Gavin,

I hope this is of
some use - it was
dead cheap in a 2nd hand
book shop - but it is
new - Anyway,

ENJOY!

Love, Damian

SOVIET ENVIRONMENTAL POLICIES AND PRACTICES:
THE MOST CRITICAL INVESTMENT

This book is dedicated to Ms Patricia Spirer, of Washington, DC, and Professor John Larner, of Glasgow, Scotland, who gave their encouragement when it was most needed.

Soviet Environmental Policies and Practices

The Most Critical Investment

M Turnbull

S Revell, *Consultant*
A Main, *Consultant*
D J I Matko
R Berry, *Translator*
W Joyce, *Translator*

Professor W V Wallace, *Project Administrator*

Dartmouth

Aldershot · Brookfield USA · Hong Kong · Singapore · Sydney

Published by
Dartmouth Publishing Company Limited
Gower House
Croft Road
Aldershot
Hants GU11 3HR
England

Dartmouth Publishing Company
Old Post Road
Brookfield
Vermont 05036
USA

British Library Cataloguing in Publication Data
Turnbull, M (Mildred), 1947 -
    Soviet environmental policies and practices: the most
    critical investment.
    1. Soviet Union. Environment. Policies
    I. Title
    333.70947

Library of Congress Cataloging-in-Publication Data
Turnbull, M (Mildred), 1947–
    Soviet environmental policies and practices: the most critical
    investment / M. Turnbull.
        p.   cm.
    ISBN 1-85521-181-5
    1. Environmental policy—Soviet Union.   2. Environmental
    protection—Soviet Union.   I. Title.
    HC340.E5T87 1990
    363.7'00947—dc20   90-45446
                                                                             CIP

ISBN 1 85521 181 5

Printed in Great Britain by
Billing & Sons Ltd, Worcester

Contents

Advisory Panel   vi
List of Tables   vii
Acknowledgements   xi

1   Environmental Investment in the Soviet Union   1

2   Municipal Waste Water Treatment   11

3   Agricultural Amelioration and the Environment   33

4   Ecology and the Pulp and Paper Industry   67

5   Fossil Fuelled Electric Power and Environmental Protection   91

6   Environmental Prospects for the Soviet Metallurgical Industries   127

7   Environmental Investment in the Soviet Chemical and Petrochemical Industries   171

8   Appendices   205

9   Index   209

Advisory Panel

Dr W H Balekjian, Faculty of Law, Glasgow University

Mr Rene Beermann, Senior Research Fellow, Glasgow University, and Co-Editor, *Co-Existence*

Mr Martin Dewhirst, Department of Slavonic Languages, Glasgow University

Professor Nigel Grant, Director, Department of Education, Glasgow University

Professor D A Loeber, Director, Department of East European Law, University of Kiel, Germany

Dr Alistair McAuley, Department of Economics, University of Essex

Dr Zhores Medvedev, National Institute of Medical Research, London

Mr Jack Miller, former Editor, *Soviet Studies*

Professor Victor Mote, University of Houston, Texas

Professor Alec Nove, Senior Research Fellow and former Director, ISEES

Dr P R Pryde, Professor of Geography, San Diego State University

Mr Frank Sebastian, Executive Vice-President, INTERACT, San Francisco

List of Tables

1.1   USSR State Committee for Nature Protection   3

Waste Water

2.1   Average Daily Supply of Water to the Population and for
      Communal-Domestic Purposes   14
2.2   Capacity of Cleansing Installations of Sewage Systems in
      Cities and Settlements of Urban Type, by Union Republic   17
2.3   The Volume of Normatively Cleansed Water Released in
      Union Republics   24

Agriculture

3.1   Capital Budget for Agriculture   39
3.2   Capital Budget for Amelioration Construction   39
3.3   Availability and Use of Ameliorated Farm Land   40
3.4   Resources of River Water and Exploitable Groundwater by
      Union Republic   42
3.5   Withdrawals of Fresh Water in the USSR by Union Republic   43
3.6   Withdrawals of Water, Losses, and Consumption by
      Agriculture in 1988 by Union Republic   44
3.7   Average Theoretical Costs of Water from the State Irrigation
      System, 1983–1984   46
3.8   Water Usage in Irrigation and Rural Water Supplies by Union
      Republic   48

3.9   Area under Irrigation and Drainage by Union Republic   51
3.10   Dynamics of Irrigated Land and its Productivity   53
3.11   Withdrawals and Consumption of Water during Transport
        by the Irrigation System in 1988   54
3.12   Volume and Mineralisation of Collector-Drainage Water in
        the Basin of the Aral Sea   56
3.13   Characteristics of Some Large Reservoirs of Collector-
        Drainage Water   57
3.14   Mineralisation and Salt Content of the Sarykamyshsk Lake   58
3.15   Estimated Costs of Irrigation Reconstruction in 1985   60

Pulp and Paper

4.1   Pulp and Paper Production in the USSR   69
4.2   Investment in Soviet Pulp, Paper, and Cardboard Industry   71
4.3   Rate of Growth of BIPF   71
4.4   Share of BIPF in Industry as a whole   72
4.5   Capital Budget by Branches of Industry   72
4.6   Commissioning of BIPF   73
4.7   Removal of BIPF   73
4.8   Commissioned BIPF by Means of New Construction,
        Expansion, and Reconstruction of Existing Enterprises   74
4.9   Incomplete Construction in State and Cooperative
        Enterprises and Organisations   75
4.10   Structure of BIPF by Type and Branch of Industry   75
4.11   Commissioning and Decommissioning of BIPF   76

Electric Power

5.1   Production of Electric Power in the USSR   94
5.2   Electric Power Generating Capacity   95
5.3   Electricity Balance in the National Economy   96
5.4   Number of Hours during which the Established Average
        Annual Capacity of Power Stations are in Operation   97
5.5   Growth of BIPF for the period 1970–1985   98
5.6   Relative Growth of BIPF   98
5.7   Gross Input to BIBF   99
5.8   Capital Assets Commissioned   99
5.9   Capital Assets Decommissioned   100
5.10   Incomplete Construction   101
5.11   Commissioning of Productive Capacity   101
5.12   Structure of Capital Assets   102
5.13   Commissioning and Decommissioning of Fossil Fuelled
        Power Stations   103

5.14 State Capital Budget for Measures to Protect Nature and
       Rational Use of Natural Resources   106
5.15 Capacity of Installations Commissioned   107
5.16 PDK Values for Some Pollutants in Atmospheric Air   110
5.17 Maximum Achievable Concentration of Pollutants   110

Metallurgical Industries

6.1 Capital Investment in the Soviet Economy   129
6.2 Structure of the State Capital Budget for the Metallurgical
      Industry in 1988   130
6.3 Return on Investment by Branch of Industry, 1970–1986   131
6.4 Return on Investment for Branches of Industry   131
6.5 Dynamics of the Basic Fund, Commodity Output, and Return
      on Investment in Non-ferrous Metallurgy   132
6.6 Technological Structure of the Capital Budget   134
6.7 Structure of the State Capital Budget for Metallurgy in 1988   135
6.8 Commissioning and Decommissioning of Capital Assets by
      Type, in 1988   136
6.9 Share of Costs Attributable to Protection of Water and Air
      Basins for Different Types of Ferrous Metallurgical
      Products   138
6.10 Structure of BIPF   139
6.11 Production of Important Types of Products   140
6.12 State Capital Budget for Nature Protection and Rational
      Use of Natural Resources   143
6.13 Use of Secondary Raw Materials in the National Economy   145
6.14 Commissioning of Systems for Circulating Water Supplies
      and Waste Water Treatment in the Metallurgical Complex   149
6.15 Commissioning of Installations for the Trapping or
      Neutralisation of Harmful Substances from Waste Gases
      at Metallurgical Enterprises   157

Chemical and Petrochemical Industries

7.1 Capital Budget in Areas of the National Economy   177
7.2 State Capital Budget for the Chemical-Forestry Complex for
      Nature Protection and Rational Use of Nature   179
7.3 Rate of Growth of Capital Assets   180
7.4 Commissioning of Capital Assets (in comparable prices)   181
7.5 Commissioning of Capital Assets (as per cent of total value
      of assets)   182
7.6 Commissioning of the Active Part of the Basic Fund   182
7.7 Use of Productive Capacity   183

7.8   Uncertified Construction in State and Cooperative Enterprises
        and Organisations   184
7.9   Structure of the State Capital Budget on Objects of Production
        in the Chemical-Forestry Complex   185
7.10 Expenditure on Repairs of Capital Assets   186
7.11 Wear and Tear of Capital Assets   187
7.12 Commissioning and Decommissioning of BIBF in 1988   189
7.13 Removing the Active Part of Capital Assets   190
7.14 Structure of Capital Assets   191
7.15 Return on Investment   194
7.16 Introduction of Measures for New Techniques and their
        Economic Effectiveness in the Chemical-Forestry
        Complex   195
7.17 Structure of the Cost of Industrial Production in 1988   196
7.18 Share of Fuel and Energy Resources Expended on
        Production of Different Types of Products   197

Acknowledgements

The work on this book began back in 1984, when Jimmy White and I set out to find a non-controversial and politically neutral topic for research. Eventually, several amongst the Institute staff became involved in activities to establish a broad-based programme of research and teaching covering environmental law, philosophy, and literature (Rene Beermann and Tanya Frisby), regional ecological concerns (Walter Joyce), environmental education and labour training (Mimi Turnbull), and environmental economics (Alec Nove, Dubravko Matko, and Mimi Turnbull). We wrote and submitted a joint proposal to the Economic and Social Research Council and to a number of other potential funders. On being rejected, we were very surprised to learn that few in Great Britain and the United States felt, at the time, that the Soviet Union actually had ecological difficulties.

The programme went into a state of limbo, and I returned to the United States in the spring of 1986, to find that one or two analysts at the US Departments of State (Mr Paul Goble) and Defense (Messrs Andrew Marshall and David Epstein), although sceptical about the issue, agreed that the subject was worth spending 'a little time on'. The operative word being 'little', the scope of the project was narrowed considerably. Under the terms of the research award, we were to study the nature of 'environmental investment priorities' and to estimate, if it were at all feasible, the burden that such investment would represent for the Soviet economy, and in particular for Soviet industry. At this juncture, one or two researchers decided their professional interests lay elsewhere.

There are political, ideological, and military connotations associated with environmental protection that have not been adequately addressed here. First,

environmental protection involves a very large amount of money and resources, and because of these factors, someone will inevitably wield a great
amount of authority and influence. Moreover, when environmental investment funds actually start flowing, it can be expected that the setting of
priorities and the allocating of resources will generate controversy. For these
reasons alone, environmental protection will have, at the very least, some
political consequences for the Soviet leadership – at any rate, it is certain that
this is no longer a politically neutral issue.

When research is conducted on matters such as environmental protection,
the implicit concerns are always reflections of basic human values. How does
one man view another? How does government or party regard the worth of
nature, man, and society? Are, and precisely how are, their declared values
implemented in daily economic activities? All governments and societies
must confront such profound issues from time to time, difficult as the process
of self-examination may be and the answers to find. Thus, any examination
of Soviet ecology must at least acknowledge the existence of domestic unrest
and political dissatisfaction. In this respect, the Soviet Union has no particular
advantage over the West, where such factors have always been a part of the
environmental scene.

Finally, the matter of linking ecology and the Soviet military. Initially, I did
not understand this point; but since President Gorbachev came to power, he
has stated time and again that environmental protection is so expensive that
a reordering of economic priorities must occur so that substantial new
resources can be directed to environmental protection. He has been insistent
that there must be substantial reductions in Soviet military expenditure if only
to release the resources that are needed to secure the ecological future of the
Soviet Union. In the interim, at least nominally, a considerable amount of new
financial resources have been directed to nature protection and resource
conservation, new bureaucracies are being created, and laws and regulations
are being promulgated. For the purposes of the research for this book, at least,
the questions of concern are: What resources are being allocated for environmental protection and resource conservation? and, crucially, How much more
is needed, and for what? Whether or not this is all because of cutbacks in
overall military spending was not investigated. If, in fact, the Soviet leadership
eventually elects to take the resources from the military that will, of course,
become a matter of general interest.

Often, when an issue such as environmental protection is the subject of
research, there is a temptation to relate to Western practices and standards
rather than to those of the subject country. That approach was resisted in
principle from the outset, as the concerns here are Soviet environmental
priorities, policies, and practices – not those elsewhere. To some extent,
therefore, where the reader might like to see some international comparisons,
these may be lacking.

A few words are needed about the source materials. Anyone working with Russian language materials these days has a 'leg up' with the tasks of identifying and translating key authors and articles. The research for this book, for instance, covered more than a hundred different journals, newspapers, and books, and there was a formidable task when it came to selecting and translating, particularly when several pages of text had to be gone over to find the half dozen lines that were relevant to this study. There are a number of general and technical translation journals, such as *Current Digest of the Soviet Press*, *Problems of Economics*, *Soviet Non-ferrous Metals*, and *Soviet Chemical Industry*, and there are several on-line data bases which index Soviet technical journals by topic. There were a number of reasons why it was impossible to rely on the translation journals, especially for current information, although they were useful for historical perspectives and references. The reports on which this book is based were written against specific contractual deadlines, while the time involved between the appearance of an article in Russian and receipt/availability of any translation journal in Glasgow is *always* several months and often over a year. Thus, by the time many excellent renditions became available here (mainly in *Current Digest*, *Soviet Geography*, and *Problems of Economics*), the articles had already been thoroughly gone over, if not fully translated. Beyond that, such sources frequently abstract the longer articles, so that the original has to be checked thoroughly for the missing, sometimes salient, items. Numerous issues of the Russian language materials were lost, mutilated, or 'off the shelves'; given issues were never received. All this made out-of-town research both frustrating and expensive. The materials used are referenced as follows: if an article was only available in one language, it is cited in that language; if it was available to the researchers in Russian and in English it is referenced to the original source; in numerous cases, both sources are cited (particularly where a non-specialist reader may find a full translation useful). Care was taken to note the published translations that were used from the outset; otherwise, no particular effort was made to indicate all cases where translations/summaries of articles might be available. The citations to Russian language publications are to materials available within the United Kingdom.

Cumulatively, over the period from 1984 until 1989, there were seven translators who tackled unfamiliar materials employing idiosyncratic vocabularies and concepts. There were also different degrees of skill in English and/or Russian amongst the translators and translation journals. An effort was made to impose some sort of uniformity, both in vocabulary and concepts, by spot-checking the translations by each translator, and in nearly every case where a translation journal was used, the original language article was checked if it could be obtained. Mr Rene Beermann was the main 'quality controller', and he is to be thanked *many* times over, indeed, for his reviews of our miserable efforts. In several cases (my own included) very many translations were checked – a necessary procedure which made the research rather more tedious than would be desirable.

A special effort was undertaken to ensure that the observations made here are as accurate as possible. From the outset, the advice of experts in and beyond the Soviet field has been sought. A number of highly respected individuals, whose names and affiliations are given as members of the Advisory Panel, monitored the research and evaluated the initial findings, an updated version of which constitutes this book. The advisory panelists contributed voluntarily, in their own ways, to the undertaking and gave constructive criticisms as research papers were written. Although he was not a member of the advisory panel, Mr Philip Joseph OBE provided insights without which the analyses would have suffered. To say a mere 'Thank You' is not enough, but it is heartfelt.

The contributions by several individuals must not be left unsung. Professor W V Wallace, Director of the Institute, undertook the financial management of the research contracts. Mr Stephen Revell, a fine linguist and an economist, was engaged for intensive stint of translating during early 1988; his efforts have been integrated into several chapters, most particularly those on fossil fueled electric power, municipal waste water treatment, and the forestry industry. Mr Walter Joyce's keen eye discerned a key article in *Izvestiya* about the pulp and paper industry that underpinned important perspectives in the original report, and he made other translations that are integrated into the various chapters. Mr Dubravko Matko and Mrs Alla Main researched issues of Soviet environmental economics.

A special 'Thank You' is due to the staff at Glasgow University's Area Studies Library, the Russian Studies Centre Library at the University of Birmingham, the British Lending Library at Boston Spa and the Science and Technology Branch Libraries of the British Library System, London, whose resources made the research possible. To the many others who helped directly and indirectly, please accept my sincere thanks.

The research for this book was undertaken with the financial support of the US Department of Defense, Office of Net Assessment. The views, opinions, and findings contained herein are those of the author and should not be construed as an official Department of Defense position, policy, or decision, unless so designated by other official documentation.

M Turnbull

1 Environmental Investment in the Soviet Union

The research for this book began in 1984, when it was noticed that a growing number of articles relating to the Soviet environment were being published over a broad spectrum of disciplines. A detailed search of Soviet journals showed that articles having an environmental theme appeared with greater frequency from late 1970s. The early articles were mainly theoretical discussions about environmental modelling or disheartened complaints about the low return from ameliorated agricultural land; Western observers tended to dismiss them as having little influence on Soviet policy-making or public expenditure. These articles generally included little or nothing by way of factual information from which economists could cull interesting titbits. By the early 1980s, formal planning for nature protection was underway in several industries, although only the programme for ferrous metallurgy was actually published. By the mid-1980s, the fact that the general theme of environmental difficulties was prominent in Soviet literature was sufficient encouragement for a reconsideration of the question of the environment in the Soviet Union.

In retrospect, it is certain that the appearance of the articles signalled that a new debate was underway over policies which had previously received little attention from the Soviet political leadership. Since Andropov, and more deliberately since Gorbachev, came to power, discussions of environmental policy alternatives have gained in respectability. But, so far, no country has undertaken a long-term investment programme for pollution controls without first being confronted in some sense with a crisis – the Soviet Union is no exception. This is not an exercise in aesthetics; the Soviet leaders are interested in the environment nowadays because the present situation is socially and,

1

therefore, politically intolerable; and, as importantly, because pollution has become an impediment to development – not just in a few localities, but for the national economy.[1] The outrage expressed by members of the Council of People's Deputies, many of whom were elected on 'green' platforms, adds further legitimacy,[2] and it reflects the general alarm over the devastating effects of industrial pollution on public health. Their complaints must be answered since the proliferating disruptions by hypercritical environmental groups – one still hesitates to label them 'organisations' with all that the term implies – are potentially destabilising for government, party, and the economy alike.

The conceptual framework for environmental management, which is discussed in this chapter, has especially intriguing implications for the on-going economic reforms, as everything in Soviet economic culture seems to weigh against success in an area which, above all else, requires efficiency. Soviet political rhetoric continues to have it that environmental management is a 'social good', the necessity of which is undisputed. Such claims are shown in subsequent chapters to be far removed from reality whenever economic decisions are made. This chapter turns on the question: How will environmental priorities be set? In answering the question, the difficulties of channelling investment are also illustrated. So far, concerns for the environment have been accorded only a peripheral role in Soviet economic planning in its centralised form. In the future – as in the past but for different reasons – the ambitions of decentralised Soviet enterprises to maximise production and profits could undermine national policies that would broaden the scope of capital investment. One hastens to point out, of course, that the industrial ministries and enterprises may become more interested if environmental investment is profit-generating. It is the desire to achieve the latter which has led to suggestions such as industry should:[3] (a) be paid to clean, (b) pay to clean, (c) pay to pollute, or else (d) pay if they fail to clean.

Environmental Leadership

The issue of leadership was not resolved with the creation in 1988 of the USSR State Committee for Nature Protection (USSR Goskompriroda),[4] which has not asserted its authority over a fragmented, competitive, and uncoordinated environmental bureaucracy or in respect of economic decisions that ultimately affect the environment. The initial remit of USSR Goskompriroda's first director, F T Morgun, was to identify environmental regulatory functions carried out by other state committees and government ministries, and to bring the dozen or so nature protection agencies under the umbrella of his state committee. Eventually, USSR Goskompriroda, and its counterparts in the republics, will review and approve all construction projects and industrial activities that affect nature – as, of course, they all do – and demand changes or stoppages as necessary. USSR Goskompriroda was also given the responsibility for public information, ecological education, and provision of ecological expertise and resources.

How well has Goskompriroda done so far? After a year 'in the trenches', FT Morgun resigned, succeeded by NN Vorontsev, a biologist of considerable reputation. Last year, the Council of People's Deputies, acutely aware of the difficulties confronting any environmental protection agency, suggested that the status of the Chairman of USSR Goskompriroda, be raised to that of Mr Gorbachev's Deputy. The promotion has not occurred, but it is now certain that Mr Vorontsev, as a Deputy himself, enjoys the backing of a very large number of elected officials – perhaps more than was the case for his predecessor – who have established an Ecology Committee (and several subcommittees) whose remit is to oversee the development of appropriate legislation and implementation of an environmental programme.

In mid-1989, the journal, *Priroda*, described the Chairman as a 'General without an Army', while others charged that all that was happening was the

1.1 USSR State Committee for Nature Protection

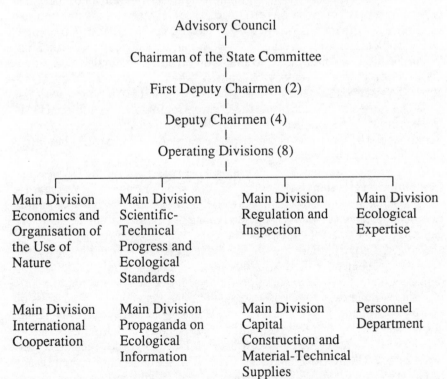

Advisory Council
|
Chairman of the State Committee
|
First Deputy Chairmen (2)
|
Deputy Chairmen (4)
|
Operating Divisions (8)
|

Main Division Economics and Organisation of the Use of Nature	Main Division Scientific-Technical Progress and Ecological Standards	Main Division Regulation and Inspection	Main Division Ecological Expertise
Main Division International Cooperation	Main Division Propaganda on Ecological Information	Main Division Capital Construction and Material-Technical Supplies	Personnel Department

Source: USSR State Committee for Nature Protection, Summer 1989.

creation of a new, amorphous, bureaucratic giant. After two years, there is now an organisational structure to the State Committee (shown above). There are at least five tiers in the national bureaucracy, and of course corresponding units in the republics, *oblasts*, *krai*, and localities. None of the nature protection agencies is fully established, but judging by reports in the Soviet press, some local nature protection units are very active. Many of the largest production ministries have established or revitalised their 'Nature Protection Committees' in the past year or so, and a few have Goskompriroda representatives on them, or send representations to the USSR Advisory Committee. USSR Goskompriroda also has the assistance of the USSR Academy of Sciences, which has placed nature protection very high on its list of priorities, and has established several committees to investigate such problems as water shortages around the Aral Sea basin and pollution at Lake Baikal.

USSR Goskompriroda is involved in a power struggle over efforts to assert its authority over other bureaucracies, with no real success so far. Such struggles are the outcome of legal manoeuvres which, like the 1988 decree that created USSR Goskompriroda, did not include enough specifics and thus left room for bureaucratic obstruction. For example, USSR Goskompriroda is to develop and promulgate the regulations against which air, land, and water protection will be achieved. Here, though, it must contend – and often appears to compete – with the USSR Ministry of Health, the USSR State Committee on Hydrometeorology, and others as well, in setting the regulatory standards. When USSR Goskompriroda becomes involved in evaluations of a new construction proposal – say, like Tyumen, which is discussed in chapter 7 about the chemical industry – cases must be made publicly and with the Council of People's Deputies and the Central Committee. In addition, USSR Goskompriroda's recommendations must be integrated into the programmatic targets issued by Gosplan, which still have the status of being state law, after the production ministries have had their say.

Other state committees and government agencies, such as the USSR State Committee on Hydrometeorology (USSR Goskomgidromet), have successfully resisted the erosion of their networks of monitoring stations, laboratories, personnel, and authority. A second round of environmental legislation is expected in 1990, part of which may clarify USSR Goskompriroda's authority and role. Of course, there are the inevitable rumours that the Ministry for Water Management (called Minvodkhoz), which is roundly criticised for construction that caused the disappearance of the Aral Sea, and the Ministry of Fishery Industries,[5] which is associated with other ecological disasters of coastal and inland waters, will escape USSR Goskompriroda's oversight altogether. Nor is there any sign that the Sanitary and Epidemiological Service (SES), run by the USSR Ministry of Health, will be transferred any time soon to USSR Goskompriroda. The SES is a vital link in the present Soviet system of monitoring local environmental conditions having an impact on public health, and it is their constant stream of reports which could often trigger environmental investigations and investment.[6] There are other agencies having great importance for environmental policy and regulation, the main one that comes to mind being the Committee on Atomic Safety, but it is unlikely that this committee will be made subordinate to the environmental agency. Finally, none of the bureaucratic restructuring has addressed the difficult question of the future role of the Communist Party, which exercises considerable influence, if not outright control (as in the case of atomic power), over environmental investment priorities.

Environmental infrastructure

When looking for signs of progress, one can be seen in the network of environmental laboratories that was announced by Mr Morgun in December 1988.[7] Apparently, there are to be nine research and scientific laboratories. The main one – called 'Ecology' is in Moscow. Others are to be located in Leningrad, Perm, Novosibirsk, Irkutsk, Khabarovsk, Vladivostok, Noril'sk, and Petropavlovsk-Kamchatka.

The locations of the USSR Goskompriroda laboratories are puzzling, as they seem to be limited to the RSFSR. They extend as far west as Leningrad (this leaves the heavily polluted Kola Peninsula without an independent laboratory), and there are several in Siberia as far north as Noril'sk and, on the mainland, as far east as Vladivostok. Everywhere else is left out of the USSR Goskompriroda network, even Central Asia, where the ecological problems could hardly be worse. The Western republics, such as the Ukraine and Belorussia, which continue to suffer from Chernobyl's radiation fall-out, are similarly excluded. The other republics may establish their own laboratories and monitoring networks, but USSR Goskompriroda's responsibilities have not been made public.

Similarly, it is uncertain what the nine laboratories will do, whether they are meant to do 'everything', or whether they will have specialisations. Mr Morgun indicated that the USSR Goskompriroda laboratories will be supplemented by facilities developed under republican auspices, some called 'Eco-centres' to be designed according to the mix of industry and agriculture in a specific *oblast* or *krai*. But relying on the republics to develop the scientific basis for environmental protection and resource conservation may be a risky tactic, if only because some of the republics are terribly impoverished. For instance, will they be able to equip the environmental laboratories or find qualified personnel to run them? In the meanwhile, USSR Goskompriroda and its sister committees are being helped out by universities and scientific research establishments associated with industry.

Nature Protection and Resource Conservation

Planners cannot be expected easily to forego the economies of scale of massive development schemes in favour of more ecologically viable investment, especially if it means losing part of their production or certain projects altogether.[8] Most Soviet planners cut their teeth on the concept of 'harnessing nature', and each of the national economic plans so far has included huge construction projects, such as building new hydroelectric stations, placing more land under the plough, or constructing long oil and gas pipelines – and many projects were undertaken in exceptionally difficult physical circumstances presented by terrain and climate in places like Siberia and the Soviet Far East. Nowadays, the economic and social burden of pollution is prompting economists to suggest an ecological approach to economic reforms.

One of the main features of the current economic reforms is the mandate to increase the return on investment capital. 'Intensification', as the concept has been termed, has special consequences for environmental protection and resource conservation as the priority has been placed on upgrading existing factories, limiting new industrial construction, and improving the infrastructure serving factories, workers, and farms. Perhaps the most important aspect of the on-going economic reorganisation is that enterprises will be assessed on the basis of their efficiency (that is, achievements in the quality and quantity of their production, profits, and environmental management). This is called *khozraschet*.

In the past, it was claimed by many in the Soviet Union that questions of the environment were addressed during the process of economic planning, and that environmental concerns were accorded greater weight than the institutional structure warranted. This is not so, and the past failure to strike a balance amongst economic and social priorities has brought about the present ecological crisis. The current approach to environmental management is proceeding along two parallel lines that purport to strike just such a balance. The first is pollution abatement and cleanup, and the second is resource conservation and waste recycling.

Under the heading of 'pollution controls' are activities to:

- reduce and treat the gaseous, liquid, and solid wastes generated by industry, which present dangers to human, animal, and other life;
- treat municipal and household sewage and manage solid waste disposal;
- rationalise the use of agricultural chemicals, irrigation, and drainage technologies; and
- clean up polluted areas and manage toxic and hazardous waste disposal.

These are the measures that are dreaded by Soviet planners and Western business, as expenditure may show little by way of increased productivity and income to the factory. And environmental protection is not a one-off expense, as pollution controls require maintenance and repair.

Cost-benefit analyses are beginning to be used by Soviet planners, although such exercises often suffer at the outset from a lack of reliable data.[9] It appears that 'damage-cost' formula will be used to estimate the necessary expenditure for pollution control equipment, and they will include evaluations of the anticipated losses to the national economy if the investment is not made. However, the 'benefit-savings' side of the regulatory picture will be measured in terms of the monetary gains for the national economy and the locality, and also according to any returns that may be realised from associated resource conservation. Presumably, then, the decision to make environmental investment will be taken in cases where a net monetary gain will occur.

There are other factors which strongly influence priority-setting. One is the legal provision that in selecting sites for environmental investment the density of population must be taken into account. This makes good sense, as there is greater return per ruble invested in populated areas, although rural areas also suffer badly from pollution. This will leave difficult political choices. However, there are already important exceptions to the population density criterion, amongst which is the level of attention, and supposedly investment, afforded Lake Baikal.

In the West, resource conservation is generally left to the market, with competition stimulating efficiency and cost cutting. Of course, the market is most effective in stimulating conservation as an economic goal under conditions of resource scarcity. Thus, many governments have grants-in-aid programmes or allow tax concessions to entice industry in such directions. Resource conservation is not cost-free, but it often generates revenue well beyond the cost of implementing the programmes.

In the Soviet economy, the underlying goal is growth, so resource conservation is an exercise in cost reduction that may have environmental spinoffs such as cutbacks in the scale of mining and forestry. Recently, Soviet law has required enterprises to:

• process extracted raw material more deeply
• recover and recycle wastes; and
• reduce the amount of water, energy, fuel, metals, and raw materials per unit of production.

Many innovative programmes are being developed, and these should eventually result in the production of saleable products and materials of value to the enterprise and the national economy. Most will require capital expenditure and some new technologies. Product substitution is viewed favourably in the Soviet Union; the most common target will be plastic for metal pipe, but production shortages will constrain progress in this area. Elsewhere, there are problems of industrial managers being unwilling to use substitutes or even knowing that they are available.

Present Environmental Priorities

It is not possible to determine from general statements of national policy where 'real' investment priorities lie. Probably, the only way to tell is by the time-honoured test – where did they spend the money? But that also leads into murky areas, since Soviet investment data are notoriously misleading. Since the policy of *glasnost'* was introduced, it has become ever more certain that not only did the central authorities deliberately publish misleading statistical information, but in some instances, the data reaching the central authorities were themselves falsified on rather grandiose scales. They reported, for instance, the completion of industrial sewerage systems where the first pipe had not been laid, and millions of tonnes of cotton that had not been sown, much less harvested. There are other points: for one thing, Soviet data are incomplete. Most statistical compilations report budget *allocations*, but it is well known that budgets can be underspent or overrun. They can be redirected and often are 'frozen' to secure savings. Most of the Soviet environmental literature treat budget data as if they were comparable to *expenditure*, which is unsatisfactory; and other useful indicators (for example, those for commissioned capacity by industrial sector and region and by nature of capacity commissioned) are usually unavailable. For another, the same criticisms can be made of cost data, which are published without indicating whether they were derived theoretically, from experiments, or after long-term usage of a given technology at multiple locations.

In such circumstances, it might be asked how can one be expected to believe the official data on environmental expenditure on which so much of the present book is based. The answer, of course, if one is strictly pedantic, is that the data are not credible. However, together with industrial literature, articles by ecology-watchers and other information sources, general impressions of priorities, achievements, failures, and future requirements are received. (Admittedly, these impressions may be distorted, but then again perhaps not unduly do.) These are the hazards of the trade, and any Soviet specialist worth his or her salt will say the same thing – you do the best you can with what you have got. Then, at best, one ends up with 'positive uncertainty'; that is, if the circumstances are these and the data are relatively correct, then given this priority, investment at such a level may be incurred.

The protection of water resources is the most frequently mentioned environmental 'priority', and large-volume water usage is a common feature amongst the economic sectors discussed in the following chapters. The same sectors are also considered to be the worst offenders in respect of air pollution – a factor which is examined in the text. The financial conditions of each industry are scrutinised, and also their past and anticipated, near-term investment patterns. Pictures are drawn of the environmental investment options being actively considered, and of the vast gap between the current levels of funding and those required to implement the ecological programmes. Most importantly, the studies endeavour to portray the monumental difficulties which must be overcome if the Soviet Union is to achieve an 'ecological' *perestroika*.

Notes

1   M Turnbull, 'Can There be an Environmental *Perestroika*? Investment in the Soviet Environment', *Conference Paper*, University of Jerusalem, January 1990.

2   Peter Lentini, a post-graduate student at the University of Glasgow, who is writing a dissertation about Soviet electoral reforms, has noted that ecology was a dominant theme in the national elections during 1989.

3   M Klybichkin, 'Zagryaznesch' prirodu? Plati!' *Ekonomicheskaya gazeta*, no. 42, 1989, p. 19. These are many such articles in this and other Soviet journals.

4   *Izvestiya*, 16–18 January 1988, carried important articles and proposals concerning nature protection. The official proclamation creating USSR Goskompriroda was published on the latter date. For further background, see also *Priroda i Chelovek*, nos. 1–3, 1988; this journal is published by the USSR State Commitee on Hydrometeorology. M Turnbull, 'The Crisis of the Soviet Environment', *Radical Scotland*, no. 1, 1989, pp. 24–25.

5   The transfer of some ecological functions associated with the Ministry of Fishery Industries (probably activities associated with Law of the Seas negotiations) was mentioned in the original decree, along with those exercised in the Ministry of Geology, Forestry, Gosagroprom, Minvodkhoz, and Goskomgidromet, and unspecified other ministries. There has not been a full transfer of authority, although there is discussion of 'erosion' in some staffs.

6   The main function of the SES is to monitor and report local health conditions. Its role in respect of the environment, however essential, is to some extent regarded as a secondary responsibility. This is an organizational difficulty confronted by a number of countries. No improvement is expected for the foreseeable future.

7   F T Morgun, 'Ekologiya v sisteme planirovaniya', *Planovoe khozyaistvo*, no. 12, 1988, pp. 53–63.

8   M Turnbull, 'Soviet Environmental Policies and Practices', in G Schopflin and S White, (eds), *Political and Economic Encyclopaedia of the Soviet Union and Eastern Europe*, London: Longman, 1990.

9   A M Satre-Ahlander, a PhD candidate at the University of Stockholm, is writing about the development of such Soviet regulations.

2 Municipal Waste Water Treatment

Introduction

Pollution of rivers, lakes and streams, inland seas and coastal areas, as well as groundwater, is highly publicised in the Soviet Union. The most common complaint is that domestic sewage and industrial waste are often processed together by municipal waste water treatment installations not having technologies appropriate to handle the industrial contaminants, resulting in very large amounts of waste water being released untreated or inadequately processed. Soviet economic and industrial literature does not give systematic attention to investment in the area of domestic and municipal waste water treatment, probably because most of the related responsibilities have been decentralised for some years. Consequently, there are no national estimates of the material, financial, and labour resources which will be needed to improve public sanitation. This chapter was pieced together from a number of articles and Soviet statistical materials in an effort to establish how much work remains to be done to provide basic urban sanitation systems and how much it will cost to do so.

The scope of the water management problem in the Soviet Union is huge. The average annual flow of nearly three million rivers, streams, and tributaries is estimated to be around 4,700 cubic kilometres, although some 80 per cent occurs in thirty-six large rivers such as the Volga, the Don, the Ob', the Amu Darya, and the Syr Darya. Additionally, there are numerous fresh water lakes having a total capacity of about 25.2 cubic kilometres (exclusive of the Caspian and Aral Seas). The water in Lake Baikal represents 91 per cent of the total volume of lake water, a factor which makes the controversy

11

surrounding its degradation somewhat more understandable given its remote location. Exploitable groundwater resources are a further 378 cubic kilometres in volume.

The main environmental concern is the protection of fresh water resources. Such a priority was spelled out in the 12th Five Year Plan (1985–1990) and no diversion from that goal seems imminent, although a growing literature suggests that greater economic gains could be achieved with enhanced attention to air pollution controls. Activities currently being undertaken to prevent water pollution are two-fold. Enterprises are required to install additional industrial waste water treatment capacity and water recycling technologies; and localities are being urged to construct municipal sanitation systems.[2] It is the latter area which is the topic of this chapter, although because of the nature of the data, other water polluting sectors are referred to intermittently.

Essential Infrastructure

Water infrastructure is commonly made up of three distinct, interconnected complexes. These comprise systems: (a) to withdraw, purify, and distribute water supplies; (b) to collect precipitation drainage, domestic sewage, and service and industrial waste water; and (c) to treat, recycle, release and dispose of waste water. The water infrastructure in a given area is designed specifically for that locale; in Soviet practice, the requirements of a regional water balance are sometimes the basis of decisions.[3] Certain aspects of these complexes and their interconnections are described below, and each ultimately influences the need for and capacity of municipal waste water treatment installations.

In urban areas, fresh water is supplied for drinking, municipal operations, industry and private gardens. Most of the water in the municipal water supply can be released after treatment into the rivers or streams from which it was taken. Soviet industry is frequently encouraged to provide its own water supply and waste water treatment facilities, especially in cases where most of it is used in cooling systems and is subsequently discharged untreated. The electric power industry, for instance, uses particularly large quantities of water for cooling purposes. Industrial processes, which consume large volumes of water and have significant volumes of effluent requiring treatment prior to release, are often located in cities, those of particular concern being the food products, pulp and paper, chemicals, oil and gas, and metallurgical sectors. Urban sewage treatment services usually require uninterrupted operations, although some enterprises may require only intermittent services.

Two approaches to water supply and waste water treatment are acknowledged in this chapter. The reader is cautioned that, largely for the sake of simplifying the presentation, the first is the basis for the analysis, while the second is mentioned as an important alternative practice which will continue, to some extent, for the foreseeable future. In general, it is the responsibility of the municipalities to provide the water supplies and waste water treatment services, and in the future this will remain the preferred route. Enterprises generally depend on the municipal services, but they can and do develop separate water purification and sewage treatment facilities. However, some parts of the Ukraine have severely limited water resources, so that much of the municipal water supply and waste water treatment which takes place is actually managed by industrial installations; the municipality acts as a purchaser of the services. The latter practice also occurs, in association with new industrial development in remote regions. Such arrangements compli-cate water management, which is then virtually held hostage to industry's responsiveness to circumstances outside the industry proper.[4]

Fresh Water Consumption

According to official Soviet tabulations published in 1987, all water with-drawn from natural resources amounted to about 6 per cent of renewable resources or 'more than 300 cubic kilometres annually'.[5] The most recent data are for 1988, when withdrawals of water from all natural sources by means of water installations supposedly totalled some 333.7 cubic kilometres (7 per cent of renewable resources), including some 31.4 cubic kilometres of groundwater.[6] But several leading economists have indicated that water taken from surface and groundwater resources reached as much as 350 cubic kilometres annually several years ago,[7] since account must be made of the fact that some volume of fresh water withdrawals (for example, well water in rural areas) is not processed through water supply installations. By the year 2000, total fresh water consumption is expected to increase to as much as 430 cubic kilometres annually.[8] Academician E Chazov, the USSR Minister of Public Health, indicated that in 104 towns and cities, one-quarter of water for domestic use and one-third of that for industrial and office use has not been sufficiently purified.[9]

The theoretical normative (planned allowance) for daily water supply is 300 litres per capita.[10] The normative varies, however, in such areas as Moscow where it is 600 litres per capita per day. In much of the country, though, the actual drinking water supplies can be as much as 20–30 per cent *below* the normative established for the locality. Official data indicate that 2172 (of a total 2190) cities have water mains, as have an additional 3429 settlements of an 'urban type' from a total of 4026. 169 million persons or 66 per cent of the Soviet population live in such areas.[11] According to Acad-emician T Khachaturov, water is supplied through central water systems in about 95 per cent of cities, but he did not specify the number or size of the cities, the percentage of population having such services, or if the word 'system' should be understood as defined above or if it simply means a central water pump and spiggot.[12]

2.1   Average Daily Supply of Water to the Population and for Communal-Domestic Purposes
(per single *urban* inhabitant, by Union Republic)

	1986	1987	1988
SSSR	319	324	334
RSFSR	303	306	330
Ukraine	310	311	321
Belorussia	235	240	252
Uzbekistan	487	485	512
Kazakhstan	288	293	297
Georgia	546	596	612
Azerbaidzhan	412	439	433
Lithuania	280	286	289
Moldavia	280	289	346
Latvia	261	256	259
Kirgizia	304	286	311
Tadzhikstan	545	576	605
Armenia	554	585	602
Turkmenia	325	321	431
Estonia	274	280	283

Source: *Okhrana okruzhayushchei sredy i ratsional'noe ispolzovanie prirodnykh resursov v SSSR*, Moscow, 1989, p. 15.

The relative distribution of fresh water supplies within the Soviet economy in 1988, as reported in percentages, is generally agreed: agriculture (inclusive of rural domestic, small towns, and some food processing industries) took 53 per cent of the total, industry (exclusive of agriculture) had 38 per cent, and municipal and domestic (exclusive of rural dwellings and small towns) 9 per cent. On an annual basis, this is estimated as 152, 107, and 26 cubic kilometres, respectively; again, the data probably refer only to water that is processed through central installations. Between 1980 and 1986, there was a 1 per cent increase in the municipal and domestic water supply, and a 3 per cent increase in industrial supplies, while water used in agriculture reportedly fell by 4 per cent. A further shift in water consumption occurred between 1985 and 1988, as industry reduced its consumption by 2 per cent and agriculture increased its by 1 per cent; although the municipal water supply maintained the same percentage share, by 1988 its volume was 1.2 cubic kilometres over that of 1985.[13]

The supply of fresh water for municipal and domestic use will continue to grow as a consequence of the central government's commitment to construct new housing. At the same time, however, if local authorities decide to upgrade the water infrastructure to reduce wastage, reduced consumption could offset some of the new demand. The potential for conservation appears to be real. One study of 52 cities and towns indicated that water consumption per capita could be cut by as much as one-third.[14] If investment does not materialise in the required orders of magnitude, drinking water supplies will continue to expand as new dwellings are accommodated. In January 1988, a decree was issued requiring a 15 per cent reduction in municipal and domestic water consumption, although how this might be accomplished was not specified and it appears to have had little effect to date.[15]

Recycled Water

Fresh water supplies to all consuming sectors are supplemented each year with recycled water (a term which mainly refers to industrial water which is used more than once without being released and includes the use of domestic sewage and drainage water). In 1988, recycled water totalled 274 cubic kilometres in all sectors.[16] The data include 'reverse' and 'reused' water in addition to recycled water; the difference is that recycled industrial water sometimes undergoes some form of treatment, while that is not common practice in respect of agricultural drainage water. Soviet authorities anticipate that recycling will provide an increasing share of industrial and agricultural water supplies. Most of the reported 274 cubic kilometres of water recycled in 1988, was used by industry. Water recycling expanded by 33 cubic kilometres from 1985 to 1988 for all sectors of the economy.[17] There is no evidence to suggest that the percentage of municipal sewage and drainage in overall water recycling is at all significant, although there is mounting literature concerning its current and potential use in some, usually isolated, metallurgical plants, pulp and paper mills, and in agriculture.

The distribution of water recycling technologies is quite obviously uneven. Overall in the USSR, industrial water supplies are provided at a rate of 72 per cent by recycling and repeat use systems. The RSFSR and the Ukraine, where four-fifths of all water consumption takes place, recycled water amounts to 74 and 81 per cent, respectively, of total industrial water supplies. The highest attainments are in Armenia and Belorussia at 84 per cent, while the lowest are in Turkmenia (22 per cent), Moldavia (25 per cent), and Estonia (26 per cent). Significant progress occurred between 1985 and 1988 in Tadzhikstan, Kirgizia, and Georgia, although in Lithuania, a marked decline (-7 per cent) in overall recycling apparently took place over the same period.[18] Industrial sectors having particularly heavy water usage made some progress towards equipping enterprises with technologies to recycle water supplies. In 1982, the amount of water supply which was met through recycling in such economic sectors was as follows: petrochemical industry – 87 per cent; pulp and paper – 52 per cent; ferrous metallurgy – 80 per cent; non-ferrous metallurgy – 46 per cent.[19] More recent information indicates that the oil refining and petrochemical industries may recycle 95 per cent of their water intake.[20] The estimated water supplies which are recycled by these industries appear to refer to calculations of 'technological water supplies', a term explored in other chapters. But a word of caution: 'technological water supplies' does not refer to all water consumed by an enterprise, and the sometimes crude recycling techniques may not be those accepted in Western practice.

Treatment Capacity

Definition

Soviet regulations require that all municipal waste water must be at a stipulated level of cleanliness prior to discharge; in effect, this means that it must be treated before it is released. In theory, the requirement for urban waste water treatment capacity equals the amount of fresh water withdrawn from surface and groundwater sources, *less* the amount of its losses through movement, use, and treatment, *plus* the amount of water that is recycled, *plus* the amount used in the process of sanitary treatment, *plus* the amount of precipitation runoff that enters the drainage system. There are variations in the quantity of effluents according to the time of day and season, so requirements for waste water treatment capacity are commonly based on the average 'peak load' over a 24-hour period. In addition, 'reserve capacity' is required to meet planned increases in demand and maintenance of installations. Implicit in the definition of 'capacity' is a calculation of the extent to which the systems should be used to obtain maximum life of the technology.

The most current data for municipal waste water treatment indicate that in 1988, 1,905 cities of a total 2,190 had sewerage systems, and that 2,132 of a total 4,026 settlements of 'urban-type' were similarly provided. These systems totalled 77.7 thousand kilometres in length. In addition, sewage treatment capacity attached to the sewers totalled 74.5 million cubic metres of daily capacity.[21] Such data correspond with representations in an article published in 1985 which stated that by 1983, 2,100 towns and cities had water supply systems and 1,750 had sewerage systems. In the same year, it was shown that approximately 91 per cent of the 'municipal socialised housing stock' were connected to a water supply system, while 88 per cent were connected to a sewerage system, 66 per cent to hot water supplies, and 81 per cent had baths.[22] Being connected to a sewerage system, however, does not mean that the municipal and domestic sewage is mechanically processed, or biologically or chemically treated. The Soviet use of the term 'mechanical treatment' implies that the wastes are collected, perhaps diluted and filtered, and then released. The fact that so much of the effluent is classed as 'inadequately cleansed' suggests that mechanical systems, without secondary stage biological or chemical processing, are insufficient.

2.2 Capacity of Cleansing Installations of Sewage Systems in Cities and Settlements of Urban Type, by Union Republic*
(at the end of the year, thousand cubic metres per day)

	1986	1987	1988
USSR	66506	70492	74470
RSFSR	41157	43734	46297
Ukraine	11330	12089	12596
Belorussia	2504	2759	3010
Uzbekistan	2699	2783	2918
Kazakhstan	2692	2682	2750
Georgia	559	557	633
Azerbaidzhan	326	511	810
Lithuania	905	917	967
Moldavia	860	922	1005
Latvia	450	500	511
Kirgizia	545	668	658
Tadzhikstan	524	562	568
Armenia	1151	923	933
Turkmenia	218	248	175
Estonia	586	637	640

Source: Okhrana okruzhayushchei sredy ..., p. 16.
*Represents capacity for all purposes

According to one Soviet source, the methods presently applied in the water supply and sewerage industry to estimate capacity have a number of deficiencies. Calculations are not based on a clear-cut definition of the expected productivity of equipment, installations, or a whole complex over a specific period of operation. The present methods do not take account of the fact that, because the capacities of water supply and waste disposal complexes are usually disproportionate, estimates of waste water treatment capacity must be on the basis of the points in the systems which limit the operations of treatment installations. For example, facilities for (a) transporting and storing water and (b) removal of waste water place limitations on throughput capacity of waste water treatment installations.[23]

There are two mutually exclusive principles. One is to calculate the capacity of the system as a whole according to the bottlenecks that determine the lowest productivity limiting the production of treated water. The other method is to base the calculation on the capacity of the points in the system which has the highest productivity. There is no definition of the criteria for evaluating the use of the productive capacity of the particular installations or of the system as a whole, and as a result there is no definition of the criteria for evaluating the efficiency of using investment funds.

At present, there are no normatives to dictate the amount of reserve capacity to be provided. Moreover, in practice, such capacity is used in daily operations and not held in reserve.[24]

The need for municipal waste water treatment is undisputed and the technologies are well known in the Soviet Union. With the possible exception of some industrial effluent, all waste water in urban locations is supposed to be collected by the network of municipal sewers, from where it flows into the treatment installation. Herein lies one difficulty, as the chemical and toxic contents of industrial waste water demand substantially more sophisticated treatment technologies. From a national perspective, there is a particular need to build installations specifically to treat industrial effluents; this is related both to the volume of waste water that is involved and the toxic contents of the effluent. When the industrial waste water treatment capacity is insufficient, managers either allow the effluent to be combined with the municipal sewage, to be placed in interim storage, or else it is released untreated.[25] The technological treatment requirements due to the chemical and toxic contents of industrial waste water create significant variations in associated capital costs.

The overall cost of municipal waste water treatment can be lowered to the extent that industrial effluents are processed separately from other municipal waste water. In locations where water supplies are abundant, Soviet authorities also reduce treatment capacity to the extent that they calculate that the volume and rate of flow of rivers or other bodies of water can dilute and neutralise the effluent. This practice, however, is outside regulatory requirements to neutralise waste water prior to release.[26]

Insofar as effluent is recycled in the industrial water supply systems, the demand for municipal waste water treatment capacity is shifted to industry. Recycling does not, however, reduce the need for waste water treatment facilities within industry.[27]

The processes of using water repeatedly or in cycles can also be considered from the standpoint of the concept of primary and secondary pollutants of water basins. It is reckoned that the use of closed systems of water consumption secures water basins against pollution, thanks to termination of discharges of waste water into them. However, the recycling of water cannot reduce the mass of primary pollutants, inasmuch as these do not depend in their formation on how the water flows, whether it is by direct flow or by recycling. The ecological effect of these methods of water use is determined chiefly by the reduction in secondary pollution, insofar as the processes of water purification are carried out significantly less frequently. But purification itself is of an uncomplicated nature for two reasons: in the first place, in reverse (repeated use) systems substantially less severe technical demands are made on the water; and in the second place, the purification of concentrated solutions results in fewer ecological costs, relative, of course, to the mass of pollutants and not to the volume of purified water. Besides which, pollutants in reverse systems at times circulate outside of water installations and are discharged along with so-called flushing waters.

Thus, as water is recycled in industry there should be treatment capacity approximately equal to the volume of recycled water. Additional treatment capacity is required, of course, for waste water including flushing water which is not recycled, while the technological requirements would be dictated by the pollutants involved.

Water Losses

On the other hand, the need for waste water treatment capacity is exacerbated in areas where there is significant leakage from the water supply distribution system due to faulty pipelines. That is, it is increased to the extent that the leaked water enters the sewerage system. Losses also can occur when water pressure is in excess of need. Unproductive losses are estimated at 13 per cent of the annual water supply for the USSR as a whole, and Soviet statistics indicate that in 1986 such losses amounted to 40 cubic kilometres, although the extent to which the leaked water was collected by the sewerage system was not stated.[28] Of the total water withdrawn in 1988, about 51 cubic kilometres were used while transporting it from source to consumer; again, some portion of the latter flowed into the treatment installations.[29]

In Moscow, for instance, the current programme is to increase water supplies by 23 cubic metres per second. In reviewing the need for additional supplies, it was found that water losses are calculated at 17 cubic metres per second (that is, 1,468,000 cubic metres/day), of which 3.0 cubic metres per second (259,200 cubic metres/day) are caused by faulty water taps. (In Moscow, water is supposedly already supplied at a rate of 680 litres per capita each day for all purposes, although this is not evenly distributed within the city.)[30] Such wastage, which could be averted with repairs to water infrastructure, should evoke a serious discussion concerning the need for additional water supplies from the Rzhev waterworks and canal. The construction of the Rhzev system continues to be a subject of concern amongst ecologists due to its environmental implications for the area around Kalinin.[31]

Moscow's water losses, and hence constant demand for increased capacity of cleansing installations, are not an anomaly. In the study of 52 cities and towns in the Russian Republic cited above, it was shown that up to 35 per cent of demand for fresh water could be eliminated by repairing the water supply infrastructure. For the localities included in the study, it was estimated that 110 million cubic metres of water could be saved each year.[32] Mention was made, for instance, of repair work in Kharkov to demonstrate the nature of the work that must be done: in 1986, automated management processes were repaired or commissioned, 1,164 valves of various diameters were replaced, as were 575 fire hydrants and 5,355 shafts of water collection plants.[33]

Water losses in Siberian cities are very high indeed. The situation was described as follows:[34]

> The losses of water are very large. On average, they come to 16.2 per cent, which exceeds by 2.2 times the average statistical data for the RSFSR (which is 7.1 per cent). The largest losses of water occur in Ulan Ude (30.4 per cent), Bol'shoi Kamen' (28.8 per cent), Andzhero-Sudzhansk (24.9 per cent), Petropavlovsk-Kamchatka (28.2 per cent), and Magadan (20.2 per cent).... In Tomsk, daily losses of water in some apartment blocks were between 77 and 130 litres per capita.

By way of contrast, the water losses (at 4.7 per cent) in Omsk and Bratsk were regarded as relatively insignificant.

Climatic variations

Common sense suggests that dry climates and areas with low levels of precipitation should equate with heavy reliance on recycled water. Maximum waste water treatment capacity is needed in areas where water supplies must be guaranteed by effluent treatment and subsequent recycling due to resource limitations. For example, water shortages will eventually force the Urals, municipalities along the Don and the Kuban rivers, and those throughout Central Asia to become heavily dependent on recycling technologies simply to meet demands for water.[35]

Severe cold weather conditions also increase the pressure on local authorities to undertake maintenance and repair work. In 1986, RSFSR authorities found that, apparently due to a shortage of appropriate equipment, there was a general lack of progress in this area. Effectively one-third of planned (as opposed to needed) work was accomplished in the Novgorod and Karelia areas. In Novgorod, for instance,[36]

> ... there is no enterprise where the director does not complain that there are insufficient excavators, pipes or fittings. Of course, when there are no transformers, it is impossible to repair the electric heating on water distribution standpipes. Last winter in the hard frost, more than once the inhabitants of small towns in the area stood with an empty bucket at a frozen standpipe.... Looking at the documents which show if the pipes are ready for the winter, we see as of 1 July that 241 collection pipes have been refitted out of 705, 30.2 kilometres out of 94 kilometres of water supply network had been flushed out, and the same amount of sewer lines out of 81 kilometres. The aim was to replace and to relay 6.5

kilometres of water supply network and 1.3 kilometres of sewers; the performance was 2 kilometres and 400 metres, respectively.

The lack of progress in commissionings and repair and maintenance is due to shortages in the supplies of needed valves and pipes. Some shortages exist because localities and ministries have overly large inventories. These are situations that are unlikely to be remedied until the consumers, by they localities, ministries, or enterprises, can depend on receiving the needed equipment from the manufacturer or supplier. That may require construction of new manufacturing enterprises in the least-served republics, although some of the bottlenecks may be removed with an improved distribution system.

Regulatory Criteria

The responsibility for ensuring the availability of clean water and the treatment of waste water throughout the Soviet economy is highly decentralised. Although the responsibility for drinking water supplies is borne primarily by the local authorities, industrial and certain republic and national bodies also play essential parts in the provision and operation of all these complexes. In the Russian Republic, for instance, local authorities operate half of the municipal water supply and waste water treatment installations, with the remainder being operated largely by the RSFSR Minzhilkomkhoz (Ministry of Housing and Municipal Management of the Russian Republic).[37] It is not clear whether or not this distribution of authority obtains in respect of waste water treatment in other jurisdictions.

Inspection and general regulatory authority over sanitary waste water treatment are vested in the Sanitary Epidemiological Service Stations (SESS). To this end, many SESS have internal units which are concerned with either surface water, drinking water, or waste water.[38] The extent to which such an organisational structure exists throughout the USSR is similarly unclear.

Normatives: Cleansing

In the Soviet Union, the regulations (the words criteria or guidelines are often seen) governing mandatory cleansing of effluent are referred to as 'normatives'. The normatives cover a range of organic, toxicological, bacteriological, and general sanitary factors that are developed on the basis of the implications of specific pollutants for human health.[39]

Soviet normatives are developed with the view that environmental protection would be enhanced by limiting the overall quantity of effluent and the concentrations of pollutants contained therein.[40] While they stipulate the minimum standard, in the future normatives will be evaluated again on a case-by-case basis with reference to the recipient environment, as in some localities the national normative may be regarded as insufficient protection. Limits are also assigned, on a case-by-case basis, to enterprises in respect of water consumption. The significance is that, in effect, water supply normatives are the first indicator of eventual waste water treatment capacity.

Other normatives govern the extent to which waste water must be cleansed by industry, municipalities and agriculture. Taken together, the supply and cleansing normatives are the basis for estimating investment in treatment capacity. Several leading economists, including A A Gusev, are worried that the cost of cleansing effluent increases exponentially according to the degree of expected cleanliness of the waste water, so that at 99 per cent it might be ten times higher than at 90 per cent, and at 99.9 per cent it might be 100 times more.[41] In their turn, such perceptions (which probably do not reflect the actual cost implications of regulatory options) discourage localities from pursuing pollution controls to higher standards of cleansing.

Normatives: Construction

In addition, there are normatives governing the design, construction, and operation of waste water treatment installations. These standards also affect not only the cleanliness of treated effluent, but also the size of investment for waste water treatment.[42] For example, there are normatives which require periodic testing of treated waste water to ascertain compliance with regulatory criteria. The currently used tests are reported to be cumbersome, time consuming, and generally ineffective in daily operations, and a number of experiments have been undertaken to find suitable alternatives.[43]

> At present, in accordance with the 'Methods of Technical Monitoring of the Operation of Treatment Plants for Municipal Sewage' (Ministry of Construction, 1977) checking of the residual organic pollutants is carried out once every ten days by biological or chemical processes. Biological processing identifies the biochemically oxidised organic substances which are primarily of human origin. Biological testing takes between five and twenty days, while chemical testing takes between two to three hours. The prolonged amount of time for these processes means that it is impossible to establish operational checks on the cleansing process. On other days, optical tests using ultra violet (UV) sensors could be carried out. This works when the optical density of the water in the ultra violet range of the spectrum is good, and suspended particles do not exceed 20–30 milligrams per litre. UV analysis of optical density of the treated water takes five to seven minutes, allows normal treatment of water to continue, and determines the industrial components of the polluted effluents.

UV testing is a 'new technology'; it is unavailable to most municipal waste water treatment installations. The usual techniques for testing the quality of cleaned effluents are similar to those used in the West, although the sensitivity of detection equipment is reportedly much greater in the West. It is likely that a goodly number, if not most, Soviet municipal waste water treatment installations are unable to comply consistently with the required norms for cleansing.

The Need for Municipal and Urban Domestic Waste Water Treatment Capacity

Soviet data are not adequate in respect of the volumes of municipal waste water for which installations or capacity must be provided. It is possible to make a rough calculation. Soviet data indicate that a total of 152.3 cubic kilometres of sewage were released, from all sources, into surface water bodies during 1988. By definition, the data exclude any volume that may have been injected into subterranean cavities, used in agriculture or rural households, or sprayed on land. There are any number of plausible definitions for the 152.3 cubic kilometres estimate. For example, the number is equal to more than the total of industrial and municipal water intake, and may include some volume of storm water drainage and/or a further volume of recycled water which is eliminated due to over-contamination. It may also include some agricultural drainage, but most such waste water does not enter the collector-drainage systems.

Insofar as releases of *untreated or insufficiently cleansed* effluent is concerned, official data indicate that the residual is 28.6 cubic kilometres, of which 8.1 cubic kilometres were entirely *untreated*.[44] There appears to be general agreement with the latter figure. For example, Yuri Izrael, the Director of the State Committee on Hydrometeorology, indicated in 1987 that 6.5 cubic kilometres of untreated waste water are released into reservoirs each year.[45] Neither source specified the sources or nature of the wastes included in the estimate. Additionally, *normatively cleaned* waste water, from all sources was reported as 12.2 cubic kilometres in 1988.[46] (This last figure is somewhat surprising because it means that the volume of normatively cleaned effluent was apparently recalculated according to the criteria obtaining in 1988, as the volume decreased from 46 per cent of total effluent in 1980 to 30 per cent in 1988.)

Thus, of the total, 111.5 cubic kilometres apparently were regarded as *not subject to regulation*. (This is calculated as total effluent [152.3 cubic kilometres] *less* untreated/insufficiently treated sewage [28.6 cubic kilometres] and *less* normatively cleansed effluent [12.2 cubic kilometres].)

In trying to make sense of the *official* estimate of untreated waste water, the following rough observations were made. First, it suggests that little, if any, of the water used in agriculture is presently treated. Secondly, judging by industrial and municipal fresh water *supplies*, it appears that a very high

2.3   The Volume of Normatively Cleansed Water Released
in Union Republics
(million cubic metres)

	1985	1986	1987	1988
USSR	22374	22968	18470	12208
RSFSR	13986	14331	9561	4576
Ukraine	4536	4749	4858	3975
Belorussia	728	812	850	895
Uzbekistan	892	936	1012	482
Kazakhstan	327	292	316	278
Georgia	279	265	230	309
Azerbaidzhan	173	206	199	252
Lithuania	88	95	116	123
Moldavia	223	155	171	197
Latvia	118	125	113	109
Kirgizia	183	152	171	177
Tadzhikstan	187	190	186	206
Armenia	359	352	352	313
Turkmenia	21	14	12	13
Estonia	274	294	323	303

Source: *Narodnoe khozyaistvo SSSR v 1988 g*, Moscow: 1989, p. 247.

percentage of industrial water is released untreated or, because it is used in cooling processes, is regarded as 'normatively clean, not requiring treatment'. It is common practice, for instance, that cooling water originating with the electric power industry is only rarely processed by treatment installations, and more often is discharged into cooling ponds where some contaminants will be filtered out. The estimate for water in this category is 70 per cent; this is the residual of total municipal and industrial water intake, less untreated or insufficiently cleansed effluent and less treated effluent.[47]

To narrow the data to municipal wastes, the calculation is made as follows:

1   107 cubic kilometres of industrial water less 70 per cent released (as normatively clean or not requiring treatment) leaves about 32 cubic kilometres remaining to be cleansed.
2   32 cubic kilometres of industrial waste water *plus* 26 cubic kilometres of municipal and urban domestic water comes to 58 cubic kilometres.
3   If 12.2 cubic kilometres of water are cleansed (assuming all or more of such water treatment refers to industrial or municipal installations), then 58 cubic kilometres less 12.2 cubic kilometres comes to approximately 45.8 cubic kilometres, which is waste water released untreated or inad-

equately treated. (This is significantly higher than the estimate of 28.6 cubic kilometres to which official sources refer in this category).

4   By this calculation, then, the residual of *municipal* waste water requiring treatment or an improvement in treatment standards is determined as: 45.8 cubic kilometres requiring treatment less the 32 cubic kilometres of industrial waste water requiring treatment leaves a residual of 13.8 cubic kilometres of municipal and urban domestic waste water requiring new treatment capacity or upgraded capacity. This is about half of the annual volume of municipal water intake.

In respect of geographical requirements for additional waste water treatment capacity, an article published in 1987 indicated that three-quarters of all waste water in the RSFSR was subjected to mechanical processing, of which 90 per cent underwent biological or chemical treatment.[48] On an all-union basis, this is on the high side, since Khachaturov indicated that two-thirds of waste water was put through mechanical treatment, of which as much as 30 per cent underwent chemical and biological treatment.[49] If a volume equal to two-thirds of municipal water supplies are mechanically processed, this leaves a residual of some 8.6 cubic kilometres of municipal sewage that are released without treatment, and a further 12 cubic kilometres needing to have the installations upgraded to provide biological and/or chemical treatment in addition to present mechanical techniques.

There is little mileage to be gained by further calculations or comparisons between 54 per cent (the calculations here) and 66 per cent (derived by Khachaturov's method), since the required investment is so very great. Its magnitude can be demonstrated in the following examples.

The estimates presented below are for both 8.6 and 13.8 cubic kilometres annually of municipal and urban domestic waste water for which no cleansing is presently provided but which are likely to be the targets of additional investment. This comparison does not take into account (a) any increase in demand up to the year 2005; (b) any additional capacity required by the processing of rain water through the sewage treatment installations; (c) any reserve or replacement capacity.

The following calculations are made on the basis of actual expenditure reported in Soviet journals by individuals associated with the responsible ministries or bureaucracies. However, the examples are not based on official data. They also suggest significant regional differences in related costs.

Example 1.   In the Russian Republic, during the 11th Five Year Plan, 177 million rubles were appropriated for building water supply capacity for 847,000 cubic metres per day. No pipeline construction was mentioned in the article in respect of the budget appropriation. This works out to 209 rubles per cubic metre of treatment capacity.[50] The advisory panel suggested that this level of investment was too high, although Academician Khachaturov wrote that it was a figure common to treatment in some *industrial* sectors.

1   Even so, at 209 rubles per cubic metre, 8.6 cubic kilometres of annual flow (or 23.5 million cubic metres daily) would amount to 4.9 billion rubles.
2   At 209 rubles per cubic metre, 13.8 cubic kilometres of annual flow (38 million cubic metres of daily capacity) would amount to 7.9 billion rubles.

Example 2.   In Latvia, where the municipal water supply and waste water treatment systems are far short of required capacity, a 1987 article indicated that forthcoming construction of 770,000 cubic metres per day of municipal waste water treatment capacity and 119 kilometres of waste water collection pipes have received an allocation of over 126 million rubles.[51] In this instance, then, the waste water treatment installation and sewerage pipe network would work out at 164 rubles per cubic metre of treatment capacity and pipeline.

1   Here, 8.6 cubic kilometres annually (23.5 million cubic metres per day) of municipal waste water treatment capacity and 2,000 kilometres of sewer pipes would cost 3.8 billion rubles.
2   Again, 13.8 cubic kilometres annually (38 million cubic metres of daily capacity) and related sewer lines would cost 6.2 billion rubles.

Example 3.   A discussion of the critical shortages in the Rostov Oblast (RSFSR) of water supply and waste water treatment capacity, stated that water supply installations with a capacity of 428,500 cubic metres per day and 373.4 kilometres of distribution pipes were planned with a capital budget of 62.4 million rubles. This works out at 146 rubles per cubic metre plus pipes.[52]

1   For 23.5 million cubic metres per day of waste water treatment capacity and pipeline, or roughly 3.4 billion rubles.
2   For 38 million cubic metres of daily capacity and proportionate sewer-line construction, the cost would be 5.5 billion rubles.

Example 4.   In Tadzhikstan, by way of comparison, development of 232,000 cubic metres per day of municipal water supply capacity and 130,600 cubic metres per day of waste water treatment capacity would require 32 million rubles.[53] The example apparently does not take into account the additional costs associated with building sewer lines. Assuming that the costs of municipal water supply and waste water treatment can be roughly equated, this equals approximately 88 rubles per cubic metre of municipal effluent treatment capacity.

1   In this example, then, 2.0 billion rubles would purchase the 23.5 million cubic metres daily of municipal waste water treatment capacity.
2   And, 3.3 billion rubles would purchase 38 million cubic metres of daily capacity.

Example 5.   This example is drawn from the following quotation:

> The general demand for water in the Urals reached 43.9 cubic kilometres per year (120 million cubic metres per day). The complex of existing plant for water supply to the economy and for protecting water resources in the Urals is valued at 7–8 billion rubles. *This figure is evidently understated.* But even if one proceeds from this figure, the water supply averages about 61 rubles of capital expenditure per cubic metre of daily capacity.[54]

1   Accordingly, the comparable outlays for 23.5 million cubic metres per day of municipal waste water treatment would be approximately 1.4 billion rubles.
2   And, for 38 million cubic metres of daily capacity, the costs would be 2.3 billion rubles.

It can be hypothesised that the middle range of costs (at 146 rubles per cubic metre of daily capacity) is the closest to actual requirements, since budgeting against such a figure appears to allow some variations in construction practices and conditions of construction. The upper range (at 209 rubles), however, may be required to cover sustained inflation at current levels.

1   Over fifteen years (three five-year plans), using the middle range costs (146 rubles per cubic metre of daily capacity), then 226 million rubles annually (1.1 billion per five-year period) are required to handle 8.6 cubic kilometres of sewage. At the lower end of the upper level (209 rubles per cubic metre of daily capacity), 326 million rubles are needed annually (1.6 billion rubles per five-year period) to handle the same volume of sewage.
2   In comparison, at 146 rubles per cubic metre of daily capacity, then 366 million rubles annually (1.8 billion per five-year period) are needed to build capacity to handle 13.9 cubic kilometres of wastes; and at the upper end, 526 million rubles (2.6 billion per five-year period) are needed.

Conclusion

During the 12th plan period (1986–1990), the state capital budget for all water protection installations will probably total 1.9 billion rubles annually or a projected 9.6 billion rubles over the period. It is possible that budgeting at the lower end of the scale is occurring in respect of municipal waste water treatment construction. The evidence in support of such a conjecture is thin on the ground, unfortunately, and the only positive proof seems to be the Soviet statistics which show an increase of approximately 8 million cubic metres per day (2.9 cubic kilometres) in treatment capacity between 1986 and 1988. At that rate of construction, over the five years of the 12th plan period an additional 5 cubic kilometres of municipal sewage treatment might be available. Therefore, by the year 2005, if construction can be sustained at such levels and if construction costs do not escalate precipitously, the condition of urban sanitation will be vastly improved although still not fully resolved.

Notes

1   *Okhrana okruzhayushchei sredy i ratsional' noe ispolsovanie prirodnykh resursov v SSSR, Statisticheskii sbornik*, Moscow, 1989, p. 63–5; *Narodnoe khozyaistvo SSSR za 70 let*, Moscow, 1987, p. 612. There is some disagreement about such data, probably due to the general lack of common definitions. For example, a 1988 publication indicated that there are 4,000 reservoirs, containing 1.5 cubic kilometres of water. Moreover, it indicated that the volume of fresh water consumed in the economy was 354 cubic kilometres, and that the volume consumed is forecasted to rise to 430 cubic kilometres by the year 2000, water conservation plans notwithstanding. G S Urvantsev, Voda: ekonomika i ekologiya, *Melioratsiya i vodnoe khozyaistvo*, no. 3, 1988, pp. 2–4.

    The number of reservoirs in the country (natural plus man-made), and the definition of a 'reservoir' itself, are not known. Apparently, the number given in most Soviet statistics includes only natural reservoirs. The issue of *Melioratsiya i vodnoe khozyaistvo* above mentioned a figure of some 4,000 reservoirs, while the 1989 statistical handbook for nature protection separates the figures for lakes and inland seas from rivers, streams, and tributaries.

2   *Osnovnye napravleniya ekonomicheskogo i sotsial' nogo razvitiya SSSR na 1986–1990 i na period do 2000*, Moscow: Politizdat, 1986, pp. 69–70.

3   I Potravnyi, V Narizhnaya, V Ogreb, Balansovoe planirovanie ispol'zovaniya vodnykh resursov, *Ekonomika Sovetskoi Ukrainy*, no. 6, 1987, pp. 74–7. The article defines a water balance as: 'In planning the use of water resources, a system of balances in the water economy has been developed, allowing for specific features of this resource, and the interdependence of water resources by volume, quality, and conditions within the limits of total river flow in the district; the changing levels in volume of river flow over specific periods of time; the use of water installations; and the addition of sewage water which results in a deceleration of water quality for purposes of consumption; and the need to release wastes into rivers.... The water balance is worked out by districts, territories, regions, *krai*, economic regions, Soviet republics, and the Soviet Union as a whole'.

4   N V Khil'chenko, A M Chernyaev, Formirovanie ob'edenennykh vodok-hozyaistvennykh sistem i vnedrenie khozraschenykh printsipov upravleniya, *Vodnye resursy*, no. 6, 1986, pp. 153–61.

5   *Narodnoe khozyaistvo SSSR za 70 let*, p. 612.

6   *Okhrana okruzhayushchei sredy ...*, op cit; and *Narodnoe khozyaistvo SSSR v 1988 g*, p. 245.

7   N Bystritskaya and V Mikhura, O plate za vodu promyshlennymi predpriyatiyami, *Planovoe khozyaistvo*, no. 1, 1983, pp. 123–5 said that consumption of water is 350

cubic km/year. M Ya Lemeshev, Nauchno-tekhnicheskii progress i priroda, *EKO*, no. 8, 1984, pp. 61–76 (translated in *Problems of Economics*), indicated that consumption of water had reached 335 cubic kilometres by 1975. 170–80 cubic kilometres are used in agricultural irrigation, of which up to 70 per cent is expended without recovery.

8   G S Urvantsev, *Melioratsiya i vodnoe khozyaistvo*, no. 3, 1988, op cit.

9   O Frantsen, Formula zdorov'ya, *Pravda*, 13 April 1987, p. 3.

10 S K Stankov, A A Kozak, Normy vodopotrebleniya – v osnovu raboty, *Zhilishchnoe i kommunal' noe khozyaistvo*, no. 6, 1986, p. 12, which cites the regulatory require- ment in SNiP 11–30.76.

11 T S Khachaturov, *Ekonomika prirodopol'zovaniya*, Moscow: Nauka, 1987, p. 112.

12 *Okhrana okruzhayushchei sredy ...*, p. 14.

13 *Narodnoe khozyaistvo SSSR za 70 let*, p. 613; *Okhrana okruzhayushchei sredy ...*, p. 75.

14 G I Volovnik, A D Lerner, Rezhim vodosberezheniya: reservy i effektivnost', *Zhilishchnoe i kommunal' noe khozyaistvo*, no. 6, 1987, pp. 20–1. S K Stankov, A A Kozak, *Zhilishchnoe i kommunal' noe khozyaistvo*, no. 6, 1986, op cit, indicated that calibration of water meters are regulated under GOST 6019–83 and GOST 14167–83, but that these are often not observed, contributing to water losses and to underesti- mates of consumption requirements.

15 V TsK *KPSS i* Sovete Ministrov SSSR, O pervoocherednykh, *Izvestiya*, 27 January 1988, p. 1.

16 *Narodnoe khozyaistvo SSSR v 1988 g*, p. 246.

17 *Okhrana okruzhayushchei sredy ...*, p. 76; *Narodnoe khozyaistvo SSSR v 1988 g*, ibid; P Poletaev, Realizatsiya meropriyatii po okhrane prirody, *Planovoe khozyaistvo*, no. 8, 1984, pp. 25–32.

18 *Okhrana okruzhayushchei sredy ...*, ibid.

19 Lemeshev, *EKO*, no. 8, 1984, op cit.

20 N A Atanov, Yu V Voronov, L L Negoda, N V Kshnyakina, Qualitative Composition of Biological Film Biocenose and Treatment of Recycled Water in Cooling Towers, *Soviet Journal of Water Chemistry and Technology*, (translation journal), vol. 8, no. 3, 1986, p. 95.

21 *Okhrana okruzhayushchei sredy ...*, p. 16.

22 S Legornev, V nogu so vsei stranoi, *Zhilishchnoe i kommunal' noe khozyaistvo*, no. 2, 1985, pp. 14–15.

23 Z S Romadinov, Kak opredelit' proizvodstvennuyu moshchnost' vodokanala?, *Zhilishchnoe i kommunal' noe khozyaistvo*, no. 3, 1987, pp. 19–21. The article cited regulations giving the formulae used in calculating the production capacity of enterprises and production associations (USSR Gosplan, USSR Central Statistical Administration no. 08.12.83, no. NL 49–D/04–66: *Osnovnye polozheniya po raschetu proizvodstvennykh moshchnostei deistvuyushchikh predpriyatii, proizvostvennykh ob' edinenii (kombinatov)*. This regulation pertains to the productive sphere of indus- trial activities, but as regards the water supply and sewerage industries it addresses both the material production and services sectors.

24 Ibid.

25 G N Krasovskii, N A Egorov, Gigienicheskaya klassifikatsiya vodnykh ob'ektov po stepeni zagryazeniya, *Gigiena i sanitariya*, no. 3, 1987, pp. 8–10. Okhrana vodnykh resursov Ladozhskogo ozera, *Ekonomicheskaya gazeta*, no. 49, 1987, p. 24. During 1986, 1.5 cubic kilometres of industrial and municipal effluents were released into the Lake Ladoga basin. Of this amount 128 million cubic metres were classed as 'insufficiently clean'.

More recent data concerning Lake Baikal and Lake Ladoga, published in *Okhrana okruzhayushchei sredy ...*, p. 66, are alarming and obviously some recalculations have been made. Here, it was stated that 1.4 billion cubic metres of waste water entered

Lake Ladoga during 1988, of which 392 million cubic metres (28 per cent) were considered polluted sewage. Thus, while the volume of waste water flowing into the lake is relatively the same, that which is classified as polluted sewage is roughly 150 per cent of the 1986 figure, raising some doubts about the rate of progress in respect of current construction of waste water treatment installations in Leningrad.

The same source stated that 252 million cubic metres of waste water flowed into Lake Baikal during 1988, of which 192 million cubic metres (76 per cent) were polluted sewage water. Of the latter, 87 million cubic metres or 45 per cent originated in the Selenga River, and would refer to the effluent from the Selenga pulp and paper complex and several towns located upstream of Baikal. However, the 1988 data are not reconcilable with other statistical sources, such as *Narodnoe khozyaistvo SSSR za 70 let*, p. 616, which stated that of 663 million cubic metres of waste water flowing into Lake Baikal, 122 million cubic metres (18 per cent) were actually processed through sewage treatment installations and reached 'normative' criteria, 66 million cubic metres (10 per cent) were insufficiently cleansed, while 475 million cubic metres (71 per cent) were not treated, but regarded as normatively clean and released. Thus, in 1988 nearly three times as much polluted sewage entered Lake Baikal than was indicated to be the case in 1986.

26   N G Ivanov, L A Komyazhenkov, A A Korolev, Ya Lazovskii, M G Novikov, E V Merkulov, Obrabotka promvnykh vod kontaktnykh osvetlitelei, *Zhilishchnoe i kommunal' noe khozyaistvo*, no. 6, 1987, p. 23: In accordance with existing USSR legislation on protection of the environment, there is a prohibition on discharge of polluted waste water into other bodies of water without prior treatment.

27   A A Mazo, Ekologicheskii podkhod k okhrane vodnykh resursov, *Vodnye resursy*, no. 1, 1987, pp. 119–24.

28   *Narodnoe khozyaistvo SSSR za 70 let*, p. 612. P Poletaev, V otvete za prirodu, *Pravda*, 5 June 1986, p. 3, confirmed the figure, stating that 13 per cent of water processed through installations is lost each year. 13 per cent of 350 cubic kilometres is approximately 45 cubic kilometres.

29   *Okhrana okruzhayushchei sredy ...*, p. 62.

30   Interview with A Yanshin, Shagi k noosfere, *Literaturnaya gazeta*, no. 5, 28 January 1987, p. 11; Kak mnogo v nem otozvalos', *Zhilishchnoe i kommunal' noe khozyaistvo*, no. 1, 1987, pp. 4–7: 'The General Plan of 1971 envisaged that by the year 2000, the per capita expenditure of water would be 1,000 litres per day, but today we already start from a figure of 680 litres of which 260 litres is used for drinking water and the remainder by industry and the municipal economy.' The author argued that the supply is not too large.

31   Moskva na poroge tret'ego tysyacheletiya, *Zhilishchnoe i kommunal' noe khozyaistvo*, no. 1, 1987, pp. 2–3; *Zhilishchnoe i kommunal' noe khozyaistvo*, no. 1, 1987, ibid, pp. 4–7.

32   G I Volovnik, A D Lerner, *Zhilishchnoe i kommunal' noe khozyaistvo*, no. 6, 1987, op cit, offers a discussion of fifty two towns in RSFSR which could reduce water losses by 25–35 per cent.

33   S Murasov, Poisk i vnedrenie ekonomicheskikh tekhnologii, *Zhilishchnoe i kommunal' noe khozyaistvo*, no. 7, 1987, pp. 8–9, and Volovnik, ibid, indicated that leaking water faucets made a significant contribution to water losses.

34   S K Stankov, A A Kozak, *Zhilishchnoe i kommunal' noe khozyaistvo*, no. 6, 1986, op cit.

35   I Potravnyi, et al, *Ekonomika Sovetskoi Ukrainy*, no. 6, 1987, op cit; V Vinogradov, Problemy sel'skokhozyaistvennoi ekologii, *Nauka i zhizn*, no. 6, 1987, pp. 2–9.

36   V Rott, Pasport gotovnosti – zerkalo predpriimchivosti, *Zhilishchnoe i kommunal' noe khozyaistvo*, no. 9, 1986, pp. 3–4. While the reasons for replacing pipe in Moscow are somewhat different, the rate of progress is similarly behind schedule. 'There is a need

to renew the pipe at a rate of about 25 kilometres each year. At the moment, we are managing 3–6 kilometres per year. What is to blame is the complex network of lanes and streets, the lack of pipes with the necessary characteristics, and the means for mechanised work in compact urban building sites, etc.' *Zhilishchnoe i kommunal' noe khozyaistvo*, no. 1, 1987, op cit, pp. 4–7.

37   Rott, *Zhilishchnoe i kommunal' noe khozyaistvo*, no. 9, 1986, op cit.

38   Z M Lazarev and F F Daitov, Kompleksnoe reshenie voprosov okhrany okruzhayushchei sredy na neftekhimicheskom predpriyatii, *Gigiena i sanitariya*, no. 1, 1987, p. 61–2; Z S Gladun, Pravovoe polozhenie sanitarno-epidemiologicheskoi sluzhby, *Gigiena i sanitariya*, no. 1, 1986, pp. 22–5.

39   G N Krasovskii and N A Egorov, *Gigiena i sanitariya*, no. 3, 1987, op cit.

40   G Shalabin, O sovershenstvovanii khozyaistvennogo mekhanizma ratsional'nogo prirodopol'zovaniya na regional'nom urovne, *Ekonomicheskie nauki*, no. 5, 1987, pp. 77–81.

41   A A Gusev, Ekonomicheskie problemy bezotkhodnykh proizvodstv, *Izvestiya Akademiya Nauk SSSR, Seriya ekonomiche skaya*, no. 5, 1985, pp. 53–63.

42   N G Ivanov et al, *Zhilishchnoe i kommunal' noe khozyaistvo*, no. 6, 1987, op cit, cited regulation SNiP 2.04.02–84, 'Vodosnabzhenie. Naruzhnye seti i sooruzheniya'; and GOST 2874–82 Voda pit'evaya. See also V F Zemtsev, I V Seryakov, L A Khristianov, Ekspressnaya otsenka kachestva ochishchennykh stochnykh vod, *Zhilishchnoe i kommunal' noe khozyaistvo*, no. 6, 1987, pp. 19–20 concerning the present technology for testing the purity of treated waste water.

43   V F Zemtsev, et al, *Zhilishchnoe i kommunal' noe khozyaistvo*, no. 6, 1987, ibid.

44   *Okhrana okruzhyushchei sredy ...*, ibid.

45   V Gubarev, Ekologiya bez kosmetiki, *Pravda*, 7 September 1987, p. 4.

46   *Narodnoe khozyaistvo SSSR v 1988g*, p. 247; *Okhrana okruzhyushchei sredy ...*, p. 62.

47   This estimate is very close to that of T S Khachaturov, *Ekonomika pridopol' zovaniya*, op cit., in which he indicates that in 1985 about 72 per cent of fresh water consumed by the industrial and municipal sectors was released as 'normatively cleansed'. It is reported that there are 133.3 cubic kilometres of fresh water intake for the industrial and municipal sectors. 133.3 cubic kilometres *less* 28.6 of normatively cleansed effluent and *less* 12.2 cubic kilometres untreated/insufficiently treated effluent leaves 92.2 cubic kilometres of waste water apparently not the subject of regulation. We call this 70 per cent for the sake of convenience.

48   Z S Romadinov, *Zhilishchnoe i kommunal' noe khozyaistvo*, no. 3, 1987, op cit.

49   T S Khachaturov, *Ekonomika prirodopol' zovaniya*, op cit, p. 113. V V Orlovskii, V N Stroitelev, Povysit' kachestvo vody, *Zhilishchnoe i kommunal' noe khozyaistvo*, no. 10, 1987, pp. 33–5.

50   V L Popov, Vesti perestroiku shirokim frontom, *Zhilishchnoe i kommunal' noe khozyaistvo*, no. 10, 1987, pp. 2–3. T S Khachaturov, *Ekonomika prirodopol' zovaniya*, op cit, p. 115.

51   V G Markot, Dobivat'sya uskoreniya na marshe perestroiki, *Zhilishchnoe i kommunal' noe khozyaistvo*, no. 1, 1987, pp. 8–10.

52   V V Orlovskii and V N Stroitelev, *Zhilishchnoe i kommunal' noe khozyaistvo*, no. 10, 1987, op cit, pp. 33–5.

53   Yu B Kostarev, Kommunal'noe khozyaistvo Tadzhikistana: perspektivy razvitiya, *Zhilishchnoe i kommunal' noe khozyaistvo*, no. 2, 1987, pp. 4–5.

54   A M Chernyaev, Yu P Belichenko, Voda: ekologiya i ekonomika, *EKO*, no. 1, 1987, pp. 102–6. In this example, there was no mention of the related sewerage network.

3 Agricultural Amelioration and the Environment

Introduction

Agricultural development, as a leading priority in the Soviet Union, has not lost its importance in the competition for investment resources. By intensifying agricultural production, the present Soviet leadership hopes to reduce grain imports and to free holdings of convertible currencies to benefit other sectors of the economy. Improvement of agriculture no longer means simply that the quantitative output of commodities and equipment must increase, although this is clearly essential. In the future, advances must occur in the agricultural infrastructure, including the provision of clean water supplies, upgraded housing, roads, electrification and sanitation, equipment appropriate to local conditions, and enforcement of child labour restrictions.

When a linkage is established between agriculture and the environment, oftentimes it can be handled expeditiously; that is, the environmental effect is preventable and assumed to have only temporary significance. The rash of public health complaints in the mid-1980s, linked to the use of an agricultural chemical, *butifos*, was one such incident and avoided by discontinuing its use. Nowadays, however, there is mounting evidence, seen in the deterioration of public health in rural areas, that agricultural practices do engender ecological damage of a more lasting nature. The impacts can no longer be considered inconsequential where they are commonly manifest as hepatitis, lung disorders, and birth abnormalities having no medical remedies, or where the effect is desertification, as is occurring throughout the Aral Sea basin. These are long-lasting environmental and economic consequences whose remedies, if indeed there are any, will be very expensive to achieve.

Soviet economic and environmental literature strongly suggests that the damage inflicted by Soviet agricultural practice is now so pervasive that it can be singled out as a cause of deteriorating conditions across the Soviet economy. But such myopic analysis is not satisfactory, as it is obvious that many preconditions for improvement in the rural economy are dependent on changes in the overall management of the national economy. The agricultural leadership does have sufficient control over the organisation and management of farming, however, to direct investment towards ecologically 'friendly' technologies and obstruct projects that are environmentally dangerous.

Soviet economists are not especially judicious in their handling of agricultural terminologies, which often simply reflect the categories of the state capital budget or else current agricultural techniques. The main concern of this chapter is the relationship between 'agricultural amelioration' and environmental investment. The term refers specifically to irrigation and drainage construction, which covers the length of some 40 million hectares of agricultural land.[1] So far, irrigation and drainage have been undertaken to expand or improve land for purposes of cultivation, and the ecological implications of the construction work appear to have been underplayed.

The fact is, the capital budget for agricultural amelioration includes funding for related areas of rural water management, which are considered in the following sections, since the ministries that are so widely criticised for the ecological damage wreaked by poor amelioration work also undertake the planning and construction activities related to provision of water supplies, waste water treatment, and some rural hydroelectric power schemes. Moreover, in its effect on the environment, amelioration work cannot be fully distinguished from a further range of management options acknowledged by the phrase 'land improvement'. This term refers, for instance, to reforestation, flood and erosion control, crop rotation, plowing techniques, fertilisation, and pest control. Water management (especially decisions to divert river flows and tap groundwater) and land improvement (in particular, the use of agricultural chemicals) have key roles in the cause-and-effect pattern of agricultural amelioration and environmental change.

Unlike other branches of the Soviet economy that have suffered from shortages of capital and financial means, agriculture has not. The overriding opinion voiced in the East and the West is that an extraordinary amount of resources has been squandered. Nonetheless, given the vast area under cultivation, it is obvious that the entire rural economy must continue to receive large-scale direct investment in order to achieve acceptable economic and social standards and, now, ecological survival. That there is great need seems obvious, but equally there is little evidence of the necessary policy reformulations. In consequence, the amelioration ministries intend to continue the massive water management construction projects that are changing the geography of some regions.

Investment Background

Agricultural policies are developed under the auspices of the 'Food Programme' (an initiative established by order of the Central Committee in May 1982 and reiterated in October 1985 to improve agricultural infrastructure and to foster productivity). The formation of the USSR Union-Republic State Agro-Industrial Committee (Gosagroprom) was announced in November 1985, with the explicit purpose of granting the agricultural sector sufficient power to influence the decisions of related ministries (for example, the Ministry of Agricultural Chemicals and the Ministry of Water Management and Amelioration [Minvodkhoz]. In April 1989, Gosagroprom was abolished. The decision to disband Gosagroprom, rather than to strengthen its remit, decentralised the national decisionmaking bureaucracy. Clearly, the changes were intended to shore up the republics' authority over regional agricultural practices. However, it did not appear to have placed limits on agricultural amelioration and other activities having ecological implications.

Since 1985, President Gorbachev has attempted to shift the direction of amelioration construction towards improvement of existing networks for irrigation and drainage, rather than in their expansion which has been the long-standing priority.[2] The change in emphasis was occasioned by the extensive damage to land and water resources resulting from amelioration activities and subsequent agricultural practices. Future decisions to undertake amelioration construction are to be considered in the context of other land improvement alternatives and also with reference to requirements for local water purification and waste water treatment.

Theoretically, decisions to undertake amelioration construction are dependent on the physical conditions under which local agriculture functions in receipt of climate, soil fertility, and water availability; the receipt of technologies and labour to compensate for such factors; and the ability to recoup the related expenditures through gains in agricultural productivity on the improved land. However, despite the very large sums of money spent on agriculture, current economic policies governing the sector are strongly criticised as Soviet agriculture's overall inefficiency is the result of decision-making of a political and administrative character.

A series of incongruent economic practices affecting amelioration investment decisions can be seen in the following:

- undue levels of price supports for agricultural commodities, caused by an hitherto unsatisfied need to establish the actual costs of production;[3]
- capital construction without guaranteed returns on investment in respect of agricultural productivity, and the lack of effective contractual relations between the collective or state farms and the builder of the amelioration systems;[4]

- expansion of irrigated agriculture in regions with inadequate water supplies to support the combined needs of industry, communal and domestic use, and agriculture; and the lack of incentives for water conservation by requiring payment for water used in agriculture.[5]
- the marginal fertility of much agricultural land, coupled with a centrally imposed crop structure.[6]
- the lack of means for agricultural mechanisation (for instance, sufficient machinery and electric power) and chemicalisation; or conversely the use of machinery and chemicals which damage the soil;[7]
- the displacement of productive agricultural land for non-agricultural purposes, in effect promoted by low valuations of agricultural land;[8] and
- the frequent interference in agricultural practices by unqualified persons having positions of political and administrative authority, as well as the lack of effective coordination amongst the administrative units involved in amelioration construction decisions.[9]

The economic situation and to a great extent the ecological circumstances in agriculture are largely conditioned by the locations of the state and collective farms. As elsewhere, those having favourable conditions receive a greater income from expenditures of capital and labour than farms found in less desirable conditions. Some actions can be taken to level out the economic conditions of farming production by means of differentiated purchase prices for produce, differentiated income tax, and other financial manipulations, but efforts in these directions have not been effective; indeed, reduced incomes underlie the depopulation of some rural districts.

It was decided in 1986 to revise the normatives that regulate rent relations by establishing them on the basis of the worst possible conditions for agricultural production. Since the beginning of 1987, state farms are supposed to be making payments to the budget from profits, while collective farms continue to pay income tax on the basis of fixed formula, that theoretically, at least, take into account an economic valuation of the land, the supply of basic funds, and labour reserves. (There is some doubt amongst the advisory panel that these changes in taxation policy have been implemented.) Other financial arrangements allow subsidies in times of natural disaster and to agricultural units having marginal incomes, and in some cases deferments of payments of interest and/or principle on debts owed to banks by unprofitable state or collective farms.[10] Nowadays, loss-generating agricultural enterprises are treated less sympathetically than in the past: there have been reports of 'bankruptcies' and the subsequent amalgamation of such collective farms with other agricultural enterprises. Several leading economists point out that either generous credit arrangements, or profound changes to the system of taxation, will be necessary to stimulate many of the state and collective farms to repair and maintain, much less pay to reconstruct the irrigation and drainage systems on their land. If the finances cannot be found within a farm's internal resources, credit is one way to remove the reluctance to expend scarce resources on amelioration work.[11]

An alternative scheme being considered, that of progressive taxation by means of differential rent, offers some potential to eliminate regional disproportion in opportunity costs of production, although it does not address the need fully to differentiate land values according to productivity and other factors – such as the presence of irrigation and drainage networks. In the West, of course, land values are established within the context of a market economy, and most economists believe that it is virtually impossible to devise a taxation system that can serve as an adequate substitute for market prices of agricultural commodities, can allow the costs of production to be recouped, and include sufficient margins to ensure agricultural organisations become profit-making. These are important factors in the consideration of agricultural-environmental economics, as a system that requires the purchaser to compensate the agricultural unit for its land on the basis of fully defined valuations might also serve to curb the procurement of agricultural land for more obviously polluting industrial purposes. Conversely, full valuations could motivate a kolkhoz manager to refrain from investment that cannot be recovered through earnings or sale of the land. In one or two regions, land values are being adjusted but, relative to the needs of the national economy, a piecemeal approach is inefficient. For example, the net result of unilateral actions by individual regions could ultimately force further inter-sectoral imbalances as, under *khozraschet* conditions, industry will locate where opportunity costs, such as the price of land, are to their best advantage. Should an adjustment of land values occur across the Soviet Union, the intent would be to stimulate change in the geographic mix of industry and agriculture,[12] although there is no evidence to suggest this would automatically prove to be more advantageous from an ecological perspective or even that agriculture would achieve a better position over industry.

It is commonly believed that capital investment in amelioration is vastly out of line with returns in agricultural productivity, stability of production, or indeed the prospects of compensation through land values. Long discussions of the situation have been published from which it can only be concluded that the big-money construction items are decided administratively and politically. The Soviet situation may not be significantly different from the sometimes bemusing relationship of the US Congress to the US Corps of Engineers, except that in the Soviet case, it seems that even the small-money items are decided politically, whereas in the United States irrigation and drainage on farm land are undertaken by the private sector. In the future, these same political accommodations could bring a positive effect as Minvodkhoz, and indeed the collective farms themselves, adjust to *khozraschet* accountability, there will be political support for the ministry to increase the accountability of Minvodkhoz for decisions to place land under irrigation and drainage in the first instance, and secondly for the construction work itself. A punitive approach to force 'rethinking' has been widely touted: it would link bonuses for completion of amelioration work not only to the quality and speed of construction but also to the subsequent productivity of agricultural land. Given past accounts of the poor quality of amelioration work and poor return on the investment, both the total of bonuses paid to Minvodkhoz's construction crews and new construction work should contract sharply, and throughout much of Central Asia, the construction workers would not see any bonuses at all![13] But such suggestions are obviously nonsensical, since allocating bonuses on such grounds as the demonstrated productivity of the ameliorated land would ensure the creation of a bureaucratic nightmare.

It is important to note that in establishing Gosagroprom, the Central Committee specifically stated that the new State Committee would assume some functions previously exercised by Minvodkhoz. These included provision of expert review of designs and estimates; setting ceilings on capital investment and financing of amelioration work; and acceptance of completed construction. Apparently, this measure was taken to impose some constraints on Minvodkhoz's expansion-oriented construction programme and to bring it in line with Gosagroprom's assessments of where and how agricultural amelioration investment should take place. However, Gosagroprom did not control the capital budget for irrigation and drainage construction, so its influence was muted from the outset.[14] It is assumed these functions were amongst those assigned to the State Planning Committee when Gosagroprom was abolished.

Some economists now argue that for expenditure on agricultural construction to be effective in respect of the Soviet economy, further integration of all investment affecting the sector must be achieved.[15] But this will be difficult as capital expenditure in agriculture absorbs approximately one-third of all investment funds in the Soviet economy, and even this one-third share is obviously not well integrated.[16] That specified for amelioration construction has been on an upward spiral since 1970. The efficiency of such concentrated investment is not only dependent on performance in the agricultural sector; it is equally dependent on a full range of related infrastructure (such as machinery, roads, transport, and interim storage) that are provided outside the agricultural economy. It also depends on rural electrification which, having been an important factor in other countries, lags behind demand. Some of the costs of electrification (plus or minus one billion rubles annually) are borne in the capital budget for agriculture.[17]

President Gorbachev has pursued a policy to restructure agricultural management, by promoting the creation of 'small cooperatives', and recently 'inheritable leaseholds'. When the problems of financial and material resources are also worked out, the new arrangements may boost the incentives amongst the workforce to move into private sector farming, which Poland's experience has demonstrated to be more efficient than giant-scale, collective

3.1 Capital Budget for Agriculture
(billions of rubles, in comparable values)

Year	Capital Budget Total	State Capital Budget Means	Means of Kolkhoz	Other Sources
1971–75	111.2	71.9	39.3	23.2
1976–80	143.2	97.3	45.9	32.0
1981–85	156.2	109.3	46.9	48.4
1986–88	104.4	71.4	33.0	37.7
1986–90*	174.0	119.0	55.0	63.0

* Projected from data for 1986–88.
Source: Narodnoe khozyaistvo SSSR v 1988 g, p. 435.

3.2 Capital Budget for Amelioration Construction
(from State Capital Budget and Kolkhoz Means, billions of rubles)

	Total Budget Amelioration Funds	of which Water Management Construction
1971–75	29.6	22.2
1976–80	40.0	27.4
1981–85	43.9	29.5
1986–88	27.8	18.7
1986–90*	46.3	31.2

* Projected from data for 1986–88.
Source: Narodnoe khozyaistvo SSSR v 1988 g, p. 445.

farms. Unfortunately, in such areas as Central Asia where water resources are severely overburdened, suitable land probably will not become available.[18] So far, the policy seems doomed to flounder, and no significant shifts to semi-private farming have occurred.

Recouping expenditure for irrigation and drainage is dependent on how the land is subsequently used. Irrigated and drained land accounts for one-third of total national crop output, including all of cotton and rice, three-fourths of vegetables, half of fruit, and a considerable part of fodder.[19] State and collective farms are assigned production targets for specific crops, but a complicating factor is sometimes reported when the natural conditions at a given site are unsuited for the designated produce. In effect, such remote decisionmaking reduces the farmer's ability to maximise the use of ameliorated land, and will continue to do so until on-site managers are allowed greater freedom to plant the crops they believe will show the greatest yield under local conditions.

3.3   Availability and Use of Ameliorated Farm Land
(millions of hectares)

	1970	1980	1985	1986	1987	1988	1990*
Available							
Irrigated	10.8	17.2	19.7	20.2	20.2	20.5	20.5
Drained	7.4	12.6	14.6	14.9	14.9	15.2	15.2
In Use							
Irrigated	10.4	16.7	19.1	19.5	19.6	19.8	19.8
Drained	6.9	12.0	14.0	14.3	14.4	14.7	14.7

* Based on 1988.
Source: *Narodnoe khozyaistvo SSSR v 1988 g*, p. 473.

There are many factors which might be considered in choosing crops to be grown on ameliorated land, and one effect of critical evaluations would be to reduce the perceived need for amelioration by specifying:

- *cultivation which cannot survive without irrigation or drainage*. This includes the production of rice, cotton and soya, which usually requires amelioration.
- *securing the stability of production where amelioration is important*. In this group are the areas requiring irrigation, where its absence retards growth, and those areas requiring a specific amount of water for even production. The production of Vegetables usually require ameliorated land, while fodder requires specific quantities of water. It is difficult, and unnecessary here, to calculate from the available data the economic benefit of cultivating fodder on ameliorated land. At present, 47.7 per cent of irrigated land is used for fodder; in another twenty years, it is planned that 64 per cent of irrigated land will be used for this purpose.
- *increasing the stability of production, where other factors are at issue*. In the third group are crops for which there are alternative means to stabilise production. The most important crop in the third group is grain.[20]

Assessing the Amelioration Option

Responsibilities for the construction and operation of water management and amelioration systems are shared amongst the all-union, republic and regional organs of Minvodkhoz (who also help decide what is built where), the State Irrigation Service, and state and collective farms.[21] Their responsibilities include:[22] provision of water intake and purification systems; maintenance of the distribution network; monitoring consumption; and waste water treatment. One or two experiments to streamline the responsibilities for agricultural water management have occurred; for example, in Georgia, the Ministry of Water Management and Amelioration was merged with the Republic's State Committee for Agricultural Production. Georgian officials note that the new organisational structure makes it much more difficult to obtain central support[23] – the very reason that several other republics have not followed suit.

Scientific and economic information are needed to evaluate the need for irrigation and drainage. These include calculations of:

- *the availability of fresh surface and groundwater resources in agricultural areas.* Such calculations are supposedly developed within the context of a regional water balance that also accounts for water consumed in industry, the municipal and domestic economy, and that needed to sustain acceptable ecological conditions.[24] Amongst the anomalies in Soviet statistical data is the fact that tabulations of the distribution of water consumption are not adequately delineated. Data for agricultural water consumption include the water supplies for irrigation and domestic consumption on collective and state farms, other rural populations, and much of the food processing industry.[25]
- *the specific demand for water supplies in respect of local climatic conditions, taking into account the most advantageous uses of farm land and available water resources.*[26] Simply put, the geographic demand for water supplies does not always reflect its immediate availability in areas with substantial dependence on irrigation, such as Central Asia and much of the Ukraine.[27]

There is growing recognition of the value of water balances, which require data on water resources, the patterns of consumption, and the nature and sources of contaminated effluent in the region. The use of such techniques started in the Ukraine, where water shortages have forced severe constraints on all sectors of the economy. But, as one author described the situation, the issue at hand is not just about water shortages, it is 'the need to stabilise demand and to ensure maximum use of water supplies by strict controls and cleansing, recycling, and amelioration technologies'.[28]

Significant strides have been made in the Ukraine not only to undertake the necessary calculations, but also to build the necessary administrative infrastructure to regulate water usage.[29] The theoretical foundations of Ukrainian water management appear to be more advanced than in Central Asia, although until 1986, the Ukrainian amelioration difficulties were a mirror-image of many Central Asian problems and 'big-money solutions'. (Since Chernobyl' there has been the additional factor of radioactive contamination for which no solutions have appeared thus far; as farm land in the fall-out zone continues to be planted and harvested, it is concluded that the surface and groundwater affected by Chernobyl' are similarly used.) The Ukraine's natural shortages of surface water, combined with the intense irrigation of agriculture, have resulted in severe groundwater contamination, although how much requires cleansing has not been reported. Efforts to satisfy the demand for water have caused the Ukraine to develop a system of reservoirs, recycling of waste water, and dependence on groundwater resources. New construction is carefully monitored to constrain new demand for water. The main controversial feature of the Ukrainian response is the construction work to divert several rivers into arid regions.[30]

Similar water balances are being developed for the Russian Republic, Dagestan,[31] and Central Asia. The difficulties encountered by Soviet authorities working on Central Asian water problems are attributed, in the past at least, to insufficient data. The gaps served to generate uncertainty when choices were required between intensifying the use of existing water supplies or developing alternative water resources, and it is partly due to the chronic

3.4   Resources of River Water and Exploitable Groundwater by Union Republic
(cubic kilometres in a year)

	Total Volume of River Flow	Potential Exploitable Sources of Groundwater	Per cent Used
USSR	4740	378	17
RSFSR	4270	228	9
Ukraine	210	21	45
Belorussia	56	18	9
Uzbekistan	108	22	25
Kazakhstan	125	44	33
Georgia	61	4	65
Azerbaidzhan	28	5	44
Lithuania	23	1	60
Moldavia	13	1	60
Latvia	32	2	25
Kirgizia	49	13	26
Tadzhikstan	95	6	37
Armenia	8	5	84
Turkmenia	71	2	50
Estonia	16	2	10

Column should read 'per cent of exploitable groundwater used'.
Source: Okhrana okruzhayushchei sredy i ratsional'noe ispolzovanie prirodnykh resursov v SSSR, Moscow, 1989, p. 64.

lack of reliable data that Central Asian scientists continue to pine for a 'quick fix' – to be found in some version of a Northern rivers diversion scheme.[32]

The most recent data giving some idea of water resources are presented above. Noteworthy is the fact that the table reflects river water as the main source of fresh water supplies, and excludes inland seas and lakes which would add 106,400 cubic kilometres of water resources, including 79,200 cubic kilometres in the Caspian and Aral Seas (a figure which should be radically reduced in keeping with the impoverished condition of the Aral Sea), and 25,200 cubic kilometres in Lake Baikal.

Table 3.5 presents recent data for withdrawals of fresh water. Noteworthy is the wide discrepancy between this table in respect of actual withdrawals of ground water and the preceding one concerning the degree to which groundwater is used. It is assumed that Table 3.4 indicates that 17 per cent of the resource base is tapped to some extent, while Table 3.5 shows that only 50 per cent of the groundwater resources that are tapped is actually withdrawn.[33]

3.5 Withdrawals of Fresh Water in the USSR
by Union Republic
(billion cubic metres)

Region	1985 Natural[1] Sources	of which Groundwater	1988 Natural Sources	of which Groundwater
USSR	329.8	29.1	333.7	31.4
RSFSR	105.5	11.4	105.8	12.6
Ukraine	30.6	4.1	30.6	4.2
Belorussia	2.8	1.0	2.8	1.1
Uzbekistan	70.6	3.0	73.9	3.2
Kazakhstan	39.0	2.1	39.4	2.3
Georgia	4.5	.7	3.8	1.0
Azerbaidzhan	15.2	1.5	14.9	1.5
Lithuania	2.8	.5	3.6	.5
Moldavia	3.7	.3	3.7	.3
Latvia	.7	.3	.7	.3
Kirgizia	9.3	.9	12.1	.9
Tadzhikstan	13.0	1.8	13.0	1.1
Armenia	4.1	1.2	4.1	1.6
Turkmenia	24.2	.4	22.5	.5
Estonia	2.6	.2	3.0	.2

[1] This column should read 'Total Volume Withdrawn from Natural Sources'.
Source: Okhrana okruzhayushchei sredy..., p. 69.

The specific usage by agriculture of fresh water resources is represented in the Table 3.6. It is noteworthy that agriculture requires 53 per cent of the total net water withdrawn for use in the national economy.

3.6   Withdrawals of Water, Losses, and Consumption by Agriculture in 1988 by Union Republic
(billion cubic metres)

	Total Withdrawals	Losses[1]	Net Consumption (all sectors)	Agricultural[2] Consumption
USSR	333.7	50.6	286.3	152.5
RSFSR	105.6	8.8	94.8	22.3
Ukraine	30.6	1.8	28.7	7.9
Belorussia	2.8	.05	2.7	.4
Uzbekistan	73.9	16.9	54.8	46.2
Kazakhstan	39.4	6.1	33.1	24.4
Georgia	3.8	.7	3.1	1.3
Azerbaidzhan	14.9	4.1	12.4	8.7
Lithuania	3.6	.03	3.6	.1
Moldavia	3.7	.06	3.6	.7
Latvia	.7	.02	.7	.07
Kirgizia	12.1	2.3	10.0	9.1
Tadzhikstan	12.8	1.2	11.7	10.6
Armenia	4.1	.7	3.5	2.4
Turkmenia	22.5	7.3	20.4	18.2
Estonia	3.0	.02	3.0	.05

[1] Losses during the transport of water from point of withdrawal to point of consumption.
[2] Taken from a table entitled 'Use of water for irrigation, irrigation canals, and rural water supplies'.
Source: Okhrana okruzhayushchei sredy..., pp. 69, 70, and 75.

In 1988, only a very small amount (2.3 billion cubic metres or about 1 per cent) of the total volume of water used in agriculture is recycled sewage or collector-drainage flows.[34]

Once the availability and demand for fresh water have been determined, there may be a rationalisation of the uses of agricultural land, especially concerning the water-intensiveness of production in areas with constrained water supplies.[35] Rational decisionmaking for amelioration by irrigation and drainage requires information on:

- the general demand for water in irrigation;
- the extent to which fresh water consumption can be reduced by recycling;
- the availability of alternative sources of water, such as cleansed sewage or industrial waste water;
- the extent to which the present irrigation and drainage technologies may be improved to reduce water losses;
- the anticipated expansion of irrigated land; and
- the technologies that are needed to cleanse water before it is recycled or discharged.

Decisions to improve the use of existing water supplies or to develop alternative water resources are not yet functions of the economics of water supplies. That is, the critical factor *should* be the cost of water. The lack of a price or prices for agricultural water in the Soviet Union has been a serious impediment to determining the opportunities associated with renewing water infrastructure (say, to reduce losses), or developing alternative, perhaps non-traditional resources. Water prices can stimulate water conservation. Moreover, in a rationalised water management situation, payments for water would be differentiated in the regions by the extent of the guaranteed supply, water quality, the conditions of its use, and other indices.[36]

Payments for water have the following economic functions:

1   *They give the consumer an economic interest in curbing waste.* Water free-of-charge, conversely, removes the interests of the user in its economic use. For instance, water protection measures, such as those announced in January 1988,[37] will have extremely limited effectiveness because, in the absence of payments, there is no economic incentive for agriculture to conserve water.
2   *They reimburse the expenses of water management.* In setting the price schedule for water consumption in agriculture, planners have much to learn from the irrationalities of the water price schedules presently used for industrial payments. For example, while industrial enterprises are required to make payments for water drawn from surface and groundwater sources and from water management systems, these charges do not fully compensate the state for its investment in water supply systems. Even though the rate structures are supposed to reflect existing conditions in various locales, they usually do not cover the costs of maintenance and repair of the water supply systems, nor do most allow for prospective investment in waste water treatment. A positive feature of the present system is that charges are assessed by enterprise; they can be reduced to the extent of water recycling and also according to the volume of purified water sold to other enterprises. Though fines exist for exceeding approved

levels of water consumption, even these are ineffective due to the fact that they are too low and, anyway there appear to be too few water metres to measure consumption accurately.[38]

3   *They allow more complete accounting of costs attributable to agriculture and specific crops.* Apparently, there is a charge levied on rural households for water taken from irrigation supplies for domestic purposes.[39]

4   *They promote efficiency in the use of labour, financial, and material investment* for both agriculture and water management, and create an index against which the appropriateness of specific water management construction projects can be judged.[40]

The following table, providing estimated costs of water supplies, also gives a sense of what must be charged, directly or indirectly, for agricultural water usage. The data cannot be regarded as definitive, however, as the hypothetical water charges reflect the assumption that all water consumed in agriculture and flowing through the state irrigation system is 'chargeable'. The rates

3.7   Average Theoretical Costs of Water from the State Irrigation System, 1983–1984

Republic	Operating Costs of SIS* from the State Budget, Use & Repair, 10^6 rubles		Volume of H_2O Supply by SIS, 10^9 metres^3		Cost of Water Supply per 1 m^3, in kopeks	
	1983	1984	1983	1984	1983	1984
USSR	854	876	146.6	153.2	.6	.6
RSFSR	166	162	25.5	25.9	.65	.6
Ukraine	89	96	7.2	8.1	1.2	1.2
Uzbekistan	237	241	42.1	45.0	.6	.5
Kazakhstan	63	66	18.3	16.5	.3	.4
Georgia	22	23	1.6	1.9	1.4	1.2
Azerbaidzhan	86	89	12.1	11.6	.7	.8
Kirgizia	31	32	9.2	8.7	.3	.4
Tadzhikstan	56	60	11.5	10.6	.5	.6
Armenia	35	36	2.3	2.6	1.5	1.4
Turkmenia	53	57	16.3	21.7	.3	.3
Moldavia	14	13	.5	.34	2.8	3.8

* State Irrigation System.

Source: L B Sheinin, Plata za vodu i khozyaistvennyi raschet v sel'skom khozyaistve, *Vestnik sel'skogo khozyaistvo nauki*, no. 8, 1987, pp. 11–15. The author is with the State Research Institute on Price Formation of the USSR State Price Committee (Goskomtsen).

probably need to be adjusted for 'actual consumption', so that if the cost at source is 6 kopeks, at the point of delivery it may actually be 12 kopeks or higher, depending on the level of water losses in the distribution network. Interestingly, if 6 kopeks per cubic metre were the average price of rural water, then the state would receive revenues of 9 billion rubles per year. Such an amount would not only cover the operating costs of the state irrigation system (as presented in Table 3.7), but also that for water management construction (as represented in Table 3.2).

It is not simply a matter of requiring payments for water consumption *per se*, but the whole spectrum of services and costs associated with agriculture should be dependent to some extent on the price structure for water. To devise a rate structure that is sensitive to the needs of the supplier to recoup the costs of supplying water, the management side of the picture needs clarification. For example, the provision of water is partly through the state-run irrigation networks, and partly supplied internally by the state and collective farms. This situation is the result of the 1984 decree allowing collective and state farms to decide whether to hand over management of their water installations to the State Irrigation Service; presumably the State Irrigation Service could decide whether the condition of the installation warranted their acceptance of management responsibility. The transfer of agricultural water management installations was scheduled to take place over the 12th plan period, so it is possible that this has not been completed.

Similarly, it is not clear how much of the responsibility for the irrigation equipment is retained by the collective and state farms or is held by the State Irrigation Service, or how costs are apportioned.[41] Such uncertainties complicate determinations of how the farms themselves could recoup payments for water, or how differentials in levels of water consumption due to the nature of a commodity would be accommodated in agricultural prices.[42] There is a further difficulty of differentiating the charges to the collective and state farms for water drawn from rivers and streams and that from groundwater resources. A rate structure sensitive to costs of water supplies would also distinguish between fresh water taken from state-run water works and that provided by repeat-use systems or by wells on the collective and state farms. Finally, there would have to be some provision made specifically for the purpose of promoting water conservation.

Sheinin's table (3.7) implies that geography is a factor in cost-formation, but he did not say how the factor is taken into account. There is, for example, no obvious reason why water in Moldavia should cost three times more than in the Ukraine. Other sources report that the cost of water supplied through the State Irrigation System in Turkmenia, even though it had been considerably reduced, was still 6.38 kopeks per cubic metre in 1980 – a very much higher rate than presented in the table above.[43] Data published elsewhere concerning agricultural water in Dagestan give a price for irrigation water supplied through the State Irrigation System as .37 kopeks per cubic metre, rising to .42

kopeks when costs of repair are included; this is in line with the prices reported in the table.[44]

Establishing rates is difficult enough on the basis of water supplied or water consumed, but when consideration is given to the vast differential in water *usage* per hectare of land irrigated, the economics are radically changed. Of course, the areas having the highest level of use-cum-wastage per hectare are 'worst off' – or at best have the greatest amount to be recouped through commodity prices or taxation. Table 3.8 demonstrates the enormous differences in the volumes of water consumed by agriculture in the various republics: the lowest level of about 1,000 cubic metres per hectare of irrigated land in Lithuania to over 13,000 cubic metres per hectare in three republics (Latvia, Armenia, and Uzbekistan), and the average in the Soviet Union at 8,900 cubic metres per hectare. In Uzbekistan, two-thirds of irrigated land are cotton-growing areas, which involve notoriously excessive consumption of water. Latvia, Kazakhstan, Kirgizia, and Armenia, however, have used more

3.8   Water Usage in Irrigation and Rural Water Supplies by Union Republic

	Total Water Consumed[1] (billion cubic metres)	Area Irrigated (thousand hectares)	Implied Usage per hectare (thousand cubic metres)
USSR	152.5	17 096	8.9
RSFSR	22.3	4 939	4.5
Ukraine	7.9	2 337	3.4
Belorussia	.4	67	5.9
Uzbekistan	46.2	3 516	13.2
Kazakhstan	24.4	1 924	12.8
Georgia	1.3	222	5.8
Azerbaidzhan	8.7	1 016	8.7
Lithuania	.1	10	1.0
Moldavia	.7	222	3.1
Latvia	.08	6	13.3
Kirgizia	9.1	848	10.7
Tadzhikstan	10.6	576	1.8
Armenia	2.4	180	13.3
Turkmenia	18.2	1 218	1.5
Estonia	.05	10	5.0

[1] Column should read 'Total Water Consumed in Irrigation, Irrigation Canals, and the Rural Economy' in 1988. The estimate is inflated to the extent that water in the rural water supply is not used for irrigation.

Source: *Okhrana okruzhayushchei sredy...*, p. 75, *Narodnoe khozyaistvo SSSR v 1988 g*, p. 475. Column three is calculated by dividing the figure in column 2 by that in column 1.

than half of their irrigated land to grow fodder, and their high levels of water consumption reflect wastage due to poorly developed irrigation infrastructure rather than the type of crops or climatic factors. The use of 13,000 cubic metres per hectare suggests that every day of the year, not just in the growing season, a field having 2.4 acres would receive 35 cubic metres of water, in addition to rainfall or other precipitation.[45]

To the extent that water is not supplied by the State Irrigation System, the expenditure per hectare is even more distorted. According to one observer, 'During the growing season between 2–50,000 cubic metres of water are used depending on the type of crop under cultivation. Half of the irrigation water is changed into waste water and drainage, which carries pesticides beyond the irrigation system.'[46] Confronted with such data, a number of economists, such as M Lemeshev, have argued for a number of years that the normatives for water use in irrigation are unduly high![47]

In the Soviet Union, the industrial rates for water are differentiated according to the source of the water, and consumption limits are assigned to each enterprise. When an enterprise's water consumption exceeds the assigned ceiling, it is obliged to pay a penalty. The penalty, a higher rate per cubic metre of water consumed, is assessed by the water authority (presumably a branch of Minvodkhoz) as an encouragement to the enterprise to undertake steps to conserve water. Additionally, the 1988 law on environmental protection envisaged that enterprises will be required to pay a penalty for polluting. Thus, an enterprise or, in this instance, an agricultural unit, will be faced with payments for water consumed and for releases of untreated waste water. There are certain reservations about the level of penalties and sanctions as devised for industry, since those rates have so far not had the effect of stimulating water conservation:[48]

> Economic sanctions [need to be] differentiated by region and over a period of the Five Year Plan, although in the case of such resources as water, they could extend over a longer period of time. The juridical levels would be threefold: (1) payment for the use of natural resources in accordance with their economic value; (2) sanctions for unauthorised levels of environmental pollution; and (3) reproduction of natural resources and nature conservation. These last would include the construction of collective purification works, recultivation of land, reforestation, and so forth. Again, such payments would have to be reckoned on the basis of the optimal economic estimate of the quality of the resources and the level of the environmental pollution, defined on the basis of ecological resources and socio-demographic forecasts of development within a particular territory.

A discussion of water payments leads to a series of questions about the selection of optimal irrigation and drainage technologies. In general, the technologies currently in use are uncomplicated: unlined ditches; cement, plastic, or clay-lined drainage and irrigation canals (that are either open or enclosed); and overhead irrigation (at varying densities of spray). Alternative technologies such as subsoil irrigation and vertical drainage are sometimes mentioned in the literature, but they have been introduced on only a very limited scale. The relatively higher technologies appear as the water intake installations, the main irrigation channels (distinguished from the intra-farm ditches and canals), and the pumping stations along their length. In the future, an additional high technology expenditure may occur with the construction of waste water treatment installations.

It is common practice in the Soviet Union, as in the West, to consider the efficiencies to be gained by automation in the context of local and regional socio-economic conditions. But maintaining employment opportunities appears to carry great weight in amelioration decisionmaking in Central Asia, where there is a labour surplus. If such factors assume a definitive role in investment decisions, they inevitably inhibit the adoption of labour-saving technologies. Soviet agricultural managers then have to compensate with improved agricultural practices across a very broad range of labour-intensive activities to achieve the environmental efficiency otherwise afforded by automation. In this respect, it is useful to recall that amelioration expenditure supposedly reflects the quality of water that is required for specific crops and ecological protection.[49] While this might evoke questions concerning the level of investment allowable under the current construction normatives, there is no evidence to suggest that the level of investment is too low; rather the conversations are about funds being wasted. It may be concluded that the available amelioration technologies do not ensure the quality of agricultural water supplies, and also that irrational consumption patterns are not fostered simply by the way in which they are being used, but by the technologies themselves. However, agricultural managers, even at the ministerial level, cannot resolve the constraints imposed by equipment manufacturers and suppliers whose priorities are established by other government agencies and state committees.

There are hundreds of other regulations governing agriculture. Most relate to the use of pesticides and their effects on human and animal health, air, land, and water.[50] There are normatives for:

- the concentration of agricultural chemicals in irrigation water, on the soil, and ground level air, as well as specific to the crop under cultivation;[51]
- the expected levels of cleansing required in a properly functioning irrigation system to protect workers and the population from exposure to toxic agricultural chemicals;
- the type of climate, subsoil, geological formations, and water table;
- each water basin that is to be protected from undue concentrations of agricultural chemicals contained in drainage water;

- the avoidance of secondary pollution (such as photooxidation when chemicals, released into the atmosphere, form secondary toxic pollutants that are subsequently absorbed into the food cycle);[52] and
- the use of sewage water and treated effluent from restricted sources.[53]

The regulations for allowable concentrations of chemicals in agricultural water and on the soil primarily concern the use of fertilisers, pesticides and herbicides. In some areas, where the soil has little natural humus, such as in Kazakhstan and Central Asia, there is a greater danger of pollution from drainage water by herbicides, than in areas with similar soils but located near open water bodies (such as rivers, lakes and seas.)[54] It is, of course, obvious that the technologies to be used in waste water recycling and treatment should be selected on the basis of the limits for maximum permissible concentrations

3.9 Area under Irrigation and Drainage by Union Republic

	Land Mass km²	million hectares irrigated 1988	million hectares drained 1988
USSR total[1]	22.4	20.8	19.8
RSFSR	17.08	6.0	7.2
Ukraine	.60	2.5	3.1
Belorussia	.21	.1	3.1
Uzbekistan	.45	4.1	*
Kazakhstan	2.71	2.3	*
Georgia	.07	.5	.2
Azerbaidzhan	.09	1.4	*
Lithuania	.07	.04	2.9
Moldavia	.03	.3	—
Latvia	.06	.02	2.0
Kirgizia	.20	1.0	*
Tadzhikstan	.14	.7	*
Armenia	.03	.3	—
Turkmenia	.49	1.3	*
Estonia	.05	.01	1.1

* denotes no land reported under drainage.
— denotes a negligible amount of land under irrigation.
[1] denotes all irrigated land in all areas of the national economy. Figures for the republics denote irrigated land use in agriculture. About 310,000 hectares of irrigated land are for non-agricultural uses.
Sources: Narodnoe khozyaistvo SSSR v 1988 g, pp. 19, 473 and 475.

and maximum permissible volumes of regulated substances, but so far there is little discussion in the literature along these lines.

Table 3.9 illustrates the location of irrigation and drainage networks; it is useful to keep in mind that land that is irrigated may also be drained, while that which is drained may not be irrigated. There are no particular surprises: it is well known that the acreage under drainage has doubled since 1970, and since 1985 has encompassed approximately 600,000 additional hectares. Similarly, the area under irrigation kept pace; since 1985 about 800,000 hectares have been included in the system. Projected to the end of 1990, an additional 1.3 million hectares of land will be under irrigation, and 1.0 million hectares more will be drained. This is half the rate of new construction that occurred in the period between 1981–1985.[55] Bearing in mind that the capital budget for amelioration construction has grown by some 7 per cent over the 12th plan period – less than the rate of inflation in real terms – these data suggest that President Gorbachev's priority of reconstruction is being implemented.

Targeting Amelioration Construction

There is no one region in the Soviet Union that will not have a valid claim for amelioration investment, and to some extent these are obvious from the general data presented below. The Central Asian region having over 50 million population and comprising the several republics with especially low standards of living and most extreme ecological problems, can make a strong case for a large share of the amelioration investment budget for the foreseeable future. The problems that make such expenditure necessary are both economic and humanitarian in their essence, and these are illustrated in a statement by the director of the USSR State Committee on Hydrometeorology, who succinctly relates that expenditures for amelioration are here to stay.[56]

> As a result of the tapping of the water which replenishes these rivers, the volume of water in the Aral Sea has fallen by 54 per cent in the last 20 years. The water table continues to fall by nearly a metre per year. The salinity of the water has risen from 9 to 24 grammes per litre, and in the south and east the shoreline has advanced by 60–120 kilometres. Sandstorms have become more frequent. The soil in the area is heavily salinated. For domestic purposes, the population uses untreated water, which is high in mineral content, drawn from rivers and the runoff from irrigation systems, causing high morbidity levels.... The Sea of Azov is experiencing salination as the result of the considerable volume of water used in the Northern Caucasus. The water tables are [also] falling in Lakes Issik-Kul' and Balkash.

The salts produced in the Central Asian region have been absorbed, in the past, by the Aral Sea. Since it is now fed with much less water than before, the sea's role as a regional stabilising factor in climate has been jeopardised, in some ways eliminated. To make the situation worse, sandstorms are depositing the salts from the dry seabed over cultivated and inhabited land hundreds of kilometres distance from the Aral. They have also been found on high terrain, and the fear has been expressed that the salts will eventually affect the permafrost.

Such effects simply multiply the health, environmental and production problems experienced by those areas since 1980, that are the consequence of the uncontrolled use of agricultural chemicals.[57] Similarly, while it cannot be expected that productivity gains on ameliorated land are uniform across the Soviet Union, the following table demonstrates that gross production actually fell in Uzbekistan. (When other indices are applied, such as the amount of water and chemicals consumed per hectare, the relative productivity in other Central Asian republics has declined as well.) Thus, the author provided specific linkages between agro-economic practices and ecological deterioration occasioned in part by amelioration programmes.

3.10 Dynamics of Irrigated Land and its Productivity

	Area of Land Irrigated, thousand hectares			Gross Annual Production per hectare irrigated land, rubles		
	1970	1980	1985	1970	1980	1985
Uzbekistan	2696	3476	3930	1563	1849	1553
Kirgizia	883	955	1009	792	986	1046
Tadzhikstan	518	617	653	1880	2409	2315
Turkmenia	643	927	1107	1351	1479	1251
Total Area	4740	5975	6699	1430	1715	1553

Source: A P Demin, Pochemu snizhaetsya produktivnost' oroshaemykh zemel' v respublikakh srednei asii?, *Melioratsiya i vodnoe khozyaistvo*, no. 9, 1989, pp. 6–9.

Accounting for water losses in any sector or region of the Soviet economy is only approximate. The most recent official estimates show that total losses of water in the national economy during transport and due to filtration and evaporation are 51 cubic kilometres annually, and 33 cubic kilometres in the rural economy.[58] The situation for agriculture is illustrated by the following table.

The greatest proportionate loss occurred in Georgia, where irrigation systems lost about one-third of water supplied, but from a national perspective this is comparatively insignificant. The greatest volume of water used in

3.11   Withdrawals and Consumption of Water during Transport by the Irrigation System in 1988

	Withdrawals (billion cubic metres)	Transport Losses (billion cubic metres)	Transport Losses (in per cent)
USSR	175.7	32.8	18.7
RSFSR	23.8	5.6	23.4
Ukraine	6.9	1.3	19.5
Uzbekistan	58.8	8.9	15.2
Kazakhstan	22.9	4.5	19.7
Georgia	1.8	.6	32.7
Azerbaidzhan	11.8	3.4	28.9
Moldavia	.4	.02	5.2
Kirgizia	11.1	2.0	17.8
Tadzhikstan	13.2	1.5	11.6
Armenia	2.5	.5	20.3
Turkmenia	22.1	4.4	19.7

Source: *Okhrana okruzhayushchei sredy...*, p. 108.

irrigation occurs in the southern republics of Uzbekistan, Turkmenia, and Kazakhstan. If their water losses are added to those of Tadzhikstan and Kirgizia, total losses (over 21 cubic kilometres annually) in the five republics are equal to about 90 per cent of the total volume, including transport losses, used for irrigation in the Russian Republic. By any account, the magnitude represents an enormous amount of unproductive expenditure. It is for such reasons that water losses in the Central Asian republics pose an economic dilemma of national proportions.[59]

But filtration and evaporation only cause some of the wastage. It is augmented by the extravagent use of water in irrigation as pointed out above. Over-consumption is the result of the outdated technology employed, inappropriate crop structures,[60] and the lack of skill of the workforce.

Unfortunately, due to evaporation, filtration, and irrational use, 60 per cent of the water consumed in agriculture is wasted. In some southern regions, water for irrigation is used 2–2.5 times more than is necessary, despite the fact that there is an increasing demand for it. Priority should be given to lowering water consumption principally through ... correct watering regimes, reconstruction of old irrigation systems, development of instrumentation, and metering of water.

This concern is echoed elsewhere,[61] although the proposed solutions differ.

In a number of regions in the Soviet Union, water demand reaches 40 per cent and more of renewable water resources, of which more than 50 per cent is used in agriculture where the use of water bears an irreversible nature. Such norms for water consumption are the maximum possible and require redistribution of water resources, increasing reserves of water for irrigation, or curtailing losses, which amount to more than 40 cubic kilometres annually (30 per cent of all water used in agriculture). Such losses decrease the possibilities for further expansion of irrigated areas, and at the same time lead to salination and bogs on ameliorated land, withdrawal of significant amounts of land from active agricultural use, or a sharp reduction in its quality.

The consumption-wastage-pollution cycle in Central Asia has, of course, devasted the Aral Sea and the lower reaches of the Amu Darya and Syr Darya river basins. (Roughly speaking, the Syr Darya river basin is where more than half the population of the Central Asian republics are found.) Given the enormous amount of water that is actually available, it is tempting to regard the water supply problems as 'paper shortages', that specialists anticipate will occur if ambitious economic development programmes are implemented. Certainly, a compelling argument can be made that existing water resources should be sufficient. Unfortunately, while resources might be adequate in better circumstances, there is extensive imbalance in the distribution of water supplies regionally and qualitatively amongst the industrial, agricultural, and rural domestic consumers. Moreover, the usable resource base will continue to shrink due to current water management practices, and lack of adequate supply purification and waste water treatment.

The extent of the water deficit is thought to be around 22 cubic kilometres annually, against annual consumption of some 100 cubic kilometres by agriculture alone. Soviet sources indicate that, with concerted efforts to improve water quality and to curb losses, water sources in the region are sufficient to support expansion in all sectors through the year 2000 or so. It was estimated that 24 cubic kilometres of additional water, or conserved sources, would allow a 177 per cent increase in agriculture and 267 per cent increase in industry, as well as growth in the daily domestic-municipal consumption from 290 to 350 litres per capita. About 10 cubic kilometres of the savings would occur in Uzbekistan.[62]

The water that used to flow into the Aral Sea came mainly from two large rivers – the Amu Darya and the Syr Darya and several other rivers, such as the Zeravshana and the Talasa, that feed into them. Growth in demand for fresh water was first promoted in the 1950s by central authorities (who simply wanted the additional agricultural produce) and then accompanied by the construction of a series of dams to retain water in the delta. The inevitably reduced flows in the Amu Darya and Syr Darya rivers have caused the water level to fall so sharply that what *was* the Aral Sea then is *now* two polluted lakes. The following table illustrates the problems of rising mineral levels in the waters of the Aral Sea basin, where the data indicate that all the water is polluted to some degree and requires treatment before use in households and food processing. While water having up to 5 grammes per litre requires

3.12   Volume and Mineralisation of Collector-Drainage Water in the Basin of the Aral Sea

Union Republic,[1] River Basin	Irrigated Land with Drainage ts ha	Volume of Collector-Drainage Water km³/yr	Collector-Drainage Water by Mineral Content, grammes/per litre		
			1–3	3–5	5–35
Kazakhstan, all Basin	418.7	2.08	.74	1.09	0.25
Syr Darya	377.9	1.89	.56	1.09	0.24
Chu	29.6	0.13	.13		
Talasa, Assy	11.2	0.06	.06		
Uzbekistan, all Basin	2590.7	20.84	11.83	4.76	4.25
Syr Darya	1261.3	9.94	6.60	1.82	1.52
Zeravshana	156.3	1.30	0.92	0.20	0.18
Amu Darya	1173.1	9.60	4.31	2.74	2.55
Turkmenia, all Basin	736.0	5.69	1.02	2.08	2.59
Amu Darya	202.0	1.41		1.41	
Murgaba, Tedzhena	108.0	0.82			0.82
Karakumsk Canal	426.0	3.46	1.02	0.67	1.77
Kirgizia, all Basin	149.3	0.92	0.92		
Syr Darya	20.8	0.10	0.10		
Chu	123.3	0.78	0.78		
Talasa, Assy	5.2	0.04	0.04		
Tadzhikstan, all Basin	430.0	3.60	3.30	0.23	0.07
Amu Darya	326.7	2.45	2.27	0.13	0.05
Syr Darya	103.3	1.15	1.03	0.10	0.02
Total for the Aral Sea Basin	4324.7	33.13	17.81	8.16	7.16

Note: This table differs considerably from the official data concerning areas under drainage. There is no immediate explanation why an author, from the USSR Academy of Science's Institute for Water Problems, would describe land as having drainage which has not been reported in official statistics for the respective republics.

Source: M V Sanin, Vodoemy-nakopiteli kollektorno-drenazhnykh vod v basseine Aral'skogo Morya, *Melioratsiya i vodnoe khozyaistvo*, no. 11, 1989, pp. 2–6.

treatment, the level of the hazard depends on the nature of the contaminant; water bearing over 5 grammes of salts per litre will, in some cases, represent life-threatening contamination in the absence of cleansing.

All the water that used to flow into the Aral obviously just does not disappear. It filters into the groundwater and it drains into the lakes, contaminating some rather badly. Elsewhere, the drainage water flows into depressions in the earth and has established new 'lakes'. The following table illustrates some lakes have an extremely high concentration of mineral salts, which, in turn, intensifies the rate of salination spreading across Central Asian soils.

3.13 Characteristics of Some Large Reservoirs of Collector-Drainage Water

Lake	River Basin	Height above Sea Level	Area of Lake km²	Volume of Lake m³	Mineral Content g/l
Arnasaisk	Syr Darya	236.5	1865	13.90	10.1
Kamyshlybash	Syr Darya	58.3	178	.96	3.4
Dengizkul'	Zeravshana	181.5	267	.27	
Sarykamyshsk	Amu Darya	-2.2	2575	26.19	12.5
Sudoch'e	Amu Darya	53.0	300	.6	2.0
Kattashop	Amu Darya		30	.09	2.3
Ashikol'	Talasa	122.0	74		9.1

Source: M V Sanin, *Melioratsiya i vodnoe khozyaistvo,* no. 11, 1989, *ibid.*

The Sarykamyshsk Lake, in Turkmenia, was a natural lake, which has been expanded into the largest reservoir formed to date with drainage water. The volume of the inflow is especially worrisome, and in 1985 was 4.8 cubic kilometres, bearing 20 million tons of salts. Of the six items represented in the following table, only hydrocarbons have dropped in concentration.

The point is that Minvodkhoz, concerned about the rapidly escalating salination of the Aral Sea basin, still appears to be looking for 'big-but-expensive' answers; in any case, for any water management programme to be workable, it will have to be devised from a regional perspective, incorporating and integrating solutions for several republics. Minvodkhoz is finding this no easy task, since each of the republics jealously protects its water supplies. Moreover, because the irrigation canals are interconnected, any water conservation strategy for one republic is usually perceived as water deprivation in the next. Economic and scientific assessments of alternative water supplies have been initiated, albeit slowly. Some of the suggestions, such as melting

3.14   Mineralisation and Salt Content of the Sarykamyshsk Lake

Year	Total Salts, g/l	including: nitrates & potassium	calcium	magnesium	chloride	sulphate	hydro-carbons
1982	10.3	2.5	0.54	0.42	3.71	3	0.14
1985	10.92	2.57	0.55	0.49	3.76	3.43	0.12
1985	11.95	3.85	0.46	0.1	3.98	3.41	0.15
1985	12.37	3.28	0.54	0.43	4.11	3.86	0.15
1986	12.54	(3.02)	0.59	0.54	4.26	(4.01)	0.12

Notes: The data for 1982 and the first and third sets for 1985 were taken by the authors from I V Rubanov; the second set for 1985 was compiled by G G Kostantinov; and the set for 1986 was from the USSR Academy of Science's Institute of Water Problems.

Source: A K Kiyatkin, M V Sanin, Sarykamyshskoe ozero – krupneishii nakopitel' kollektorno–drenazhnykh vod, *Melioratsiya i vodnoe khozyaisstvo*, no. 1, 1989, pp. 20–4.

the glaciers in times of low precipitation,[63] appear to be 'Mad Hatter' schemes. Other approaches are along more traditional lines. For example, research is being undertaken to establish guidelines for using substandard water for domestic and industrial purposes; to make water having a high mineral content (3–5 grammes per litre) safe for irrigation by means of genetic engineering; to improve water distribution technologies; and to stimulate rainfall by artificial means.[64] It is important to note, however, that nowhere does one find serious discussions about dismantling the existing irrigation systems.

However, the key Minvodkhoz solutions seek to redistribute the water resources, and a particularly good example of what this would entail concerns Turkmenia. One version would require water to be drained away from the Sarykamyshsk Lake into collector-drainage systems that would be constructed over a significant part of the republic, with several large engineering works proposed to irrigate additional land there. A second suggestion involves the construction of a series of small and large canals to divert yet more water from the Amu Darya. A third concept would redirect part of the drainage water from the Ozernyi collector (which flows into the Dar'yalyk and eventually into the Sarykamyshsk Lake) into a new canal that would ultimately cross through Uzbekistan into the depleted Aral seabed. A fourth proposal would be, in effect, an extension of the first two.[65]

Elsewhere, the agricultural authorities and kolkhoz managers have recommended solutions specific to their existing systems, insisting that the obvious goals for Central Asia are to reduce evaporation and filtration, place curbs on new sources of demand, and stabilise consumption. The priorities reflect assessments such as one by A Egrashev, that out of 232,200 hectares of irrigated land in the Syr Darya basin, construction work is needed on 65,000 hectares (28 per cent); reconstruction work on 36,800 hectares (17 per cent); and amelioration improvements on another 40,000 hectares (17 per cent).[66] But stabilising consumption may also require changes to the crop structure – an unpopular option from the perspective of central planners who want to see more textiles on the consumer market.

The costs of increasing agricultural water supplies, even by the more conservative tactics, are estimated at 2 rubles per cubic metre of water.[67] On an arithmetical basis, then, one cubic kilometre of additional water would command an investment of 2 billion rubles and 24 cubic kilometres would require 48 billion rubles. The prospect of regional investment on this scale, even though it might be supported by income from water rates, should push the Soviet authorities to establish priorities based on an economic evaluation not just of agricultural efficiency, but also of the ripple effect in other sectors of the economy and beyond Central Asia.

Future Investment Requirements

This section is purely speculative, attempting to illustrate the magnitude in monetary terms of certain amelioration options. There is one clear advantage to be gained if decisions are taken as environmental investments. In contrast to the more highly politicised process for agricultural decisions, environmental investments are supposed to be made on the basis of cost-benefit analysis, where benefits in monetary terms outweigh the costs. Also a much broader range of environmental factors is taken into account in both the costing and the calculating of benefits. In theory, by applying environmental criteria, amelioration investment would not proceed where only marginal gains in productivity would be achieved at the cost of environmental disruption such as that now seen in all of the Central Asian republics.

It appears that the Central Asian crisis has stimulated some changes in long-term amelioration objectives and methods across the Soviet Union. In the future, the leading priorities must include: avoidance and abatement of health hazards; reduction of unproductive water consumption; and abatement of soil salination, water pollution, and rising water tables. These, then, underlie the following calculations, although further amelioration, land improvement, and other water management objectives will surely claim a share of capital budget allocations.

Option One. The 12th Five Year Plan indicated that by 1990, 23.1 million hectares will be under irrigation, and by the year 2000, 32 million hectares. The Plan targeted an increase of land under drainage to 18.5 million hectares by 1990, and up to 21 million hectares by the year 2000. Such economic goals may not be compatible with the present priorities of responding to a wider range of competing economic, social and ecological considerations. So far, the cutback appears to be by half, although Gosagroprom, which competed for investment resources, was understandably reluctant to publish the revised targets for the year 2000.

The question addressed here is how much of the existing irrigation and drainage networks require to be reconstructed, and what selection criteria would be applied. Unfortunately, there are no official data, only anecdotal accounts. In 1984, for instance, M Loiter, an economist, observed that 38 per cent of all irrigated land and 11 per cent of drained land required improvements.[68] N Minashina, a specialist with the USSR Academy of Sciences, indicated that 'of 8.5 million hectares of irrigated land in semi-arid and desert areas, 40 per cent is subject to serious problems of rising groundwater.'[69] Thus, according to the following table, fully one-half of irrigation system reconstruction would take place in Central Asia.

3.15   Estimated Costs of Irrigation Reconstruction in 1985

	Irrigated Area (million hectares)		Investment (billion rubles)
	Actual	Reconstruction	
USSR total[1]	17.1	6.4	32.0
RSFSR	4.9	1.9	9.3
Ukraine	2.3	0.9	4.3
Belorussia	.07	—	—
Uzbekistan	3.5	1.3	6.7
Kazakhstan	1.9	.7	3.6
Georgia	.2	—	—
Azerbaidzhan	1.0	.4	2.0
Lithuania	.01	—	—
Moldavia	.2	—	—
Latvia	—	—	—
Kirgizia	.8	.3	1.5
Tadzhikstan	.6	.2	1.1
Armenia	.2	—	—
Turkmenia	1.2	.4	2.0
Estonia	.01	—	—

[1] denotes irrigated land under cultivation in 1988.
— not calculated
Sources: N G Minashina, Nash sovremmenik, no. 1, 1987, pp. 124–126, indicated that about 38 per cent of irrigated land requires reconstruction due to problems of rising groundwater. Investment is calculated at 5,000 rubles per hectare to allow 2,732 rubles per hectare for improvements in irrigation plus 1,246 rubles for closed drainage. Narodnoe khozyaistvo v 1988 g, p. 475

The above estimate, totalling 32 billion rubles for reconstruction of the irrigation system alone, represents a manageable outlay in the context of medium-term amelioration investment. The normatives used in budgeting reconstruction of irrigation systems were estimated in 1985 at 2,732 and 2,912 rubles per hectare for surface and overhead irrigation respectively, and at 698 and 1,246 rubles per hectare for open and closed drainage respectively.[70] It is noteworthy that the normative costs vary dramatically from actual experience, which in Central Asia are reported between 16,000–25,000 rubles per hectare for irrigation, and between 40,000–50,000 rubles per hectare for drainage construction.[71] Minashina reported that the higher figure relates to hill areas in Uzbekistan.[72]

If a decision were made to reduce water losses due to evaporation, then enclosing irrigation canals would be required. Roughly 68 per cent of irrigated land in the Soviet Union would be subject to reconstruction.[73] This variation suggests that the required investments would rise sharply to about 60 billion rubles.

Option Two. If protection of public health were to assume a higher status in amelioration decisions (in descending order of the probable occurrence of risk), then greater resources would be directed, first, to separate domestic and agricultural water supplies, and to purify the former to potable standards; and, second, to subject all waste water from rural domestic and rural industrial sources to treatment prior to release into the waterways.

This option involves a decision to separate agricultural water into that consumed by households and by rural industry. This is potentially a very expensive option. If it is assumed that Central Asia is targeted for such construction, calculation of costs can be made on the basis of the volume of water supplies that must be purified to potable standards, and the volume of sewage that must be treated for reuse or discharge.

If it is assumed that water supply purification and waste water treatment installations can be costed in a manner similar to that indicated in chapter 2 it works out on an all-union basis as follows: If (and this is a guess) an amount equal to one-third of the water for municipal-domestic use would be supplied to agricultural homes, then about 8.6 cubic kilometres must be purified to potable standards.[74] For water purification alone, 8.6 cubic kilometres should involve outlays similar to those seen in chapter 2 for municipal waste water treatment – or 3.3 billion rubles at the middle range cost.

While it can be envisaged that rural household sewage would be collected in septic systems and then transported to regional sewage treatment facilities, no estimates have been made because it is virtually impossible at this level of aggregation to calculate the scale of facilities required.

Option Three. A decision to cleanse *agricultural* water supplies, irrigation and drainage water collected for reuse, as well as agricultural waste water would demand greater levels of sustained capital outlays. The potential benefit of this approach, particularly in combination with reconstruction of faulty irrigation and drainage systems, is that it could contribute to a significant reduction in salination of surface and groundwater, and soil. There are two possible starting points – the intake installations for irrigation water or the 30 cubic kilometres of water in collector-drainage systems. The latter is the more manageable target, involving an outlay of nearly 12 billion rubles.

Taken together, these three options could involve investments of between 47 and 75 billion rubles; of course, it must be remembered that these 'solutions' do not take into account Minvodkhoz's large-scale water management projects.

Notes

1   The total of irrigated and drainage construction equals 40 million hectares. However, irrigation and drainage often coexist on the same land, so that the total hectares covered by the systems may be substantially lower.

2   M S Gorbachev, Agropromyshlennomu proizvodstvu – intensivnoe razvitie, *Ekonomicheskaya gazeta*, no. 37, September 1985, pp. 5–7; and V Tsentral' nom Komitete KPSS i Sovete Ministrov SSSR, *Ekonomicheskaya gazeta*, no. 48, November 1985, pp. 17–18. See also I Avilin, V interesakh zemlepol'zovatelei, *Khozyaistvo i pravo*, no. 8, 1986, pp. 18–23, and for earlier references see Razvitie melioratsii zemel', *Ekonomicheskaya gazeta*, no. 35, 1983, pp. 1–2; L I Brezhnev, O prodovol'stvennoi programme SSSR na period do 1990 goda i merakh po ee realisatsii, *Ekonomicheskaya gazeta*, no. 22, 1982, pp. 4–6; and Prodovol'stvennaya programme SSSR na period do 1990 goda, *Ekonomicheskaya gazeta*, no. 23, 1982.

3   A Dobrynin, Problemy ucheta differentsial'noi renty v sel'skom khozyaistve, *Ekonomika sel'skogo khozyaistvo*, no. 10, 1987, pp. 73–7; K Gofman, M Vitt, Platazhi za prirodnye resursy, *Ekonomicheskaya gazeta*, no. 37, 1987, p. 4.

4   Interview with A Yanshin, Shagi k noosfere, *Literaturnaya gazeta*, no. 5, 1987, p. 11; Yu L Dzhavadyan, Peristroika ne terpit blagodushiya, *Melioratsiya i vodnoe khozyaistvo*, no. 1, 1988, pp. 7–9.

5   L B Sheinin, Plata za vodu i khozyaistvennyi raschet v sel'skom khozyaistve, *Vestnik sel'skogo khozyaistvo nauki*, no. 8, 1987, pp. 11–15.; N Bystritskaya, V Mikhura, O plata za vodu promyshlennymi predpriyatiyami, *Planovoe khozyaistvo*, no. 1, 1983, pp. 123–5.

6   V A Tikhonovym, O khlebe nasushchnom, Argumenty i fakty, no. 48 (393), 28 November 1987, p. 1.

7   B Kerner, *Yearbook of Soviet Economics 1985*, p. 187; V Vinogradov, Problemy sel'skokhozyaistvennoi ekologii, *Nauka i zhizn*, no. 6, 1987, pp. 2–9; A V Postnikov, Programma khimizatsii sibirskogo zemledeliya, *Zemlya sibirskaya, dal'nevostochnaya*, no. 12, 1985, pp. 2–4; N P Starov, et al, Otsenka sostoyaniya meliorativnykh sistem pri obosnovanii ocherednosti rekonstruktsii, *Melioratsiya i vodnoe khozyaistvo*, no. 1, 1988, pp. 21–4.

8   V P Plyukhin, KATEK: ekzamen na ekologicheskuyu zrelost', *Zemlya sibirskaya, dal'nevostochnaya*, no. 4, 1987, pp. 33–5; R R Mukhamadnev, Okhrana sel'skokhozyaistvennykh zemel' kak odna iz problem ratsional'nogo ispol'zovaniya territorii (na primere Tadzhikskoi SSR), *Nauchno trudy po okhrane prirody (Tartu)*, no. 8, 1985, pp. 31–5; V Vinogradov, *Nauka i zhizn*, 1987, op cit.; V N Kornilov, A A Subbotin, Vozmeshchenie krupnomasshtabnogo ushcherba, prichinyaemogo ob'ektam prirody, *Sovetskoe gosudarstvo i pravo*, no. 6, 1987, pp. 67–73; Yu Bystrakov, Ekologicheskie problemy APK, *Voprosy ekonomiki*, no. 10, 1984, pp. 81–9 (translated in *Problems of Economics*); G Kukushkin, Planirovanie ratsional'nogo ispol'zovaniya prirodnykh resursov, *Planovoe khozyaistvo*, no. 3, 1985, pp. 64–70 (translated in *Problems of Economics*).

9   M Ya Lemeshev, Ratsionalizatsiya prirodopol'zovaniya i ekonomicheskii analiz, *Vestnik Akademiya Nauk SSSR*, no. 6, 1986, pp. 63–70, (expressed as 'perfecting the organisational structure'); G A Khilinskii, Vedomstvennyi kontrol' v meliorativnom stroitel'stve, *Melioratsiya i vodnoe khozyaistvo*, no. 1, 1988, pp. 15–17.

10   A Dobrynin, *Ekonomika sel'skogo khozyaistvo*, no. 10, 1987, op cit.

11   M Loiter, Intensifikatsiya i fondootdacha v melioratsii, *Voprosy ekonomiki*, no. 6, 1985, pp. 72–81. At present, the internal reclamation fund is 20 billion rubles, and it will grow to 34 billion rubles by 1990. In most regions, internal irrigation and drainage are financed from the kolkhoz and sovkhoz accounts. The costs of maintenance and repair are shared with water management organisations at 30 per cent of costs from the state budget and 70 per cent on their own accounts.

12   T Khachaturov, Intensifikatsiya ispol'zovaniya zemli, *Voprosy ekonomiki*, no. 4, 1985, pp. 73–82, gives normative data on land prices; A Nabiev, Tselevaya programma prirodopol'zovaniya respubliki, *Ekonomika stroitel'stva*, no. 7, 1985, pp. 7–10, gives land value figures.

13   A P Demin, Pochemu snizhaetsya produktivnost' oroshaemykh zemel' v respublikakh srednei asii?, *Melioratsiya i vodnoe khozyaistvo*, no. 9, 1989, pp. 6–9.

14   *Ekonomicheskaya gazeta*, no. 48, November 1985, op cit. For details of the reorganisation of the agricultural bureaucracy, see *Izvestiya*, 11 April 1989, p. 1 and *Izvestiya*, 12 April 1989, p. 2.

15   P Guzhyin, Otdacha zemli i struktura vlozhenii, *Kommunist*, no. 8, 1986, pp. 28–39.

16   *Narodnoe khozyaistvo SSSR v 1988 g*, pp. 421 and 543.

17   Ibid, p. 435.

18   M S Gorbachev, Myslit' po-novomu, deistvovat' energichno, *Pravda*, 8 April 1988, p. 1.

19   Yu Bystrakov, *Voprosy ekonomiki*, no. 10, 1984, op cit.

20   I P Boiko, Ekologicheskie problemy povysheniya ustoichivosti sel'skokhozyaistvennogo proizvodstva, *Vestnik Leningradskogo Universiteta, seriya 5*, no. 3, 1987, pp. 59–65.

21   G A Khilinskii, *Melioratsiya i vodnoe khozyaistvo*, no. 1, 1988, op cit.

22   N N Burtsev, Planirovanie razvitiya eksplutatsionnykh vodokhozyaistvennykh organizatsii v sisteme APK, *Melioratsiya i vodnoe khozyaistvo*, no. 1, 1988, pp. 12–14.

23   D V Kadzhaya, Sosredotochivayas' na nereshennykh problemakh, *Melioratsiya i vodnoe khozyaistvo*, no. 1, 1988, pp. 2–3.

24   M Ya Lemeshev, *Vestnik Akademiya Nauk SSSR*, no. 6, 1986, op cit.

25   L B Sheinin, *Vestnik sel'skogo khozyaistvo nauki*, no. 8, 1987, op cit.

26   M Ya Lemeshev, *Vestnik Akademiya Nauka SSSR*, no. 6, 1986, op cit; V Vinogradov, *Nauka i zhizn*, no. 6, 1987, op cit; S T Voznyk, B I Strelets, Osnovnye napravleniya nauchnykh issledovanii v oblasti gidrotekhnicheskikh sel'skokhozyaistvennykh melioratsii, *Gigiena i naseleniya mest*, 1986, pp. 3–8.

27   P S Neporozhnyi, *Gidroenergetika i kompleksnoe ispol' zovanie vodnykh resursy SSSR*, Moscow: Energoizdat, 1982, water resources in rivers, table 2, p. 41; groundwater resources, table 2.4, p. 45; water resources in lakes, tables 2.5 and 2.6, pp. 49–50.

28   V Vinogradov, Problemy sel'skokhozyaistvennoi ekologii, *Nauka i zhizn*, no. 6, 1987, pp. 2–9, op cit.

29   I Potravnyi, V Narizhnaya, V Ogreb, Balansovoe planirovanie ispol'zovaniya vodnykh resursov, *Ekonomika Sovetskoi Ukrainy*, no. 6, 1987, pp. 74–7; N I Gadzhiev, Deistvovat' chetko, reshitel'no, soglasovanno, *Melioratsiya i vodnoe khozyaistvo*, no. 1, 1988, pp. 5–7. There are a number of books about the Chernobyl' accident. See, for example, Z Medvedev, *The Legacy of Chernobyl'*, Oxford: Basil Blackwell, 1990.

30   Yu P Belichensko, Kak zdorov'e, Severskii Donets? *Zhilishchnoe i kommunal'noe khozyaistvo*, no. 6, 1987, pp. 17–18.

31   M L Lishanskii, Plata za vodu dla orosheniya, *Finansy SSSR*, no. 3, 1987, pp. 24–6.

32   I F Rusinov, Eshche raz o perebroske chasti sibirskoi vody na yuzhnyi sklon, *Melioratsiya i vodnoe khozyaistvo*, no. 7, 1989, p. 4.

33   Calculated as follows: .17 × 378 billion cubic metres (bcm) = 64 bcm. 31 bcm divided by 64 bcm × 100 = 48 per cent.

34   *Okhrana okruzhayushchei sredy i ratsional'noe ispol'zovanie prirodnykh resursov v SSSR*, Moscow, 1989, p. 75.

35   V Vinogradov, *Nauka i zhizn*, no. 6, 1987, op cit.

36   M Loiter, *Voprosy ekonomiki*, no. 6, 1985, pp. 72–81, op cit; M L Lishanskii, *Finansy SSSR*, no. 3, 1987, op cit; M Ya Lemeshev, *Vestnik Akademiya Nauk SSSR*, no. 6, 1986, op cit.

37   V TsK KPSS i Sovete Ministrov SSSR, O pervoocherednykh merakh po uluchsheniyu ispol'zovaniya vodnykh resursov vo strane, *Izvestiya*, 27 January 1988, p. 1.

38   N Bystritskaya, V Mikhura, *Planovoe khozyaistvo*, no. 1, 1983, op cit.

39   L B Sheinin, *Vestnik sel'skogo khozyaistvo*, no. 8, 1987, op cit.

40   Ibid; N Bystritskaya, V Mikhura, *supra*.

41   Intra-farm amelioration systems were to be transferred during the 12th plan period from the books of collective and state farms and other state agricultural enterprises to those of the State Irrigation System, by order of the USSR Council of Ministers. The transfer was to include drainage and collector-drainage networks, intra-farm irrigation, hydraulic engineering installations, electric pumping stations, and wells. Such transfers, however, were dependent on the consent of the collective and state farms and on the condition of the installations and equipment being transferred. V Sovete Ministrov, *Pravda*, 31 October 1984, p. 2.

42   Yu A Melyugin, K oplata za voyu podkhodit' differentsirovanno, *Melioratsiya i vodnoe khozyaistvo*, no. 11, 1988, pp. 12–15; G Shul'gin, Plata za vodu: pervye itogi eksperimenta, ibid, pp. 15–17; and V M Legostaev, Nuzhna li plata za orositel'nuyu vodu? *Melioratsiya i vodnoe khozyaistvo*, no. 8, 1989, pp. 14–15.

43   B Ya Dvoskin, V I Makalkin, Napravleniya ispol'zovaniya vodnykh resursov Sibiri, Srednei Azii i Kazakhstana, *Geografiya i prirodnye resursy*, no. 3, 1986, pp. 3–7.

44   M L Lishanskii, *Finansy SSSR*, no. 3, 1987, op cit.

45   Roughly calculated on the basis of 166 growing days, which is of course longer than irrigation needs to be applied.

46   N A Popovich, Nekotorye gigienicheskie voprosy melioratsii v sel'skom khozyaistve, *Gigiena i sanitariya*, no. 1, 1986, pp. 69–70.

47   M Lemeshev, Prodovol'stvennaya programma i okhrana okruzhayushchei sredy, *Voprosy ekonomiki*, no. 12, 1985, pp. 79–89, (translated in *Problems of Economics*).

48   M Lemeshev, *Vestnik Akademiya Nauk SSSR*, no. 6, 1986, op cit.

49   G Shalabin, O sovershenstvovanii khozyaistvennogo mekhanizma ratsional'nogo prirodopol'zovaniya na regional'nom urovne, *Ekonomicheskie nauki*, no. 5, 1987, pp. 77–81.

50   A V Pavlov, Prodovol'stvennaya programma i problemy gigieny primeneniya pestitsidov, *Gigiena i sanitariya*, no. 4, 1987, pp. 4–6.

51   Ibid.

52   V M Perelygin, Pervoocherednye zadachi v oblasti gigieny pochvy v dvenadtsatoi pyatiletke, *Gigiena i sanitariya*, no. 1, 1988, pp. 4–5; Yu I Kundiev, O I Voloshchenko, V I Smolyar, Itogi issledovanii po probleme 'Nauchnye osnovy gigieny sela', zadachi na dvenadtsatuyu pyatiletku, *Gigiena i sanitariya*, no. 3, 1987, pp. 4–7.

53   N A Romanenko, Sanitarnye trebovaniya k sel'skokhozyaistvennomu ispol'zovaniyu stochnykh vod i ikh osadkov, *Gigiena i sanitariya*, no. 7, 1986, pp. 12–15, references SNiP 2.06.03–85, 'Melioratiunye sistemy i sooruzhe-niya. Norma proektirovaniya'. The author explained that the use of waste water as a supplement to fresh water in agricultural irrigation is presently a subject of much interest in the Soviet Union. Decisions to build processing facilities for waste water to be used in agriculture are taken jointly by Minvodkhoz, the Ministry of Agriculture, the Sanitary and Epidemiological Service, veterinary authorities, agencies concerned with the use and preservation of water, and territorial hydrological services. Given the extensive involvement of a number of interested authorities, sanitary regulations governing the use of waste water in irrigation are frequently ignored. A Popovich, *Gigiena i sanitariya*, no. 1, 1986, op cit, indicated that the regulations governing the use of sewage water in agriculture have not been fully developed; there is some urgency since the regulations are an important guarantee of public health and safety. It is not a matter of permitting the use of sewage sometime in the future, but of issuing regulations to govern an existing situation. At present, there are regulations which:
*   prohibit the use of effluent from certain sources (such as, animal farms, biological research facilities, and food processing centres);
*   restrict or prohibit its use in specific locations (such as, humus or peaty soils, near towns or reservoirs);
*   specify the amount of waste water or sludge that can be used per hectare;
*   restrict their use for certain crops (such as, potato, fruit, and berry growing); and
*   set stringent regulations for biological treatment of water prior to its use and for the technologies themselves.
*   specify the treatment that must occur prior to the use of sewage or sludge by agriculture.

54   V I Asin, et al, Zagryaznenie vodnykh ob'ektov gerbitsidami, postupayushchimi s kollektorno-drenazhnymi vodami risovykh sistem, *Vodnye resursy*, no. 6, 1986, pp. 101–11.

55   *Narodnoe khozyaistvo SSSR v 1988 g*, p. 473.

56   V Gubarov, Ekologiya bez kosmetiki, *Pravda*, 7 September 1987, p. 4. See also an interview by I Tsarev, Kaplya reki berezhet, *Trud*, 7 February 1988, p. 1, in which D Ratkovich from the USSR Academy of Sciences, Institute of Water Problems, mentions 'outbreaks of illness that occur several times more frequently than the average for the whole country. This happens because people drink untreated water directly from streams and irrigation ditches'. Ratkovich referred to people living in the Kalmyk ASSR (which is in the southern part of the Russian Republic).

57   V Kotlyakov, Mozhna li spasti more? *Pravda*, 14 April 1988, p. 3.

58   *Okhrana okruzhayushchei sredy ...*, p. 71.

59   M Loiter, *Voprosy ekonomiki*, no. 6, 1985, op cit. It is useful to note at this point that the term 'Central Asia' is imprecisely used. It usually means the semi-arid areas in the south, variously including all or part of Kazakhstan, Uzbekistan, Turkmenia, Tadzhikstan, and Kirgizia. Sometimes, the discussions of 'Central Asian' water problems also mention those of Azerbaidzhan and the southern RSFSR, where similar conditions obtain.

60   V Vinogradov, *Nauka i zhizn*, no. 6, 1987, op cit.

61   I P Boiko, *Vestnik Leningradskogo Universiteta, seriya* , seriya 5, no. 3, 1987, op cit.
62   N R Khamraev, O razvitii vodokhozyaistvennogo kompleksa Uzbekistana na base imeyushchikhsya vodnykh resursov, *Obshchevtvennye nauki v Uzbekistane*, no. 5, 1987, pp. 34–41.
63   Ibid.
64   Ibid.
65   A K Kiyatkin, M V Sanin, Sarykamyshkoe ozero – krupneishii nakopitel' kollektorno-drenazhnykh vod, *Melioratsiya i vodnoe khozyaistvo*, no. 1, 1989, pp. 20–4.
66   A Egrashev, Rezervy ispol'zovaniya vodnykh resursov, *Voprosy ekonomiki*, no. 7, 1987, pp. 122–4. These figures are probably understated as according to M S Gorbachev, Uspekh perestroika – v rukakh naroda, *Pravda*, 10 April 1988, pp. 1–2, about half of the irrigated land in Uzbekistan needs serious ameliorative attention. Further, according to M I Aliev, Otvetstvennost' za konechnyi rezul'tat, *Melioratsiya i vodnoe khozyaistvo*, no. 1, 1988, pp. 3–5, the actual programme for the twelfth plan period for Azerbaidzhan was shaped as follows: 300,000 hectares of the irrigation network will be reconstructed and receive additional water supplies; 130,000 hectares of ameliorated land will be improved; planning for capital outlays will cover 110,000 hectares, and irrigation will be constructed on 75,000 hectares. Other reasons for poor productivity, involving the full spectrum of resources and external decision-making, are reported in N I Gadzhiev, *Melioratsiya i vodnoe khozyaistvo*, no. 1, 1988, op cit.
67   N R Khamraev, *Obshchestvennye nauki v Uzbekistane*, no. 5, 1987, *supra*.
68   M Loiter, *Voprosy ekonomiki*, no. 6, 1985, op cit, cited *Gidrotekhnika i melioratsiya*, no. 9, 1984, p. 5, as his source.
69   N G Minashina, Soizmeryaya dokhody i poteri, in Ekologiya. Ekonomika. Npravstvennost', *Nash sovremmenik*, no. 1, 1987, pp. 124–6.
70   T Khachaturov, *Voprosy ekonomiki*, no. 4, 1985, op cit.
71   M Loiter, *supra*; A Nabiev, *Ekonomika stroitel'stva*, no. 7, 1985, op cit.
72   N G Minashina, *Nash sovremmenik*, op cit.
73   *Narodnoe khozyaistvo SSSR za 70 let*, p. 249.
74   *Narodnoe khozyaistvo SSSR v 1988 g*, pp 18 and 245. This is calculated as follows: 26 billion cubic metres were attributed to the municipal and urban domestic economy. This volume provides water for some light, probably service, industry, although consumption by most industrial enterprises is excluded. No data were found that specified how much within the 26 billion cubic metres is attributable to households, but it is assumed that rural domestic water supplies are equal to at least one-third of the municipal and urban domestic. Even though the population is numerically smaller, rural consumption includes some food processing industries which, in turn, draw on the same water supplies.

4   Ecology and the Pulp and
Paper Industry

Introduction

Public dismay over the environmental impact of the pulp and paper industry
in the Soviet Union is widespread, and reactions were especially noticeable
after the prolonged press coverage of damage caused by the industry to Lakes
Ladoga and Baikal and of biologically active sewage that spoiled a number
of popular holiday spots during the summer of 1989. This is an essential
industry as its products are necessary to all sectors of society, the military, and
the economy. The industry is described by Aganbegyan as 'occupying first
place amongst the sources of water pollution',[1] which suggests that damage
is in disproportion to the size of the industry within the Soviet economy. The
Soviet pulp and paper industry ranks third in world production of paper and
pulp, having 22 locations with 157 operating enterprises.[2]

In general, environmental problems associated with pulp and paper production have emerged due to a combination of factors. The main cause is a
result of an emphasis over the years on quantitative production at the expense
of maintenance and repair of basic production units, of product quality and
diversification, while environmental protection was shunted aside pretty
much altogether. But, despite official policy, significant increases in production
tonnage have not been achieved since the 1970s, and as the lack of investment
has led inevitably to the physical deterioration of both plant and equipment,
no improvement is imminent.

The industry currently has little access to waste-free or waste-reducing
technologies. This is a situation due, in part at least, to an insistence within the
ministerial leadership on technologies of domestic origin, even though Soviet

technologies are often inadequate for operating conditions and their reliance on out-of-date designs cannot advance the technological base of the industry. Under the new *khozraschet* conditions, enterprise managers are confronted with a requirement to finance modernisation mainly from enterprise earnings. Their former, relatively easy access to government grants and bank loans is no longer guaranteed, and in the future such means of finance are to be dependent on the financial viability of a given enterprise. Some financial alternatives may be found in joint venture or other commercial undertakings, where in exchange for timber, wood products, or pulp, there may be an injection of foreign technologies. No 'hard' information has been found to support an analysis here of the Soviet industry's reliance on such arrangements, although commercial linkages are underway, for example, with Japan and Finland. The extent to which other countries of the Western and Eastern hemispheres become similarly involved depends, of course, on the long-term capacity of Soviet forestry reserves to sustain a stepped-up pace of exploitation; but in that respect there is growing fear amongst many observers that forestry management in the Soviet Union is badly neglected indeed.[3]

The ecological outlook for the pulp and paper industry is especially grim, because its ability to make ecological improvements is constrained by unresponsiveness on the part of the machine-building industry, which simply does not manufacture pollution control equipment in the quantities, range, and qualities sufficient to meet the competing demands from a diverse spectrum of industrial enterprises. These circumstances, in their turn, may trap the industry within a catch-22 situation, as it is the declared intention of nature protection authorities to levy heavy fines against enterprises for pollution with the proviso that such penalties are taken from the profits that could otherwise be reinvested in modern technologies. Should this set of circumstances materialise without central action to relieve such effects (for example, by allowing price increases for pulp and paper products), it may make it impossible for the pulp and paper enterprises having limited funds at their disposal to invest in pollution controls or, alternatively, may force some of the least cost-efficient enterprises to shut down if the authorities actually enforce the environmental laws.

Production Targets and Goals

'The Basic Directions for Economic and Social Development in the USSR for 1986–1990 and for the Period to the Year 2000' envisage an increase during the 12th Five Year Plan in the production of pulp by 19–22 per cent, paper by 17–20 per cent, cardboard and chipboard by 33 per cent, as well as diversification in products. The industry's goals are to double production by the year 2000, by achieving an annual growth rate of 5.0–5.2 per cent.[4] In the period 1971–1985, production in the pulp and paper industry grew by 4.3 per cent per annum, which was somewhat less than for industry as a whole.[5] In 1986, pulp production was up by 3.4 per cent by volume; in 1987, production in the pulp, paper, and cardboard sectors was stagnant. In 1989, the output data are uncertain, although there was overall growth during 1988.[6] Present levels of paper production are effectively half of what is needed in the Soviet economy, and per capita consumption of paper and paper products such as cardboard lags in forty-second place in the world.[7] Pulp and paper imports amount to 800 million rubles annually, which in value terms is strikingly high.[8] The Soviet Union cannot immediately reduce the level of commodity imports, which are not the results of the industry's productive capacity and raw material resources; rather, such imports are linked to external trade agreements conducted in commodities.

4.1   Pulp and Paper Production in the USSR
(in thousands of tonnes)

Year	Pulp	Paper	Cardboard
1989	–	6300	4300
1988	8749	6322	4499
1987	8633	6191	4375
1986	8663	6156	4240
1985	8374	5986	4035
1980	7123	5288	3446
1970	5109	4185	2516

Source: Izvestiya, 28 January 1990, p. 3, for 1989 figures which are obviously rounded. The other figures are found in *Promyshlennost' SSSR*, Moscow: Finansy i statistika, 1988, p. 212, and *Narodnoe khozyaistvo SSSR v 1988 g*, p. 403.

In the future, as part of an initiative to ensure qualitative improvements in the industry's performance, the variety of products is to be expanded and efforts will be made to ensure 'homogeneity of production' (oft-used Soviet jargon which refers to the need to standardise production processes and to improve product quality).[9] Some qualitative improvements are anticipated as automation and monitoring devices are installed, although significant advances in product mix are limited by the lack of advanced technologies and chemicals.

Investment Background

The foremost reason that the pulp and paper industry has problems with productivity and environmental protection is its dependence on obsolete technologies. The situation obviously constrains the potential for growth based on existing plant and has led to an extraordinary level of pollution. The industry's representatives uniformly agree that without commissioning new capacity or 'technical re-equipment' of existing pulp and paper mills, the targets for production increases cannot be met.[10] The term 'technical re-equipment' means that a significant increase in production capacity at existing sites will be accomplished by installing up-to-date technologies and equipment.

Modernisation initiatives in the past were supposedly devoted primarily to increasing production capacity; because output has not grown significantly, one is led to the conclusion that such investments were largely to keep existing production units in operation. Now and in the future, such decisions are to be based on research sufficient to guarantee productivity increments and on cost-benefit analyses of alternatives which take into account the requirements to protect nature and conserve resources. The latter are of special concern because renovation costs of older plants (over 60 years in service) can escalate to 350 per cent over that of newer facilities (under 30 years in service). In the future, investment decisions will be based on a positive evaluation that the net product of renovation will result in performance equal to a new facility.[11]

The current crisis over pollution caused by the pulp and paper industry can be attributed to the structure of investment. In the 1970s, for example, investment for environmental protection amounted to 15 per cent of total capital investment funds allocated to the pulp and paper industry.[12] There were some successes seen at the time, largely in the area of water conservation and incineration of sludges, which critics claim 'fostered a false complacency within the industry'. By the 1980s, however, investment in nature conservation had fallen off and such construction projects were routinely ignored.[13] In 1987, the USSR State Planning Committee (Gosplan) approved a construction programme for nature conservation installations at pulp and paper enterprises over the remainder of the 12th plan period and extending to the year 1995. The plan has not been published,[14] although some references to it appeared in *Bumazhnaya promyshlennost'*, the industry's journal, during 1988 and 1989.

Judging from past performance, the accomplishments of technological re-equipment and reconstruction are very few indeed. *Izvestiya* reported in 1988 that of the 157 enterprises and assocations in the pulp and paper industry, 25 (16 per cent) were built after 1960; 40 (26 per cent) have undergone reconstruction and technical re-equipment; and the remainder (58 per cent) went into production at the beginning of the century or earlier.[15] Over the past 15 years, the annual average retirement of plant industry-wide was 1 per cent, and the replacement rate has been 2 per cent per annum. 'This means that no more than 10 paper and cardboard producing machines have been replaced.'[16] 200 (45 per cent) out of 440 operating paper and cardboard producing machines have been in service for more than 45 years; at pulp and paper plants half of the curing pans are more than 25 years old. As a result, the physical deterioration of basic equipment is between 43 per cent and 73 per cent at the majority of plants in the industry. Between 1971 and 1985,

200 paper and cardboard producing machines were 'modernised', and in the 12th plan period a further 120 were scheduled for modernisation.[17]

4.2   Investment in Soviet Pulp, Paper, and Cardboard Industry
(in per cents)

| | Five Year Plans | | | | | |
	VII	VIII	IX	X	XI	XII
Actual Capital Investment, allowing for indexing & other cost increases	100	71	67	54	51	48
Construction-Installation Work	100	64	57	33	29	25
Average annual rate of growth of capacity in pulp, paper and carton industry	8	9.4	5.8	2.3	1.9	1.6

Source: Izvestiya, 5 February 1988, p. 1.

A review of investment activities in the Forestry Products Industry (FPI), of which pulp and paper is a part, is warranted by two circumstances. The first is the marked shortfall in the output of pulp and paper which has affected the FPI's overall performance, and the second is the reportedly high proportion of old plant and machinery in use. Since the introduction of new machinery and technology is necessary to make good the shortfall in output that cannot be achieved through production increments at existing plants, there is also the opportunity to integrate into the investment process features which cause less damage to the environment.

4.3   Rate of Growth of BIPF[1]

1970	1975	1980	1985	1986	1987
100	145	199	258		
		100	130	135	139
			100	104	107

Note: 'Basic Industrial Production Funds' is Soviet jargon for capital assets and is referenced variously hereinafter as capital assets or BIPF.
Source: Narodnoe khozyaistvo SSSR v 1985 g, p. 115; and *Narodnoe khozyaistvo SSSR v 1987 g*, p. 100.

Overall, there has been growth in the capital assets ascribed to the Forestry Products Industry, but the picture expressed in indices based on 1970, 1980 and 1985 values, permits only fleeting optimism.

However, the net outcome of the investment activity in the Forestry Products Industry has been a decline in its share of BIPF in relation to industry as a whole. Again, this is presented on a value basis:

4.4   Share of BIPF in Industry as a Whole

1970	1975	1980	1985	1986	1987
5.1	4.8	4.5	4.2	4.2	4.1

Source: *Narodnoe khozyaistvo SSSR v 1985 g*, p. 122; and *Narodnoe khozyaistvo SSSR v 1987 g*, p. 112.

Further, the level of capital investment in the Forestry Products Industry, and especially within the pulp and paper industry, has declined relative to the overall volume of industrial development:

4.5   Capital Budget by Branches of Industry

	1971–75	1976–80	1981–85
Capital Investment in Forestry Products Industry, in comparable prices, millions of rubles	9 000	10 500	10 400
as a per cent of all investment	4.6	4.2	3.5
In Pulp and Paper Industry, in comparable prices, millions of rubles	2 600	3 600	3 000
as a per cent of all investment	1.3	1.4	1.0

Source: *Narodnoe khozyaistvo SSSR v 1985 g*, p. 368.

The net decline in the FPI's share of basic industrial production funds is not so clearly expressed when a further indicator, that of the value of capacity brought into service, is examined.

4.6   Commissioning of BIPF
(as percentage of the overall value of funds,
at the end of the period under review)

	1971–75	1976–80	1981–85	1986	1987	1988
All industry	40	37	33	6.9	6.6	6.1
FPI	43	37	32	6.3	6.4	6.3

Source: Narodnoe khozyaistvo SSSR v 1985 g, p. 123; and *Narodnoe khozyaistvo SSSR v 1988 g*, p. 357.

In this sense, the FPI has kept pace with the rest of industry. This indicates that there is a further reason for the decline in the industry's share of basic industrial production funds apart from the way in which investment in the FPI has fallen behind the industrial average.

What also contributes to the relative decline in the value of the FPI's capacity is the rate at which facilities are being taken out of service.

4.7   Removal of BIPF
(as percentage of overall value of funds,
at the beginning of the period indicated)

	1981–85		1986		1987		1988	
	total removed	due to age	total removed	due to age	total removed	due to age	total removed	due to age
All industry	14	8	3.0	1.8	3.6	2.1	3.5	1.8
FPI	22	15	4.5	3.0	5.7	4.1	8.7	3.7

Source: Narodnoe khozyaistvo SSSR v 1987 g, p. 106, and *Narodnoe khozyaistvo SSSR v 1988 g*, p. 359.

In this respect, the FPI has decommissioned plant and machinery relative to its existing park at a rate roughly twice that of the average for industry as a whole. This may be explained by the age structure which necessitates retirement of old facilities, but the rate of commissioning does not keep pace. If, then, the value of new capacity or the re-equipping of existing facilities are measures of an opportunity for the simultaneous introduction of pollution control features into production processes, there is relatively less opportunity for the FPI to innovate in this way. In reality, the age structure of the production units in this industry offers an exceptionally good chance to weed out particularly damaging processes.

A further indication of these opportunities could also be expressed in terms of the introduction and retirement of capacity for producing physical output of various types. In this respect, the data are incomplete, as there are no comparable figures for capacity taken out of service. However, data for the commissioning of major production capacity (from the construction of new enterprises and the extension or reconstruction of existing enterprises) are cited here as they indicate a further feature of investment activity in the FPI.

4.8   Commissioned BIPF by Means of New Construction, Expansion, and Reconstruction of Existing Enterprises

New Production Capacity	1971–75	1976–80	1981–85
paper, 1000 tonnes/year	509	271	714
cardboard, 1000 tonnes/year	803	350	461
pulp, 1000 tonnes/year	2 100	900	600
cut timber, million cubic metres/year	5.3	4.5	2.9

Source: Narodnoe khozyaistvo SSSR v 1985 g, p. 359.

The new capacity in 1976–80 showed a general fall over the preceding period in each type of output; the fall was more than one-half with the exception of cut timber. The following period showed a recovery in new capacity for paper and cardboard, most marked in the case of paper, and a continuing decline in new capacity for pulp and cut timber. The initial general decline in new capacity apparently does not accord with the pattern of rising gross investment in value terms noted above, given the expected correspondence of investment costs with volume of capacity within the relatively homogeneous conditions of one branch of industry; nor does it seem to fit the history of newly commissioned basic industrial production funds.

For the value of FPI investment to move in roughly the same magnitude as the rest of industry and yet incorporate the general decline in new output capacity after 1971–75, there has to have been a similar decline in new physical capacity throughout industry as a whole. This is indicated as incomplete construction.

**4.9 Incomplete Construction in State
and Cooperative Enterprises and Organisations**
(at the end of selected years, as a
percentage of the volume of capital investment)

	1970	1980	1985	1986	1987	1988
Whole Economy	73	87	78	79	78	83
FPI	89	116	84	82	86	85

Source: Narodnoe khozyaistvo SSSR v 1988 g, p. 558.

The period 1976–80 is flanked by years in which the proportion of incomplete construction was higher than in the whole economy, markedly so in 1980. As a general pattern, the FPI's performance in this respect has been consistently poorer than the average and shows an apparently disporportionate decline in years when the economy as a whole did not fare so well.

The main problem for the FPI has not been so much the flow of investment funds, which have held up fairly steadily, but translating these funds into usable output capacity. This difficulty is related to features that are endemic to the structure of the production processes themselves. The structure of the industry's capital assets had the following profile in 1988:

4.10   Structure of BIPF by Type and Branch of Industry

	All Industry	FPI
Total	100.0%	100.0%
Buildings	27.1	32.4
Installations	19.5	16.1
Transmission Devices	10.4	4.5
Power Plants	7.5	4.6
Operative Machinery	29.2	35.0
Measuring, regulating, and laboratory equipment	1.8	0.5
Computer Technology	1.2	0.5
Means of Transport	2.3	5.7
Other	1.0	0.7

Source: Narodnoe khozyaistvo SSSR v 1988 g, p. 352–3.

In relative terms, the FPI is more dependent than industry overall on the supply of funds for buildings and operative machinery, and any bottlenecks in this connection, together with delays in construction activity or the installation of equipment, for example, would probably be reflected in the outcome of the FPI's investment process. As is discussed below, the selection of production technology (shown above to be a relatively more costly item in the FPI's capital structure), is a difficult question.

In any case, it is the element of machinery and equipment which figures most prominently in the value of funds put into and taken out of service, since these need replacement more frequently as well as being (in historical terms) an increasingly larger element in investment value than buildings or installations.

4.11 Commissioning and Decommissioning of BIPF
(in 1988, as a percentage of the overall value of funds)

	Commissioned		Decommissioned	
	All Industry	FPI	All Industry	FPI
Total	6.6	6.8	1.8	3.7
Buildings and Installations	6.0	4.5	0.8	1.7
Machinery and Equipment	7.3	8.9	2.9	5.3
Other	6.8	9.8	2.2	7.0

Source: Narodnoe khozyaistvo SSSR v 1988 g, p. 361.

These data show a replacement rate for machinery and equipment that is higher than that for other elements both in industry as a whole and in the FPI in particular. Activity in the FPI in the aggregate of replacement has the same pattern as noted above: commissioning on a par with the rest of industry, and decommissioning twice the average. In the category of machinery and equipment, the FPI's activity in commissioning new funds exceeds that of industry as a whole, but it is appreciably lower in the category of buildings and installations, which perhaps reflects the relative importance of re-equipping in the FPI as opposed to establishment of entirely new operations. On the other hand, the value of decommissioned machinery and equipment in the FPI relative to all industry is lower than the corresponding figure for aggregate decommissioning, which suggests that the FPI's basic industrial production funds are older than the average and have a lower valuation.

Given the shortfall in the FPI's output, there is pressure to increase the value of investment, and in this respect the FPI is subject to the usual difficulties in the allocations of capital funds. This, in turn, would inhibit any attempts to make production less damaging to the environment whether by means of new technologies of production or through add-on technologies, since the priority in increased capital outlays would be the expansion of production capacity and not higher capital costs, much as these might be offset by benefits from recycling in terms of current costs or reduced environmental damage. Similarly, the environment's claim on capital investment is impeded by the fact that the industry's investment apparently has a history of being particularly susceptible to fluctuations in the completion of facilities, so that when the economy as a whole is in difficulty it can be expected that the outlays on capital investment in environmental protection will be squeezed by the need to make up for the delayed introduction of new output capacity. On the other hand, the age structure of facilities in the FPI extend the scope for making investment that is less damaging to the environment, as there is relatively more machinery that needs replacing. This potential benefit to the environment enhances the opportunities that are offered by the fact that the FPI is retiring facilities at a higher rate than industry as a whole.

Thus, criticism of the slow pace of retirement of plant and equipment must be understood in respect of the age and condition of the industry, even while the rate for decommissioning is generally higher than in other sectors. Pulp and paper industry officials indicate that the fault for this should be placed squarely on the shoulders of the machine building industry.[18] Its sluggishness, coupled with the pulp and paper industry's aversion to foreign equipment purchases, have been especially devastating to the pulp and paper industry in respect of environmental protection. Still, one solution may be trade deals involving turn-key arrangements, which are available from Canada, the United States, Japan, or any of the Scandinavian countries. An alternative approach would be for the Soviet pulp and paper industry to establish its own machine building capacity, but no assessments of the feasibility of such an undertaking have been published. Other, obviously wealthier, industries have made similar investments, although in the immediate future the FPI's emphasis will be on the repair and service branches.

Other Economic Concerns

The unwillingness to make foreign purchases can be attributed at least in part to leading researchers in the industry, who fear that going to foreign markets could undermine prospects for significant strides by domestic scientific initiatives.[19] Given that scientific research by this industry is substantially underfunded, that scientists are anyhow engaged in daily operational issues rather than in research *per se*, and that the lead time in commissioning new mills is reportedly upwards of 15 years, this seems a perspective based largely on wishful thinking. It does not reflect a reasoned programme for the industry's recovery based on an assessment of the opportunity costs associated with the purchase of foreign technologies in comparison to reliance on some non-specific developments in the future of domestically produced equipment.[20]

The lack of construction, reconstruction, and repair work, which are vital for nature protection and resource conservation, cannot be blamed solely on the lack of funds. In 1986, state capital investment allocations were underspent, and investment from enterprise resources, especially the pulp and paper industry, were far below planned levels.[21] The pulp and paper industry's capital budget during 1987 was 710.2 million rubles. Of this, 447.2 million (62 per cent) was for development of the mills, 92 million (13 per cent) for nature protection, 15 million for the cardboard industry, 10 million for goods of cultural and domestic significance, and 50 million rubles for production of yeast feedstocks.[22] The pattern of incomplete construction, however, has been repeated each year of the 12th Five Year Plan (1986–1990), and in 1988 even the extraordinarily modest allocations for nature protection construction were not fully used. That year, about 85 per cent of total capital investment funds were expended; but only 79 per cent of funds for retooling and repair work were used. This was very poor performance indeed when it is recalled that the rate of inflation was hovering, officially, around 10 per cent per annum. At 25 enterprises, 'large' nature protection installations were to be constructed during 1988; but at 14 enterprises, such activities were about 50 per cent behind schedule.[23]

In 1987, the structure of investment in the pulp and paper industry was substantially unchanged, although the investment programme specifically mentioned some environmental protection concerns.[24]

> Significant investment is devoted to ensuring growth of capacity for producing pulp, paper and cardboard. It is envisaged that the output of these commodities will be increased by 81,000, 169,000, and 61,000 tonnes, respectively. It is necessary to ensure the commissioning of evaporation devices with a capacity of 550 tonnes per hour of evaporated water, biological cleansing stations with a capacity of 446,000 cubic metres.

What appeared to be going on then was a policy of continued expansion at existing sites and technical improvements nominally addressed to the resource conservation mandate that may result, eventually, in (a) greater attention to saving the usable wastes, and products, and (b) decreased levels of pollution in effluent. The investment priorities are somewhat puzzling in respect of the several aspects of resource conservation investment discussed below.

The recalcitrant posture of the machine building industry is probably under-estimated, since it is not just a matter of a 'willingness' to address the pulp and paper industry's requirements. For example, there are not enough qualified engineers to supervise all of the construction and capital repair activities that are needed by the pulp and paper industry.[25] More importantly, as Soviet designs in this sector are substantially inferior to analogous foreign technologies (and who wants to produce machinery they know is inferior?), this deficiency is compounded by construction flaws which limit the likelihood that plants can achieve and sustain design performance indicators.[26] Further, so long as the technology for this industry is being designed on a piecemeal basis, the machine building industry cannot respond adequately by means of serial production. Finally, and as important as the availability of modern technologies and equipment, the range, volume and quality of chemicals now significantly determine technological efficiency, productivity, and product quality. Despite the priority afforded by the Gorbachev government to modernisation and improved performance by the chemical industry, the standard and quantity of chemicals available to the pulp and paper industry remain 'dispiritingly low'.[27] These factors represent serious disincentives for the machine building industry to place the pulp and paper industry any higher on its list of priorities.

Pollution Problems

The pulp and paper industry is a heavy consumer of water, which is used for flushing, transporting intermediate products and waste at various stages of the production process, and as a solvent for chemical reagents. Pollution from pulp and paper mills takes the form of waste water containing organic and chemical wastes, gaseous emissions containing a high concentration of sulphur, chlorine, and other chemical elements, and toxic sludges. Industrial wastes from this industry have a noxious smell, and there are 'negative reactions' with flora and fauna due to the presence of suspended organic and inorganic substances in the effluent and the high acidity. Industrial effluent from sulphur-consuming processes is distinguished by its high corrosivity.[28]

In recent years, a decision has been made to reclaim the chemicals used in production from the waste by-products, sludge, waste water, and gaseous discharges. A Tipisev, an official of the Ministry of Timber, Pulp and Paper Industry's Department of Nature Conservation, outlined the investment strategy in the 12th plan period as follows: wide introduction of waste-reducing and waste-free technologies, more effective use of nature conservation installations, and completion of programmes for building purification structures in the basins of the Volga and Ural rivers, the Baltic Sea, and other regions.[29] In mid-1989, the goals were restated: 'to completely eliminate by 1995 the releases of polluted sewage'. The main body of work, starting in 1989, included the elaboration of permissible levels of pollution in gaseous and liquid wastes.[30]

The strategy for the industry will centre primarily on the introduction of waste-reducing processes. There are several points that the industry will observe in their organisation, including:

- modification of production processes to achieve maximum use of raw materials and to reduce wastes (such as, the transition to lower density paper and other products and increased output of semi-finished products);
- introduction of complex technologies in the production process, so that the waste from one form of production can be used in other sectors (for instance, the use of fibres accumulated in the course of pulp production for the manufacture of wood fibre, insulation, and other boards);
- repeat-use or recycling of raw materials, chemicals, and other resources (for example, reverse use of water to be accompanied by repeat use of fibres, fillers, and thermal energy);
- use of waste by means of their inclusion in natural processes (for example, the use of bark and sediments filtered from drainage for fertilisers).[31]

An important operational indicator of subsequent pollution control problems is the amount of sodium sulphate used in boiling pulp. The losses that occur in the course of boiling determine the volume of pollutants in the drainage water and also the amount of sulphur and dust emitted into the atmosphere in the absence of pollution controls.[32] In paper and cardboard manufacturing, the degree to which effluent results in pollution is estimated on the basis of the volume of fibrous semi-finished products and fillers that are consumed.[33]

The implementation of waste-reducing technology is only possible if the capacities of the separate production units at a given mill are approximate in size, or if there is sufficient capacity to accommodate excess volume flows due to bottlenecks. For example, the consumption level of sodium sulphate depends on the efficiency of electric filters and the system of liquor sampling. The sodium and sulphur contents of industrial effluent, usually monitored by periodic laboratory sampling of waste in the enterprise's general collector, indicate the efficiency of the alkali regeneration processes. As the sulphur content of waste water increases, it causes a deterioration in technical and economic indicators and increases the difficulty of neutralising the effluent.

Monitoring analyses are used to evaluate the loss of chemicals in the production cycle and to anticipate the load on the treatment installation. However, the lack of automated monitoring of the sulphur in the effluent halts operations at the very stage where chemicals can be recovered. In turn, unscheduled stoppages generate heavy demands on the cleansing installations, and force the treatment installations to operate out of step with actual need, because the peaks of concentrated pollutants in effluent are not detected by intermittent laboratory monitoring.[34]

Discussions on the strategy of using waste-reducing and waste-free technologies, described by Tipisev in 1985, noted that environmental solutions are dependent on developing waste-free, ecologically clean technologies for semi-finished fibres and paper, as well as closed systems of water supply, full or partial exclusion of water from paper production, and waste recovery. These require the creation of new equipment and chemicals that are not widely available in the Soviet Union. Some observers argue that scientific research is the 'weakest link' in the industry, although the previous discussions suggest that if this aspect is not fully successful, it is only one of several features that need to be addressed.[35] In any event, the fact that industrial scientists want to go back to the drawing-board may delay systematic environmental investment.

Resource conservation policies have implications for the amount of raw materials used, and in this respect performance by the Soviet industry can be judged against that of other countries. In 1985, for instance, for each ton of paper and cardboard produced, Soviet mills consumed 5.2 times the amount of wood as in the United States, and nearly six times that in Finland.[36] This suggests that if raw materials are used less wastefully, production could be expanded without broadening the industry's share of exploited wood and timber.

The raw material base, in its turn, also has significant impact on pollution control requirements. It is regarded in the industry as follows:[37]

The harmful effects on the environment of drainage water from production of various types of wood pulp are derived chiefly from fibres, non-organic salts, and toxic compounds, biochemical pollutants, and the colour (chromacity) of drainage water.

Soviet researchers link the degree of pollution in drainage and recycled water from production of different types of wood pulp to various factors: the species of timber, use of recycled water and means for its clarification, basic technological parameters for production of semi-finished products of high yield, temperature of the preparatory treatment, duration of thermo-hydraulic action, pressure in steaming, bleaching regime, and use of chemical reagents. It is reported that processes of producing wood pulp to improve the quality of semi-finished products, widening of the raw material base, and lower consumption of energy are linked, as a rule, with increased processing of the timber and use of chemical reagents that are ultimately concentrated in drainage waters. It has also been concluded that using chemical reagents at any stage of the technological process will form an additional source of pollution in drainage waters; the degree of toxicity is affected above all by the type and volume of chemical reagents consumed, the duration and other parameters of treatment. It is also stated that the 'most harmful' effect on the quality of drainage water is from the treatment of wastes generated by the grading of wood pulp at high temperatures under pressure.[38]

Scientific research lags for all the traditional reasons: poorly developed educational and laboratory resources; research emphases on current problems which should be resolved by technicians; requirements that researchers respond to daily production emergencies; and lack of an economic context that would encourage basic scientific research in the first instance. One article expressed the situation as follows:[39]

> The lack over a prolonged period of any precise policy and organisational economic mechanism for stimulating the development and implementation of work of a strategic nature has led to the paradoxical fact that researchers are not interested in the creation of fundamentally new processes, materials, and equipment, even though enterprise managers are in favour of implementing such developments. Until now, for both researchers and managers it has been simpler and more convenient not to carry out fundamental changes in technology, but to adapt developments to existing processes and equipment.

There are a number of criticisms concerning cleansing installations at pulp and paper enterprises. In 1987, inspections of the facilities at 14 locations (including Arkhangel, Kotlass, and Turin) cited numerous inappropriate practices such as the inadequate evaporation of alkaline and fermented masses; inefficient work of the internal cleansing stations; and lack of extraction filters in the waste water treatment systems, which consequently allowed active sludge to enter the cleansing systems.[40] The inspections showed that because evaporation and precipitation stations often do not work, cleansing installations were forced to handle waste water and fermented wastes in excessive quantities. As a result, waste water commonly contained several times the permitted concentrations of pollutants.[41] Experiments involving pollution controls in the Forestry Products Industry indicate that recycling and repeat-use of waste water plus off-site waste water treatment work well together. The practice of reducing the volume of waste water was found to be insufficient on its own, as the toxins in the effluent are more concentrated and, in result the required degree of treatment increased.[42]

Water recycling was reportedly about 52 per cent in 1982. During the 12th plan period water recycling was projected to increase by 5 per cent (that is, by 1.2 cubic kilometres). Information is incomplete in this area, but suggests that under 60 per cent of water used by the pulp and paper industry is recycled.[43] The figures above indicate that total water consumption by 1990 will be about 40 cubic kilometres annually, of which 24 cubic kilometres will be recycled. (Calculated as 1.2 cubic kilometres × 20 = 24 cubic kilometres of recycled water; 24 cubic kilometres is 60 per cent of 40 cubic kilometres of annual water supply.) While this is a very large volume of fresh and recycled water consumption, a further indicator suggests that it may be somewhat understated. The highest indicators of specific water consumption, at 300 cubic metres of fresh water per tonne of pulp, is not matched by comparable measures for paper and cardboard. At 300 cubic metres per tonne of pulp, fresh water consumption for that sector alone would be 26 cubic kilometres annually, which would imply an additional volume required for paper and cardboard production.[44]

The volume of fresh water consumption notwithstanding, the percentage of water recycling confirms a picture of an industry beset by outdated technologies, and one which is loath to invest scare resources on what might yield marginal financial returns and no increases in productivity. Locational factors (such as, the availability of large quantities of water from rivers and lakes) and the structure of water costs (preferential rates for industry-supplied water which further erode the effects of very low user-charges) do not encourage such investments. Aganbegyan suggested in 1984, for instance, that '…given there is no efficient means at present for decontaminating waste water from pulp mills, special care must be taken to locate in areas with sufficient water and to avoid gigantic installations'.[45] He mentioned, in particular, the planned expansion at Ust'-Ilimsk, where sewage already contaminates the Buguchansk reservoir, making the planned development of a second pulp mill there illogical, 'especially since other installations at Bratsk draw on and pollute the same water resources'.

Apart from the difficulties presented by the lack of monitoring equipment, there are other shortcomings in the use of purification installations. For example, at the Sokol paper mill, capacity for dehydration of drainage sediments was added at the water purification plant at a time when ferric chlorite, which is essential to the neutralisation process, was not available. Despite this, the installation was commissioned and subsequently released inadequately processed effluents.[46] Elsewhere, a waste water treatment plant was so poorly constructed that the installation to deal with hydraulic and corrosive loads failed,[47] while at many other sites, there are insufficient aerators and at most the biological treatment installations cannot handle abnormal loads.[48]

Problems with boiling installations are widespread. Boiling technologies are used to remove water from pulp, to extract sulphur and other chemicals, and to produce an organic mass that can be used in agricultural fertilisers, feedstocks, and fish food. There are discussions of 'extreme situations' such as when, due to lengthy repairs of boiling-down stations, the Turin combine directed the whole of the 'mash' into the cleansing equipment.[49] A similar situation occurred at the Perm combine, when the lye burning equipment was shut down.[50] Whether or not such failures and subsequent misuse of cleansing equipment are routine cannot be determined, although frequent references in *Bumazhnaya promyshlennost'* imply that this may be the case. Sulphur extraction can be accomplished in connection with the boiling-down stations.

This technology is experimental, although rates of extraction at 97–98 per cent efficiency have been reported.[51] In respect of air quality, the priority locations for investment in the 12th plan period appear to be the Bratsk and Arkhangel combines;[52] but the main effort for the foreseeable future will be the development of regulations for permitted quantities of pollutants in exhaust gases.

Problems with sludge disposal and interim storage are widespread. Even though sludge is routinely incinerated, interim storage must take place on some scale. However, long-term storage represents a new area for investment. Storage facilities will be essential at sites experimenting with recycling of waste products. Any shortage here mainly reflects the lack of investment rather than insufficient know-how.

Permissible Concentrations of Pollutants in Effluent and Permissible Volume and Concentrations of Pollutants in Emissions

Unlike other Soviet industries where the permissible concentrations of pollutants (PDK) have been more fully elaborated, this is not the case for the pulp and paper industry. For water, the difficulty is implicit in the formula for effluent, in which the limits for pollutants contained therein are linked to the ability of the recipient water body to tolerate them. Thus, in every instance (that is, for every point at which sewage is released at each of 157 enterprises) such calculations have to be made, alongside ecological appraisals for the new technologies. This creates a certain amount of room for enterprises to resist pressures to invest in pollution controls; the enterprise director's recalcitrance at the Lake Ladoga mill stands as a very good example of this type of obstacle. The situation becomes more complicated as reconstruction and retooling of pulp and paper mills are of an 'adaptive' nature, rather than by means of standard equipment.[53]

In respect of air pollution, compliance with the pollution control regulations is complicated by the formula for permissible volume of pollutants (PDV), as measured by the rate and method of dispersion (see chapter 5 where this concept is discussed). Most pulp and paper mills were built in relatively undeveloped areas, but many have been subsumed into towns and cities. As a result, PDV standards now also take into account the detrimental effects of toxic emissions on local populations.[54] Because research has lagged, the response of Soviet regulators is to issue permits for temporarily approved emissions (VSV). In this way, they establish the parameters for emissions based on incomplete information, and allow substantial deviations from design performance indicators (where those indicators exist and are adequate, which may be in very few instances given the age of the plant). In 1985, there were 39 draft standards for PDV and VSV applicable to the Ukrainian and Moldavian wood processing industries. The goal in the Ukraine is that PDV normatives will be applied and developed for air pollution, with the goal of 75 per cent efficiency of control by means of cyclones and wet filter technologies. Although it is not certain that pulp and paper mills are presently included in this process, an article about the wood processing industry (the other main part of which is the pulp and paper industry) indicated that, in the Ukraine, VSVs are based on the following documentation:

- materials provided by the Ministry (Minlesprom) listing sources of emissions of harmful substances into the atmosphere. (This was done by direct measuring with instruments and indirect calculations of balances at 213 wood processing enterprises.)
- methodological guidelines to determine the quantities of industrial emissions into the atmosphere at wood processing enterprises. (The degree of pollution hazard for ground-level air is determined in accordance with the highest calculated value for ground-level concentrations of pollutants (milligrams per cubic metre) that can be established at a prescribed distance from the point of emission under unfavourable meteorological conditions.)
- categorisation of enterprises according to the quantity of emissions and degree of impact on the adjacent area. (The PDV for pollutants in the atmosphere is established on the condition that the emissions from the source of the aggregate of sources [and accounting for future development of the plant and dispersion in the atmosphere] do not create a ground-level concentration which exceeds PDK for inhabited areas.)
- methodological guidelines for industry on how to measure emissions of harmful substances into the atmosphere in the health protection zones where some of the wood processing enterprises are located; and
- methodological guidelines for elaborating proposals for PDV and VSV for enterprises.[55]

Enterprises have been required to pay substantial fines for pollution. For example, the combine located at Bratsk reportedly paid more than 2 million rubles in fines, and similar amounts were levied against the Tallinn combine.[56] Consistent application of penalties on such a magnitude should create an incentive for enterprises to change their practices. However, while the pulp and paper complex at Bratsk is one of the largest in the Soviet Union, fines are certainly not the only incentive to change investment priorities at the enterprise. External political pressures centring on pollution of Siberian rivers are considerable and equally good reasons to invest in pollution controls there.

Investment Requirements for Pollution Controls

Given the financial state and technological condition of the industry, it might be simpler and more efficient to enter world markets to purchase mills on a turn-key basis, with guaranteed performance of waste-reducing features and pollution control technologies. This would be the fastest route to advancing the Soviet pulp and paper industry to world class standards, while simultaneously increasing productivity and recouping expenditure. This, of course, would fly in the face of the current national investment strategy to modernise existing production units, and would also necessitate a change of mind concerning reliance on technologies of domestic origin.

In any case, if the industrial base of the pulp and paper sector is to be renewed whilst also providing for environmental management, then the question must be asked whether the current levels of investment, sustained over the long-term, are (a) sufficient for purposes of entering foreign markets; or (b) sufficient for purchases within the Soviet economy. If, as is suggested by Soviet scientists, the piecemeal, adaptive approach to the pulp and paper industry is to continue, then the resource conservation and pollution control strategies require a series of technical renovations and add-on technologies. From 1988 and over the years of the 13th plan period, 1990–1995, the official estimate is that 2 billion rubles will be needed for construction of water and air pollution controls.[57] This estimate, which would mean provision within the 13th plan period (by 1995) of funds roughly equal to four times the allocations of the 12th plan period, can be examined in the context of the following calculations.

Water Recycling

If the whole of the Soviet pulp and paper industry consumes a total of 40 cubic kilometres of water annually, and if perhaps 60 per cent will be recycled by 1990, then additional recycling capacity is required for 16 cubic kilometres of water per year to achieve 100 per cent recycling based on no water losses against supply. The volumes of water consumed without prospects for recovery in the production of pulp and paper and related electric power are not known. It is likely that 16 cubic kilometres is more water than really could be recycled, but without additional information, further estimates here will not be productive.

Automatic Processes

Very little has been spent on this sector, especially for automatic testing of process liquors, waste water, and exhausts. While up to 15 per cent of total investment is reported in respect of pollution control generally in the pulp and paper industry, 'measuring, regulating and laboratory equipment' account for

0.4 per cent of total basic industrial production funds within the whole forestry products industry. It seems apparent that this amount is insufficient to include pollution controls, and Soviet manufacturers are unlikely to be able to provide the necessary equipment quickly enough anyway. Installation of such equipment would result in temporary decommissioning of plant and production losses, but these should be offset by production gains and energy conservation.

Air Pollution Controls

It is not known how much is being spent on this type of equipment, but it is unlikely to be significant given that the emphasis in the 13th plan period (that is, until the year 1995) will be on waste water treatment. No data on which to base cost estimates (such as volume of gaseous emissions or tons of ash) are presently available. There is no reason to believe that ash filters or desulphurisation equipment are more expensive per unit than for electric power stations in respect of technologies used to regenerate sulphur from gaseous emissions. 'Wet scrubbers' appear to be the preferred technology, which can be linked to Soviet interest in recovery of sulphur wastes (see the discussion of gas cleaning technologies in chapter 5, the electric power industry).

Waste Water Treatment

Process Filters

Similarly, there are no examples of costs on which to base an estimate of the installation of filters for waste water. This is achieved by means of technical re-equipping, and in the past has been a major expenditure.

Biological and Chemical Treatment of Effluent

Information concerning pollution on Lake Ladoga provided data on the volumes of waste water cleansed and on costs for two pulp and paper mills. At the Okulovsky Pulp Plant investment outlays are estimated at 0.393 rubles per cubic metre of annual capacity of water treated. This allows processing of 15 million cubic metres/year for 5.9 million rubles. (Calculated as 0.393 rubles times 15 million cubic metres equals 5.9 million rubles.) At the Pitkyaranta Pulp Plant investment outlays are estimated at 0.543 rubles per cubic metre of annual capacity. This will allow about 30 million cubic metres/ year of water to be treated with a total estimated investment of 16.293 million rubles. (Calculated as 0.543 rubles times 30 million cubic metres equals 16.293 million rubles.)[58]

The use of water recycling technologies does not remove the need for purification of the recycled water or the waste water. This could mean, however, that cleansing is occurring to some extent for 60 per cent of total water supply to allow its reuse, leaving 40 per cent of the present annual consumption of 40 cubic kilometres requiring treatment prior to discharge. However, if part of the water supply is used by associated electric power plants, calculating waste water flows as 40 per cent of annual consumption may be too high, particularly since cooling water from electric power stations is not routinely subjected to treatment. If, as suggested above, required investment for treatment technologies ranges between 0.4 and 0.5 rubles per cubic metre of annual capacity of water treated (on the basis of the annual flow-through, 40 per cent of 40 cubic kilometres equals 16 cubic kilometres), then it can be expected that between 6.4 and 8 billion rubles are needed for waste water treatment installations to cleanse 100 per cent of all waste water. This type of investment can be reduced if additional recycling capacity is provided.

Organic Waste Storage

There is no particular reason to believe that this technology is unavailable. For long-term storage some of the preferred membrane technologies, used as liners in landfills, will be hard to obtain from domestic suppliers in a period of petrochemical expansion in the Soviet Union. An estimate of investment requirements depends on types of preferred technologies, numbers of sites, and volumes of waste to be stored. No such information was found and for this reason no estimate is offered.

Notes

1   A G Aganbegyan, Chtoby prirastat' sibir'yu, *Priroda i chelovek*, no. 10, 1984, pp. 18–23.

2   V K Antonov, Narodnokhozyaistvennye problemy tsellyulozno-bumazhnoi promyshlennosti, *Bumazhnaya promyshlennost'*, no. 9, 1989, pp. 7–8; Yu Grin'ko, Bumazhnyi bum so znakon "minus", *Izvestiya*, 5 February 1988, p. 1; A P Vikulov, A P Ivanov, Modernizatsiya oborudovaniya. Ne kolichestvo, a kachestvo! *Bumazhnaya promyshlennost'*, no. 1, 1988, pp. 15–16.

3   T S Khachaturov, N G Fetel'man, N V Bazileva, et al, *Investitsionnaya politika prirodopol'zovaniya*, Moscow: Nauka, 1989, pp. 213–25. Forestry reserves in the European part of the USSR, including the Urals, are about 25 per cent of total Soviet reserves, but it supplies 59 per cent of exploited wood.

4   A P Vikulov, A P Ivanov, *Bumazhnaya promyshlennost'*, no. 1, 1988, ibid.

5   Ibid.

6   Yu Grin'ko, *Izvestiya*, 5 February 1988, op cit.; Itogi raboty predpriyatii tsellyulozno-

bumazhnoi promyshlennosti za 1986 god, *Bumazhnaya promyshlennost'*, no. 3, 1987, pp. 1–3 indicates that production plans were not uniformly fulfilled in all sectors, and the closure of the Priozersk combine at Lake Ladoga, in November 1986, had considerable impact on production of cellulose.

7 A P Vikulov and A P Ivanov, *Bumazhnaya promyshlennost'*, no. 1, 1988, op cit; Yu Grin'ko, *Izvestiya*, 5 February 1988, ibid.

8 *Bumazhnaya promyshlennost'*, no. 3, 1987, op cit.

9 Tsellyulozno–bumazhnaya promyshlennost' SSSR. Problemy, perspektivy, *Bumazhnaya promyshlennost'*, no. 10, 1987, pp. 1–6.

10 A P Vikulov and A P Ivanov, *Bumazhnaya promyshlennost'*, no. 1, 1988, op cit.

11 Ibid.

12 Okhrana prirody na novyi uroven', *Bumazhnaya promyshlennost'*, no. 6, 1987, pp. 1–3.

13 Ibid.

14 Ibid.

15 Yu Grin'ko, *Izvestiya*, op cit.

16 A P Vikulov and A P Ivanov, *Bumazhnaya promyshlennost'*, no. 1, 1988, op cit.

17 Ibid.

18 *Bumazhnaya promyshlennost'*, no. 10, 1987, op cit.

19 Ibid.

20 Yu Grin'ko, *Izvestiya*, op cit.

21 *Bumazhnaya promyshlennost'*, no. 3, 1987, op cit.

22 Ibid.

23 Nastoyatel'noe trebovanie vremeni, *Bumazhnaya promyshlennost'*, no. 6, 1989, pp. 1–3.

24 Ibid.

25 Yu Grin'ko, *Izvestiya*, op cit.

26 Ibid.

27 Ibid.

28 A discussion of the ecological problems caused by the Ukraine's pulp and paper industry are found in S A Gensiruk, *Ispol'zovanie i vosproizvodstvo lesnykh resursov USSR*, Kiev: Naukova Dumka, 1986, Chapter 8.

29 A Ya Tipisev, Malootkhodnaya tekhnologiya – glavnoe napravlenie v okhrane prirody, *Bumazhnaya promyshlennost'*, no. 6, 1985, pp. 1–3.

30 L K Korovin, V F Nevolin, V V Smetanin, Sovershenstvovanie prirodookhrannykh trebovanii – klyuchevaya zadacha zashchity okruzhayushchei sredy, *Bumazhnaya promyshlennost'*, no. 6, 1989, pp. 4–6.

31 A Ya Tipisev, supra.

32 Ibid.

33 Ibid.

34 G A Kondrashkova, L B Glazov, Avtomaticheskii beskontaktnyi konduktometr dla kontrolya stochnykh vod, *Bumazhnaya promyshlennost'*, no. 2, 1988, p. 29.

35 *Bumazhnaya promyshlennost'*, no. 10, 1987, op cit.

36 V K Antonov, *Bumazhnaya promyshlennost'*, no. 9, 1989, op cit.

37 S S Puzyrev, G S Tsvetkova, V V Smetanin, Drevesnaya massa: problemy i perspektivy. Stochnye i oborotnye vody, *Bumazhnaya promyshlennost'*, no. 9, 1987, pp. 16–17,

38 Ibid.

39 *Bumazhnaya promyshlennost'*, no. 10, 1987, op cit.

40 *Bumazhnaya promyshlennost'*, no. 6, 1987, op cit.

41 Ibid.

42 S A Gensiruk, *Ispol'zovanie i vosproizvodstvo lesnykh resursov USSR*, op cit.

43 Povysit' effektivnost' mer po okhrane prirody, *Bumazhnaya promyshlennost'*, no. 8,

1986, pp. 1–4. This degree of recycling was reported in T S Khachaturov, *Ekonomika prirodopol'zovaniya*, Moscow: Nauka, 1987, p. 116.

44   L K Korovin, et al, *Bumazhnaya promyshlennost'*, no. 6, 1989, op cit. See also I I Savel'eva, Dla sokrashcheniya raskhoda svezhei vody, *Bumazhnaya promyshlennost'*, no. 7, 1988, p. 5, which gives an example of a pulp mill at Balakhninsk which has 87.5 per cent water recycling; and Otdadim dolgi prirode, *Bumazhnaya promyshlennost'*, no. 7, 1988, pp. 1–3, which gives an example of a mill at Ust'-Ulimsk which requires 100 cubic metres of fresh water per ton of pulp produced.

45   A Aganbegyan, *Priroda i chelovek*, op cit.

46   *Bumazhnaya promyshlennost'*, no. 8, 1986, op cit.

47   *Bumazhnaya promyshlennost'*, no. 6, 1987, op cit.

48   *Bumazhnaya promyshlennost'*, no. 8, 1986, op cit.

49   Ibid.

50   Ibid.

51   *Bumazhnaya promyshlennost'*, no. 6, 1987, op cit.

52   Ibid. Other installations will also receive some equipment for cleansing of exhaust gases, but there is reported to be a shortfall in equipment supplies.

53   L K Korovin, et al, *Bumazhnaya promyshlennost'*, no. 6, 1989, op cit.

54   S F Lositskii, P P Shkabura, T A Chekin, Normirovanie promyshlennykh vybrosov v atmosferu na predpriyatiyakh Minlesproma UkSSR, *Derevoobrabatyvayushchaya promyshlennost'*, no. 5, 1985, pp. 25–6.

55   Ibid.

56   *Bumazhnaya promyshlennost'*, no. 6, 1987, op cit.

57   *Bumazhnaya promyshlennost'*, no. 7, 1988, pp. 1–3, op cit.

58   Okhrana vodnykh resursov Ladozhskogo ozera, *Ekonomicheskaya gazeta*, no. 49, 1987, p. 24.

5   Fossil Fuelled Electric Power and Environmental Protection

Introduction

The electric power industry in the Soviet Union is closely studied by Western observers having interests in world oil and gas markets and others who follow the advances in power engineering and long distance transport of electricity and heat. Despite such attention, little has been written about the Soviet electric power industry in environmental terms, even though this is easily one of the dirtiest of Soviet industries. Nonetheless, while the conceptual foundations of preferred environmental technologies are well established, the industry appears to have no environmental strategy or near-term pollution control priorities. The electric power industry has three main routes it can take to improve its ecological situation: to use cleaner fuels; to improve combustion technologies; and to apply pollution controls.

The extent to which environmental investment is needed by the electric power industry is, above all, a function of the fuel supply. Ecological goals involving shifts in fuel supplies will not be easily achieved for several reasons. Firstly, the two alternatives traditionally regarded as ecologically 'clean' – nuclear energy and hydroelectric power – are under intense public scrutiny for a variety of ecological and economic reasons. Secondly, the demand for electric power is being strengthened by dint of other energy-intensive industries' moves to electricity as an ecologically efficient alternative. Thirdly, the electric power industry competes with petroleum supplies from other industrial sectors which are attempting to respond to the government's priority programmes to develop chemicals, plastics, textiles, and pharmaceutical manufacturing. And, fourthly, the demand for fuel supplies is on the

91

upswing, but the quantity of coal and oil extracted has gradually slowed due to factors involving the resource base and the magnitude of investment required to extract them. Meanwhile, any extention of domestic natural gas consumption must be weighed against its potential to generate hard-currency earnings.

The remaining strategic routes to improved environmental conditions necessitate heavy and sustained capital investment to repair, upgrade, and relocate existing electric power and regional heating plants. From this perspective, the environmental outlook is gloomy – but not entirely so. The technological base is aging and many polluting plants are scheduled for reconstruction, when environmental features can hopefully be introduced. The environmental forecast would improve if funds allocated for the construction of cancelled hydro and nuclear power installations were shifted into the coal, oil, and gas-fired sector; such rationalisation of investment would require central government intervention to circumvent the obstacles presented by the bureaucratic organisation of energy construction. Environmental investments will also reflect (1) the extent to which regulations require the neutralisation of exhaust gases; (2) the nature of combustion technologies; and (3) the choices of electric and other filtering devices fitted at the power plants. These factors are discussed in the sections below.

Characteristics of the Industry

The fact is, there are conflicting policies and priorities at play. On the one hand, Soviet energy policy stresses the benefits of fuel substitution as a route to environmental protection. On the other, the environmental programme emphasises recovery and recycling of wastes as a means of offsetting the cost of environmental protection. The latter policy ensures the use of high sulphur fuels, which are advantageous to the recovery of commercial quantities of sulphur from the wastes. Meanwhile, the industry itself indicates that existing capital budget allocations can in no way support the level of investment needed for modernisation, much less environmental protection. Although this type of argument is common outside the Soviet Union and is usually resolved by raising user charges, a look at the investment profile of the electric power industry seems to be warranted. The profile here considers activity in the fuel and energy sector in general and the electric power industry in particular, taking into account several of the factors at play. The fuel industry, as the other main component of the sector, is reviewed because of its role in the generation of electric power and its relationship to pollution control options.

Most electricity in the Soviet Union is generated using fossil fuels, which in 1988 yielded about three-quarters of total output. The remaining quarter was produced by hydroelectric and nuclear power plants.[1] The most significant relative growth until 1988 was in nuclear power, which was 134 per cent of its 1985 level, although the increase in nuclear generating capacity was somewhat lower at 125 per cent. Overall, electric plants produced 178 billion kilowatt hours (bkWh) more power in the four years (1986–1989) of the 12th plan period.[2] Such growth is a striking achievement, although one price is obviously the industry's environmental impact that has long been criticised by domestic and foreign observers alike.[3]

Roughly speaking, both capacity and output have doubled over the period 1970 to 1988, which serves as an indication of the scale of the new environmental problems, associated with fuel extraction and processing, as well as with electricity generation itself. It also flags the fact that roughly 50 per cent of electric power generating plants are over 15 years old. Over the next twenty years, these older plants are the most likely targets for replacement or radical reconstruction in the normal course of things. Some additional opportunity is thus offered to combine economic and ecological investment objectives largely within the anticipated investment schedule.

Fuel Supplies

The raw materials used to generate electricity are of environmental concern because the development strategy was devised on the basis of the expanded use of low-quality coal, locally available energy resources, and nuclear power. The strategy is outlined in the 1983 Energy Programme, which is still in use although an updated version is under review. From an environmental perspective, the Energy Programme represented difficult investment choices, as the coal deposits having high sulphur content are primarily found in the Western-most regions of the USSR, which is also where the greatest share (about three-quarters) is consumed.[4] Equally unfortunate, the future growth of coal consumption by the electric power sector must rely on the mining of Kuzbas, Ekibastuz and Kansk-Achinsk coal, and the construction of additional coal-fired plants in Siberia, Kazakhstan, and the Urals.[5] Coal from the latter two deposits are relatively low in sulphur, but they have high ash (around 40 per cent) and moisture (between 8 and 12 per cent) contents and, consequently, only moderate calorific values; significantly, their use also presents formidable dust trapping and solid waste disposal problems. The aims of the Energy Programme notwithstanding, the declining calorific values of Soviet coal supplies make the expansion of coal-fired electricity less economic.[6] Nonetheless, three factors – the escalating cost of coal production in the Moscow and Donets Basins, deeper refining of oil which in turn will reduce the availability of residual fuel oil (*mazut*),[8] and of course the cancellation of the construction of several nuclear plants in the aftermath of Chernobyl' – continue to increase Soviet reliance on coal as a key factor in the industry's energy balance.

The 12th Five Year Plan (1986–1990) indicated that the balance of fossil-fuelled and nuclear power installations in electricity production would be significantly changed by 1990. The major shifts would have occurred in the share of power generated by fossil-fuelled stations (reduced to 65 per cent) and nuclear power (reaching 20 per cent).[9] The plan was to expand nuclear power production in the highly populated European areas of the USSR, to decommission a series of coal-fired power stations known to cause urban air pollution, and to expand the use of coal in areas east of the Urals. The distribution of electric power generation by type of fuel is presented in the following table.

5.1   Production of Electric Power in the USSR
(billion kilowatt hours)

	1970	1980	1985	1986	1987	1988	1989	1990p
Total Production	741	1294	1544	1599	1665	1705	1722	1860p
of which:								
FFEP	601	1016	1139[2]	1198	1233	1233	1247	1225p
Oil		370						
Gas		248						
Coal		416						
Nuclear	4	73	167	161	187	216	217[3]	390p
Hydro	124	184	215	216	220	231	233[3]	245p
Other[1]	12	21	23	24	25	25	253	-

[1] Wood, shale and peat are of negligible value; estimated by L Dienes and T Shabad, *The Soviet Energy System: Resource Use and Policies*, New York: John Wiley & Sons, 1979, pp. 124–8, as under 2 per cent of total produced power. *Narodnoe khozyaistvo SSSR za 70 let*, Moscow 1987, p. 163, reported the production of alternative fuels as 1.8 per cent of total fuel extracted. *Promyshlennost' SSSR*, p. 141, reported the share of alternative fuels at 1.7 per cent in 1987.
[2] Estimated as 'total power less hydro, nuclear and other'.
[3] Estimated on the basis of the previous year.
p = planned.
Sources: Razvitie energetiki SSSR v 1986 g i zadachi na 1987 g, *Electricheskie stantsii*, no. 1, 1987, pp. 2–4; *Narodnoe khozyaistvo SSSR v 1988 g*, p. 379; *Izvestiya*, 8 January 1990, p. 3.

An initial sharpening in the public's awareness of the Energy Programme's implications for the environment occurred before Chernobyl'; but even though hydroelectric construction is still often criticised, the projects are not in the same league of disrepute as nuclear power. Post-Chernobyl' public opposition is formidable and the government has simply walked away from some new construction elements of the nuclear programme – especially from construction based on designs used at Chernobyl' and in ares having seismic faults. Even so, in 1988, 26 nuclear installations were scheduled for expan-

5.2 Electric Power Generating Capacity
(million kilowatt hours)

Year	All Electric Stations of which:	Hydro	Nuclear
1970	166	31.4	0.9
1980	267	52.3	12.5
1985	315	61.7	28.1
1988	339	63.8	35.4

Source: Narodnoe khozyaistvo SSSR v 1988 g, p. 379.

sion or were under construction.[10] The expansion of hydro power is now being more keenly monitored, and for many ecology-watchers the cancellation in the late 1980s of the Katun project was a landmark result due to such scrutiny.

One oft-mentioned economic dispute centres on the flooding of arable land, as that effectively brings the hydro power concept into conflict with the government's declared priority of increasing agricultural production. Another is the high cost of construction in remote areas, involving not just power plants but the spectrum of social and economic infrastructure. Even so, the new element in the opposition argument is that Siberian construction damages ecologically fragile terrain that is not only unlikely to recover from the disruption, but where left unattended the initial damage breeds further deterioration. The recent record of hydroelectric power reflects the expansion of this form of electricity generation onto sites that are relatively less well suited in that they lack seasonal continuity of water flow.

Should hydroelectric construction continue to be regarded as a viable option, it may take the form of smaller production units; and, in any event, the most likely immediate targets are in Siberia. There is also considerable discussion of greatly expanding hydro power in Central Asia,[11] but it would be extraordinary if such investment occurred before some sort of solution is devised for Central Asian water supplies and pollution abatement.[12] Nonetheless, the record serves to emphasise that the path for operating and developing the electric power industry still lies in conventional fossil fuels and nuclear fission.

Energy Conservation

Soviet economic strategy requires improvements in energy efficiency (the usual jargon is 'to reduce the energy intensiveness of production per unit of output and overall').[13] A 10 per cent saving in electric power consumption, to cover 80 per cent of new demand, is one hoped-for outcome of the present programme of industrial modernisation.[14] Soviet economic strategy also requires savings in the oil and natural gas used in the generation of electric power.[15] According to the 1983 programme, the proportion of coal could increase from about 35 per cent in 1980 to 42–45 per cent at the end of the century, using between 60 and 70 per cent of the overall consumption of coal to generate electric power. Since, as Caron Cooper has written, the year 2000 target has already been met,[16] of the 467 million tons of coal (in values of standard fuel) mined in 1988, at least 326 tons were used by the electricity industry.[17] In any event, a further shift to coal means that the majority of power stations, particularly those in the European regions, are increasing their dependence on fuel of diminished quality. As the plants were not designed to use low quality coal, this is gradually eroding their efficiency.[18]

The fact is, available Soviet data do not identify those technological areas where industrial leaders envisage either the need or possibility for energy conservation. Broadly speaking, of course, it is assumed that 'industry', consistently absorbing 57 per cent of total electricity supplies, is the most obvious target by virtue of its consumption which is expanding at a very fast pace indeed. Such rapid growth is also characteristic of the agricultural-rural economy, but in 1987 it took only 10 per cent of total available power and is probably under-supplied. Electric power for municipal and urban domestic purposes was 9 per cent of total available supplies, and for transportation about 8 per cent. It is difficult to see how significant savings can be achieved in the non-industrial sectors given their proportionately small shares. The much-needed modernisation of the Soviet transport sector should ultimately promote energy efficiency, although not savings of electric power as such.

5.3   Electricity Balance in the National Economy
(billion kilowatt hours)

Year	Total Output	Industry	Agriculture[1]	Transport	Other	General Branches[2]	Export Uses[3]
1980	1294	773	111	103	181	107	19
1985	1544	894	146	120	222	134	29
1986	1599	922	152	128	230	137	29
1987	1665	957	160	131	240	142	35

[1] From the total, 24.6 billion kilowatt hours of electric power were consumed by rural households.
[2] No explanation was given for the power used by 'other branches'.
[3] 'General uses' apparently refers to municipal-domestic consumption, exclusive of transport.
Source: Promyshlennost' SSSR, Moscow: Finansy i statistika, 1988, p. 136.

Increased demand can be met through improvements in efficiency at power stations (for example, reductions in transmission losses and the amount of fuel consumed per unit of electricity generated, or increases in the operating time of the power generating units). Overall, there seems to be some, but not much, scope for improvements of this kind. This is demonstrated by the following indicators of how power stations operate.

5.4   Number of Hours
during which the Established Average Annual Capacity
of Power Stations are in Operation

	1970	1980	1985	1988
All Power Stations	4735	5029	5110	5117
(% of 1970)	100	106	108	109
Power Stations for General use	5136	5251	5231	5311
(% of 1970)	100	102	102	103
Fossil Fuelled Stations	5423	5692	5676	5643
(% of 1970)	100	105	105	104
Hydroelectric Stations	4146	3646	3612	3679
(% of 1970)	100	.88	.87	.89
Specific Consumption of Standard Units of Fuel at Power Stations for General use in grammes per kW hour of electric power generated	367	328	326	325
(% of 1970)	100	.89	.89	.89

Source: Narodnoe khozyaistvo SSSR v 1988 g, p. 380.

Other Conservation Opportunities

Whatever the improvements in the efficiency of fuel consumption and operating hours, they are of much less significance than the expansion of capacity and electricity generated. The following table expresses the rate of growth of capital assets.

5.5   Growth of BIPF
for the Period 1970–1985
(1970 = 100)

	1970	1980	1985
All Industry	100	217	300
Fuel and Energy Sector	100	200	279
Electric Power Industry	100	190	247
Fuel Industry	100	212	321

Source: *Narodnoe khozyaistvo SSSR v 1985 g*, p. 115.

With particular reference to the electric power industry, it should be noted that the value of funds has more than doubled; either this reflects a form of inflation or the fact that additional capacity costs more in real terms and is given a higher valuation (or conceivably a combination of both). In comparison with the growth of funds as a whole, the electric power industry has fallen behind, though there is no particular reason why such a structural shift should have negative consequences if net savings were being made in electricity consumption per unit of output throughout the economy. By contrast, the stock of basic funds in the fuel industry has risen by more than the average for all industry.

These respective shifts in the growth rate are reflected in the basic industrial production funds of the respective industries:

5.6   Relative Growth of BIBF
(as a proportion of the value of capital assets as industry as a whole)

	1970	1980	1985
Fuel and Energy Sector	30.5	29.1	29.8
Electric Power Industry	17.4	15.9	15.1
Fuel Industry	13.1	13.2	14.7

Source: *Narodnoe khozyaistvo SSSR v 1985 g*, p. 122.

Over this period, the proportion of funds in the electric power industry has undergone a general decline, whereas growth in the fuel industry has been sufficient to push up its share of funds. This, then, represents the net outcome of investment activity.

The gross input into the stock of funds shows a similar pattern to net growth and is expressed here both absolutely in comparable prices and relative to investment in industry as a whole:

5.7 Gross Input into BIPF

	1971–75	1976–80	1981–1985	1986–88
Billions of Rubles				
All Industry	196.0	251.4	300.7	225.5
Electric Power	20.0	22.9	28.7	20.5
Coal Industry	9.9	11.4	13.5	10.3
Oil Industry	17.9	29.3	50.3	}58.1
Gas Industry	8.2	11.3	15.9	
As a Percentage				
All Industry	100	100	100	100
Electric Power	10.2	9.1	9.5	9.1
Coal Industry	5.1	4.5	4.5	4.6
Oil Industry	9.1	11.7	16.7	}25.8
Gas Industry	4.2	4.5	5.3	

Source: Narodnoe khozyaistvo SSSR v 1985 g, p. 368; Narodnoe khozyaistvo SSSR v 1988 g, p. 356.

From these data, there is clearly a decline in investment performance in the electric power industry relative to industry as a whole, although the absolute level of investment funds has grown. As the data here are more fully disaggregated, it is possible to identify the more dynamic elements in the fuel industry: the outstanding leader is oil which has undergone extensive expansion.

Again, the addition to the stock of funds can be evaluated in terms of the commissioning of basic industrial production funds as a percentage of the overall value of funds in a given industry at the end of the period stated:

5.8 Capital Assets Commissioned

	1971–75	1976–80	1981–85	1986	1987	1988
All Industry	40	37	33	6.9	6.6	6.1
Fuel and Energy Sector	34	32	31	6.9	7.0	6.7
Electric Power	28	24	21	4.2	4.4	3.8
Fuel Industry	41	41	40	9.6	9.6	9.5

Source: Narodnoe khozyaistvo SSSR v 1985 g, p. 123; Narodnoe khozyaistvo SSSR v 1988 g, p. 357.

In this context and relative to the existing stock of funds, the electric power industry has invested consistently at a rate roughly two-thirds of that for industry as a whole (that is, at a rate which, if matched by a similarly proportionate rate of decommissioning, would generate a net decline in the industry's portfolio of assets). Performance in the fuel industry provides a striking contrast: whereas the rate of commissioning for industry as a whole has declined over the period under review, the rate for the fuel industry has held steady, so that the advance of this industry's proportion of funds that was noted above appears to be closely associated with the sustained rate of investment.

The corresponding data for the rate of decommissioning capital stock (as a percentage of the overall value of BIPF at the beginning of the period) confirm in the first instance the proportionality of the decommissioning rate in the electric power industry relative to the rate for industry as a whole:

5.9   Capital Assets Decommissioned

	1976–80	1981–85	1986	1987	1988
All Industry	15	14	3.0	3.6	3.5
Fuel & Energy Sector	16	15	3.5	3.8	3.2
Electric Power	8	7	1.7	2.4	1.9
Fuel Industry	26	24	5.3	5.3	4.5

Source: *Narodnoe khozyaistvo SSSR za 70 let*, p. 149; *Narodnoe khozyaistvo SSSR v 1988 g*, p. 359.

The decommissioning rate in the fuel industry has fallen more rapidly than that for industry as a whole and thus has boosted this industry's proportion of basic industrial production funds. Moreover, the decommissioning rate for fuel is not only above average for all industry, it ranks only second in this respect to the pulp and paper industry. By contrast, the rate for electric power ranks lowest amongst the major branches of industry. The rate of decommissioning may be explained by the fact that most of the electric power industry's plant still operate within their normal life expectancy.

In general, these data show that the fuel industry has developed a high turnover since it is a major branch of industry with easily the highest rate of commissioning. By contrast, the electric power industry not only decommissions at a low rate, it also takes new plant into operation at a rate lower than that found amongst the other major branches of industry; that is, it has an especially low turnover in capital stock.

This impression is confirmed by the data on incomplete construction, shown here as a percentage of the volume of capital invested:

5.10   Incomplete Construction

	1970	1980	1985	1986	1987	1988
Whole Economy	73	87	78	79	78	83
Electric Power Industry	102	123	125	142	147	164
Coal Industry	126	120	106	104	109	114
Oil and Gas Industries	82	82	71	74	73	77

Source: Narodnoe khozyaistvo SSSR v 1988 g, p. 558.

In this respect the electric power industry is well above the average for the whole economy and responded favourably to the rise in the proportion of incomplete investment in 1980; the industry thus appears to have a relatively long lead time between starting and completing construction and has grown at an extraordinary pace since 1980. By contrast, both the main components of the fuel industry detailed here have suffered reductions in their respective proportions of incomplete investment. Between them there is a further contrast: the proportion is substantially and consistently higher in the coal industry than in the oil and gas industries.

These configurations point to the dominant characteristics of the industries themselves. Typical features are to be found in the commissioning of the most important productive capacity on the basis of construction in new and extended enterprises and reconstruction at existing enterprises.

5.11   Commissioning of Productive Capacity

	1971–75	1976–80	1981–85	1986–88
Power Station Capacity (million kW)	58.1	54.0	51.2	26.7
Extraction Wells (1000)				
oil	2.5	2.2	2.4	na
gas	20.8	29.8	53.6	na
Capacity for Extracting Coal (million tons/annum)	114.2	90.4	61.6	78.8
Gas Pipeline (1000 km)	33.7	30.0	48.1	32.2
Pipeline for Oil and Oil Products (1000 km)	22.6	14.9	16.9	6.5

Source: Narodnoe khozyaistvo SSSR v 1985 g, p. 360; *Narodnoe khozyaistvo SSSR v 1988 g*, p. 546.

It should be stressed that these are not the sole components of the industries, but as key elements they roughly represent a diminishing return on outlays in terms of rubles which, as noted above, may derive from a combination of inflation and actual increases in the cost of providing a unit of output capacity. In the case of the fuel extraction industries, there is some reason to expect a real rise in the cost of construction as deposits are opened up that have less favourable geological conditions and lie further from existing population centres. This spatial dimension also plays a role in the location of power plant investment, inasmuch as the very low rate of retiring existing facilities, which typically are located in established urban centres, suggests that much of the new capacity (in effect replacement capacity) is being placed in *new* centres of population and industrial operation.

Some idea of the relative importance of these various capacities is given by examining the structure of basic industrial production funds by types, as on 1 January 1989.

5.12   Structure of Capital Assets
(in per cents)

	All Industry	Fuel and Energy	Electric Power	Fuel Industry
Total BIPF	100	100	100	100
Buildings	27.1	11.2	15.2	7.4
Installations	19.5	37.1	14.9	57.7
Active Assets	53.4	51.7	69.9	34.9
Transmission				
Devices	10.4	21.7	31.8	12.4
Power Plants	7.5	17.4	33.7	2.2
Operative				
Machinery	29.2	9.8	1.8	17.3
MRLE*	1.8	1.2	1.3	1.1
Computers	1.2	0.4	0.6	0.3
Transport	2.3	1.0	0.5	1.4
Other	1.0	0.2	0.2	0.2

*Measuring, Regulating, and Laboratory Equipment
Source: Narodnoe khozyaistvo SSSR v 1988 g, p. 352–3.

In the fuel industry, the largest item is 'installations', in a proportion far exceeding anything to be found in other branches of industry. The other large items are 'transmission devices' (such as, pipelines and conveyor belts for coal) and machinery. The electric power industry naturally has the highest concentration of 'power plants', the single largest item in the composition of its funds; the second largest item is 'transmission devices', again the largest proportion to be found in any industry, which represents power lines.

The point is to bring attention to the specific parts of these industries that are associated with industrial pollution. There are problems with open cast mines and deep mines in the extraction of solid fuel, as well as with the disturbance and pollution of deep strata in the extraction of oil and gas: these are likely to continue. On the other hand, the initial treatment of the extracted fuels is more amenable to technological intervention as the usable material is separated from the waste (for example, mining spoil or sulphur), as is the transportation of these fuels where spillage causes environmental damage. In the electric power industry, potential damage is mainly associated with the use of fuels as sources of energy rather than with the transmission of output, although the latter, too, occasions environmental disruption.

The present comments are confined to the opportunities for environmental protection in the electric power industry. When technical considerations limit the possibilities for adding pollution control devices to existing plant, new construction or radical reconstruction offer the main path for introducing pollution controls. There is, however, the further complicating factor in that the relative concentration of problems is associated with pollution in the area of generation; downstream damage (that may be at once remote and hard to detect), must also be taken into account. The data on commissioning and

5.13 Commissioning and Decommissioning of Fossil Fuelled Power Stations

	All Industry	Fuel & Energy	Electric Power	Fuel
Commissioned				
Total	6.9	7.6	5.5	9.7
Buildings & Installations	5.7	8.3	5.5	9.7
Machinery & Equipment	8.3	7.3	6.2	9.1
Other	6.6	6.5	4.6	10.8
Decommissioned				
Total	1.4	1.1	0.4	1.8
Buildings & Installations	0.4	0.5	0.2	0.7
Machinery & Equipment	2.5	2.1	0.5	4.9
Other	1.5	0.9	0.7	1.4

Source: Narodnoe khozyaistvo SSSR v 1985 g, p. 124.

decommissioning of power stations (1985, as a percentage of the overall value of funds at the end and beginning of the year respectively) give a general picture. The key area, of course, for the electric power industry is machinery and equipment, which includes boilers, generators, and turbines. The value of all newly commissioned funds relative to the existing stock is, as in previous years, roughly two-thirds of the ratio for industry as a whole. Decommissioning runs at a rate of only one-fifth of that in industry as a whole.

This set of data once more underlines the contrast in the investment activities of the fuel and energy sector: the rate at which plant and equipment are commissioned and decommissioned in the fuel industry ranks highest amongst branches of industry, whereas this rate in the electric power industry ranks amongst the lowest. Where the opportunities for introducing pollution control equipment are limited by technological considerations, again there is relatively little scope in the electric power industry as presently financed to introduce pollution control features that are dependent on changes in power generating technologies. Until recently, most power stations have operated within service age, so the slow rate of decommissioning is to be expected. An increased pace of decommissioning will occur unless the industry decides it is economically efficient to keep the old plant in operation. A power station can be run as long as it can be maintained and repaired, or technologies replaced within an existing installation. In contrast, the life-span of a given fuel extraction site can be short, as a mine or an extraction well operates until the resource base is exhausted in economic terms and abandoned.

On this basis, there are two possible scenarios. The first is the optimistic view that at least 50 per cent of the existing plant appears to be at least 15 years old, and in the next two decades will undergo routine reconstruction. This is a rather extraordinary amount of plant maturing within a very short space of time. While it does not necessarily mean that ecological combinations of technologies will be brought into service, at least an unusually good opportunity exists to address polluting emissions by a substantial part of the industry within the normal servicing arrangements, thus alleviating the need to decommission new plant outside normal service periods and incur additional burdens. This does not, however, say anything about whether or not the existing level of investment in reconstruction and retooling is adequate, for obvious reasons of differences in the valuations of old compared with new plant.

The pessimistic view is that resource conservation technologies and pollution controls will be seen primarily at new power stations, since there is considerable pressure to expand capacity and to replace only the very old plant. The economic argument is that installation of pollution controls will also be circumscribed by the preference for fuelling power stations with coal. This necessitates some redirection of investment. In this respect, the running down of gas extraction would present no great problems given the relatively high turnover of plant, though no doubt any switch in fuel strategy toward gas is motivated by considerations of demand for gas in other industries and the prospects for further gas extraction from new sites (anyway, gas is not expected to pose a resource-supply issue until well into the twenty-first century). The expansion of coal production is especially hampered by the long lead-time between initiating investment and commencing extraction. In general, the faster pace of commissioning in the fuel industry appears to give it an overall flexibility, which is needed to accommodate planned shifts in fuel consumption by new generations of power stations. Nonetheless, the relative cost of establishing a unit of extraction capacity is rising; but since the electric power industry is similarly constrained by the cost of generating capacity, the choice of fuel for new power stations will be limited as much by the economics of its transportion as the original investment in fuel extraction.

Environmental Options

Because there is no environmental programme as such for the electric power industry, a discussion of its environmental 'priorities' must refer back to the broad goals established in the 'General Programme for Social and Economic Development' and the 1983 Energy Programme. It is these guidelines and discussions in the nature protection journals and the electricity industry's literature which constitute a basis for describing the 'environmental regulations' confronting this industry. Thus, a discussion of 'goals', 'investment priorities', and 'regulations' assumes the contradictory posture of 'positive uncertainty' – in other words, given the regulatory approach, this is what remains to be done, all other things being equal.

The implementation of laws and resolutions to combat air pollution is subsumed under briefs assigned to several government agencies, supposedly coordinated by the USSR State Committee on Hydrometeorology (Goskomgidromet) and the USSR State Committee on Nature Protection (Goskompriroda). Goskomgidromet keeps track of atmospheric conditions in towns and industrial centres by means of a network of monitoring stations.[19] In 1979, the A I Voeikov Main Geophysical Observatory, operated by Goskomgidromet, provided annual summaries of 'the state of atmospheric pollution' in about 300 cities,[20] the data for which originated with Goskomgidromet's monitoring stations. Nowadays, in addition, the State Sanitary Inspectorate under the USSR Ministry of Health identifies and reports local pollution problems, and the USSR Ministry of Health, amongst others, sponsors scientific research on which the air pollution control regulations are based.[21] A further source of data originates with Soviet enterprises, which have been required for several years to submit annual reports to the USSR State Committee Statistics (Goskomstat) on the quantities of harmful substances they discharge.[22] So far, the official data originated with Goskomgidromet and were issued by Goskomstat.

To further complicate the picture of regulatory organisation, the actual operations of gas decontamination systems at industrial enterprises are inspected by the State Inspectorate for Monitoring the Operations of Gas Treatment and Dust Extraction Devices. The Inspectorate was subsumed under Goskomgidromet in 1985, and presently embraces a network of 59 regional inspectorates.[23] The Inspectorate's brief (which excludes any responsibility for enforcement as such) is to establish whether individual industrial enterprises observe the regulations and instructions governing the operations of gas treatment installations, if their operational indicators correspond with the design specifications, and that the installations have the instrumentation needed to determine the performance efficiency of cleansing equipment. The Inspectorate also undertakes evaluations prior to the commissioning of new facilities.[24] It is not clear how, or indeed if, the findings of inspections and subsequent remedial activities are coordinated with the USSR State Committee for Nature Protection, which is responsible in law for all areas of environmental protection.[25]

Some funds have been expended by the fuel and energy sector for environmental controls; the currently available data are presented below. Until mid-1990, when new data emerged, Soviet statistics did not distinguish amongst the branches of industry – fuel or electric power – that invested the funds. It seems most likely that the investment occurred in the fuel side (at the refineries, fuel-processing plants or nuclear installations) rather than at fossil-fuelled power stations. This is a point that is illustrated by 1989 data presented in Appendix 1.

5.14   State Capital Budget for Measures to Protect Nature and Rational Use of Natural Resources
(millions of rubles)

	1981–1985	1986–1990*	1986	1987	1988
Total FEC	1745	2605	494	448	621
of which:					
Waste Water Treatment	1235	1548	268	316	345
Air Pollution Controls	110	305	71	64	48
Land Protection	120	250	30	34	86

Source: *Okhrana okruzhayushchei sredy i ratsional' noe ispolzovanie prirodnykh resursov v SSSR*, pp. 148–149.
* Projected on the basis of 1986–1988.

In effect, the data tell us that the FEC is receiving an increasing amount of funding with which to address pollution caused by one or other branches of the complex. For this, the FEC complex commissioned the following.

5.15 Capacity of Installations Commissioned

	1981–1985	1986–1990*	1986	1987	1988
Waste Water Treatment (ts cubic metres/day)	2845	2170	474	504	324
Circulating Water Systems (ts cubic metres/day)	87855	89090	18596	23433	11425
Air Pollution Controls (ts cubic metres gas/hr)	62610	57500	8995	16564	8915

*Projected on the basis of 1986–1988.
ts cubic metres/hr = thousand cubic metres per hour.
Source: Okhrana okruzhayushchei sredy..., pp. 152–3.

Since 1986, it has been increasingly difficult to spend the environmental budget anywhere in the national economy; judging by the irregular pace at which new waste water treatment capacity has been commissioned by the FEC, this sector has not been excepted from the national trend. However, the FEC continued to allocate more resources into environmental investment, with roughly 70 per cent of the 1986 capacity being commissioned in 1988. This poor performance occurred in spite of a 25 per cent increase over the 1986 budget – a real increase even after allowing for inflation. It was caused by the dual problems of too few material resources and rising costs; in fact, there was probably money left over. In 1989, the situation apparently deteriorated further (see Appendix 1).

Before the 1989 data appeared, Soviet statistics did not indicate in which sector of the FEC the recirculating capacity was commissioned. This is unfortunate as the data represent a large amount of new capacity. (See Appendix 2 for 1989 data). The data are especially unhelpful for environmental assessment purposes, since they do not tell from which budget (for example, from nature protection or the reconstruction of existing plant, etc.) they were taken. The items in the budget do not add up to total resources available, so that some part of the necessary funds *may* have originated within the capital budget for environmental controls. It is noteworthy that the level of commissioned capacity in 1988 was well below that for any year since 1980.

Finally, there is capacity being commissioned for air pollution controls although, at the average rate for 1986–1988, the signs are that total capacity commissioned during the 12th plan period will be less than that for the preceding one. The rate at which capacity is commissioned reflects the availability of funds for the purpose, which in 1988 was below that of the previous two years. Air pollution controls have a low priority within the FEC and the national economy generally. In fact, the

FEC's environmental budget for this purpose sustained a budget reduction in 1988, although Appendix 1 shows an increase in 1989.

Finally, the budgetary data for protection of land are surprising, as concern about land reclamation is not identified in the industry's literature as an investment priority. Land improvement will occur as a long-term benefit of waste reclamation, but even then the concern is only implied. It is unlikely that the capital budget in this category (which was larger than that for air pollution controls) was expended by the fossil fuelled electric power industry.

Regulated Substances

The general Soviet strategy for environmental protection envisages a hierarchical regulatory process in which normatives (regulatory criteria) stipulate the 'permissible volumes of contaminants' (*predel' no dopustimykh vybrosov* or PDV) which may be released, as well as the permissible concentrations of pollutants' (*predel' no dopustimykh kontsentratsii* or PDK). Both classes of normatives are developed primarily on the basis of the impact of the substance on humans,[26] though there is some evidence that the impact on nature is also considered in the development of PDV.[27] The PDK normatives are adjusted on a site-specific basis, taking into account regional assessments of environmental factors, local climatic conditions and prevailing concentrations of pollutants.[28]

> Development of energy producing enterprises can be ecologically valid only in such cases where the generation or releases of harmful substances are not in excess of the permissible concentrations (PDV). In connection with GOST 17.2.23.02–78, emissions from a given enterprise are considered the maximum permissible, when together with the releases of other enterprises, they do not lead to ground-level concentrations exceeding the health normatives at any point of the urban area (precisely, its residential area). Only in the case indicated does the operation of energy enterprises not contradict the USSR Law for the Protection of Atmospheric Air.

In theory, the regional assessments embrace local 'thermal conditions' (that is, temperature, humidity, and wind speed), light conditions, noise, the extent and composition of green spaces, and sources and concentration of pollutants in the area.[29] The assessments are supposed to be used in decisions involving power plant siting, mandatory allowances for sanitary zones around the installations, and selection of the normatives applied in the designs and during the construction of new electric power stations. In addition, the environmental protection strategy emphasises the use of waste-free or low-waste technologies in the designs for all new construction, the implications of which are discussed below. All indications are that the regional assessments are handicapped by insufficient automation which forces monitoring personnel to conduct the tests manually.[30]

The number of air pollutants for which PDK have been published has grown rapidly. There are three sets of PDK normatives: those governing releases of pollutants (a) into high altitudes, (b) affecting ground-level concentrations, and (c) into the work place. In 1979, the list of normatives included 114 substances, for which two PDK were published. (One category of PDK related to occupational exposures, and the other to releases into the atmosphere.) By 1981, the list included 160 regulated elements relative to atmospheric emissions, and 494 relative to releases into the working areas of industrial enterprises. By 1986, the former had been developed to include 200 substances.[31]

There are few normatives governing the overall volume of gaseous emissions (PDV) into the atmosphere.[32] It is probably reasonable to assume that the absence of relevant discussions means that this class of normatives has not been extensively developed. In theory, the reason for a limit on the absolute volume of gaseous emissions is that atmospheric pollution (even when emissions are below the levels prescribed in the PDK) also reflects the gross volume of pollutants in the atmosphere. For example, the quantity of solar energy absorbed by aerosols contained in the atmosphere depends not only on the concentration of solid particles and their dispersion, but the depth of the polluted layer of air which, all other things being equal, is a function of the total volume of emissions from all sources. Thus, PDK normatives, which are based on the implications of specific substances for human health and hygiene, have not been devised to regulate on the basis of the cumulative effects of low concentrations of pollutants on the atmosphere. Examples involve acid rain and, potentially, the 'greenhouse effect'.

A fully developed system of PDK and PDV normatives would simplify the implementation of pollution controls, as it would remove at least one obstacle to compliance. The effectiveness of the PDV system is constrained by the unavailability of pollution control technologies (whose development would be stimulated by the PDV system) and, crucially, by the absence of reliable data on the long-term effects of cumulative low-level concentrations (which are essential for setting the PDV). At present, it seems that the limitations on emissions of pollutants, whether by PDV or PDK standards, have been primarily in industrialised regions, but in general they have occurred incidentally rather than as the result of specific policy initiatives.

Oxides of sulphur, nitrogen, and carbon, as well as dust, cinder, and ash are characteristic components of gases emitted by coal, gas, oil, shale, and wood-fired electric power installations. The following is a list of substances commonly found in the gaseous wastes from power plants. The formula concern the maximum permissible concentrations in the emissions once the gases have been combined with air outside the smoke stack. Thus, if a power plant emits sulphurous gases in a location characterised by little wind, the concentration of sulphur should not exceed the values for hourly checks of daily totals as expressed in the table.

5.16   PDK Values for Some Pollutants in Atmospheric Air
(maximum permitted concentrations mg/m³)

	maximum at any one time	daily average
Nitrogen dioxide	0.085	0.085
Vanadium pentoxide	—	0.002
Arsenic	—	0.003
Dust, non-toxic	0.5	0.15
Soot	0.15	0.05
Sulphuric acid	0.3	0.1
Sulphur dioxide	0.5	0.05
Hydrogen sulphide	0.008	0.008
Carbon monoxide	3.0	1.0
Formaldehyde	0.035	0.012
Fluorine compounds*	0.02	0.005
Chlorine	0.1	0.03
Benzopyrine	—	0.000001

*By fluorine content.
Source: N G Zalogin, L I Kropp, and Yu M Kostrikin, *Energetika i okhrana okruzhayushchei sredy*, Moscow: Energiya, 1979, p. 37.

The Soviet experience in meeting PDK is as follows:

5.17   Maximum Achievable Concentration of Pollutants
(as per cent of the volume of waste sample)

Sulphur dioxide	0.01–0.3
Carbon monoxide	1–10
Nitrogen oxides	0.01–0.05

Source: M A Styrikovich, A K Vnukov, Kachestvo vozdukha v gorodakh. Issledovaniya i normirovanie. *Vestnik Akademiya Nauk SSSR*, no. 1, 1984, pp. 45–51.

In principle, this makes the normatives for cleansing dependent on the volume of atmospheric air, as measured by wind dispersion (displacement by wind velocity that causes movement horizontally and vertically).[33] Thus, for areas with air inversion problems and urban areas, a higher standard of cleansing is required, while in areas where wind velocity dilutes the concentrations of sulphur, the standard of cleansing is lower. It is usual in the Soviet Union for the dilution of the concentration of exhaust gases to be dependent on the use of tall smoke stacks which, in turn, increase the long-distance transportation of sulphur gases with concomitant downstream damage. Officially, the 'standard of cleansing' prescribed for a given power station is to be established on the basis of the regional assessment of atmospheric conditions, mentioned above. It is claimed that chimneys of 250 metres in height can achieve reductions of *local* concentrations of smoke from some thermal electric stations to 99 per cent; after the assessments were made, chimneys of 320 metres were built at the Zaparozhsk, Karmanovsk, Uglegorsk, Perm, and Kashirsk State Regional Power Stations.[34] The problem with the tall chimneys, other than their questionable benefits for pollution control *downstream*, is that the material costs conflict with the government's policy 'to reduce the raw materials content of production'.[35]

Soviet calculations of the need for gas cleansing technologies require knowledge of the dispersion rate of the specific substances contained in the flue gases. (Such estimates are often highly controversial in the West, where the best data are derived with automated point-source and downstream monitoring systems, and subsequently with the assistance of sophisticated computer models.) But there are also indications that flue gas controls should in future be selected on the basis of the behaviour of airborne pollutants by transformation and deposition. This is because some pollutants undergo chemical and physical transformation in the atmosphere, and in so doing they may form 'secondary pollutants' – such as hydrogen sulphide, sulphuric acid and photochemical oxidants. These are often mentioned as problems in Central Asia, where climatic conditions, emissions from industry and power plants, and certain pesticides act together to produce toxic substances that, on entering the food chain, then endanger public health.[36]

Locations

Even in the absence of a published environmental programme for the electric power industry, it is frequently assumed that investment activities will occur first in urban centres, as human health is the primary concern of the environmental regulations. This, then, is a good example of 'positive uncertainty', because as it was shown above there are equally strong arguments suggesting that, given shortages of investment capital, the immediate targets are in remote locales where population density is lower, but cheap fuel is plentiful.

On the side of the socio-economic argument, it is understood that some cities are especially vulnerable to air pollution – partly because the density of tall buildings inhibits the ability of wind to cleanse the air. In towns with populations in excess of 500,000 the concentration of pollution is believed to be generally 1.5–2 times higher than in small towns.[37] A general definition of urban pollution is as follows:[38]

> The city environment is considered polluted if, as the result of direct or indirect input by sources of human origin of substances and energy, it causes a change of

its physical, chemical, and biological properties up to the levels exceeding established norms and the environment becomes unfavourable for one or other type of use.

Of the diverse pollutants released into the atmosphere, the ones with the most significance for energy facilities located in urban settings are sulphurous gas and nitrogen dioxide:[39]

> ...inasmuch as they are practically always present at the same time in the product of burning fossil fuels ... . (Regulation SN 245–71 addresses some of the contaminants which must be contained, but the scientific basis has not been completed.) ... . The problem is that the rapid development of motor and air transport, which are not fitted with means to prevent emissions of nitrogen oxides, makes it more difficult or precludes the construction of fossil fuelled electric power stations in populated areas even on the basis of natural gas unless health legislation is contravened.

A glance at Soviet demographic statistics is sufficient to see that a great number of people will be affected by uncontrolled emissions from urban power plants. In 1985, there were more than 1200 cities in the USSR; and if towns and villages (not classified as urban) are taken into account, this increased to over 5,000. At the time, the Soviet population was 276 million, of whom 180 million (65 per cent) lived in urban areas, and 16 per cent (46 million) lived in cities having more than 1 million inhabitants.[40] Since 1981, when it was observed that 350 cities suffered from air pollution, Goskomgidromet appears to have concentrated on a much smaller number of urban centres. In 1987, the Director of Goskomgidromet, noted that the air quality assessments show 104 cities as suffering from severe air pollution,[41] and his data apparently do not yet cover all Soviet cities.

Power plants generate over half of the total sulphur dioxide emissions in urban areas, and a significant volume of sulphur and nitrogen oxides are also caused by urban automotive transport:[42]

> Twenty-eight per cent, of ground-level concentrations of sulphur and nitrogen oxides are due to energy and industrial enterprises, and transport vehicles release additional sulphur and nitrogen oxide gases.

A further socio-economic justification for immediate investment in urban air pollution controls is implicit in the following observation concerning the unproductive and preventable outlays of several billion rubles for health care services and institutions each year:[43]

> Any environment, which is unusual in evolutionary terms and liable to change rapidly, is capable of causing irreparable damage to public health. According to

the data of a number of authors, 18–20 per cent of all expenditure on health protection is connected to illnesses caused by atmospheric pollution alone.

It was not for reasons of pollution, according to Shabad, but rather 'due to shortages of fossil fuels in Western regions of the USSR' that fossil-fuelled power development virtually ceased from the beginning of the eighties, 'except for district heat and power stations in the large cities'.[44] Municipal hot water and heating supplies, sometimes co-generated at the electric power installations, are usually dependent on fossil fuels. The provision of district heating and hot water by electric power plants effectively dictates the placement of boilers within a few kilometres of consumers. Still, given the heavy reliance on coal in Western regions, this factor alone ensures that plants in the vicinity of cities must invest heavily in pollution controls.[45]

When socio-economic reasoning is pushed aside, as it frequently is with power engineers and economic planners, there are strong motivations not to invest in cities. A S Nekrasov expressed the alternative case as follows:[46]

> The necessity of burning low quality fuel at power stations and in boilers has led Soviet planners to consider a scheme wherein power stations which are located close to coal and shale basins and deposits are reconstructed to use this fuel. The purpose is to free up higher quality coal which can then be shipped to thermal power stations and boilers some distance from the fuel base.... . An analysis of the relative locations of fuel base and power stations intended for reconstruction and modernisation before the year 2000 has shown that almost all are located within a radius of 500 kilometres from the centre of production associations of coal extraction enterprises and some 50 per cent of their capacity is located within a radius of 100 kilometres. These power stations [and the boilers of coal extraction and processing plants] can be regarded as prime candidates for using fuel with low calorific value.

Nekrasov's views seem to coincide with those of M A Styrikovich, who summarised the economic benefits of using high ash coal from basins such as Ekibastuz and Kansk-Achinsk, by saying 'We have our ways of dealing with it'[!] noting that, in his view, 'serious' ecological problems arise with the use of high sulphur coal.[47] It remains for the population of Kazakhstan to question what exactly these methods are, given an assessment in 1988 that their power industry 'accounts for over 50 per cent of the total volume of dust emissions, 40 per cent of sulphurous gases and 70 per cent of nitrogen oxides, and annual damages of some 450 million rubles.'[48]

These unresolved splits in the discussion are typical of the industry's literature; taken at face value, they suggest that immediate investment may be in environmentally efficient systems at plants located near the coal basins, so that urban plants can obtain high-quality coal. Given the shortages of investment capital, the strategy outlined by Nekrasov will inevitably result in delaying ecological improvements at urban plants.

Equipment

The technological options for environmental protection by the electric power industry reflect a combination of factors that are more or less inseparable. These concern the fuel supply; combustion, resource conservation, and pollution control technologies; the quality of installation work; and finally the efficiency of subsequent equipment operations. Moreover, all power plants require large volumes of water, which are consumed primarily as cooling tower evaporative losses. Recycling is not practised in this industry as in others, although ideally, cooling water effluent should be processed to adjust pH levels and remove or neutralise suspended solids, chloride, organic salts, salts, and metal ions, but again this is uncommon in Soviet practice.

When it comes to the fuel supply, it is possible to use secondary combustible materials such as timber waste, domestic waste and methane from land-fill sites, and so forth. Some efficiency can be gained by using secondary heat from exhaust gases and incandescent slag to produce electricity and heat. Electric power plants and boilers can also be built to use exhaust heat from rotary kilns and blast furnaces. As often as not, however, the type of fuel to be used is not open to discussion, so that the only alternative is to determine whether or not it is necessary and feasible to clean the fuel so that the environment can be protected.

The characteristic emissions from gas, oil, and coal-fired power stations are sulphur, nitrogen, and carbon oxides, trace metals, and dust which appear in varying concentrations. Those contained in natural gas can easily be reduced prior to use during the gas preparation stage at a processing plant located at or near the site of extraction. But this is not often the case with crude oil since cleansing must take place during the refining process. Typically, when crude oil is refined, sulphur compounds will become highly concentrated in the heavier fractions, and especially in residues, which are used as furnace oil. Ideally, the removal of pollutants takes place in the refining process, so that the *mazut* can be used under any ecological conditions;[49] however, the removal of sulphur by refining becomes progressively more costly in both economic and energy terms the heavier the residual fraction.[50] The expenditure associated with desulphurisation of *mazut* was estimated in 1979 at 3 rubles per tonne for every 0.5 per cent of sulphur that is extracted.[51] For large residual fuel oil consumers like power plants, flue gas desulphurisation is more cost-effective than fuel oil desulphurisation,[52] although the concentration of sulphur in exhaust gases can also be reduced by combining low and high sulphur fuels. Trace metals are present in the exhaust gases of power plants if they are contained in the fuel; this is most likely to occur with the use of *mazut* and, again, they can be removed with intensive refining.[53] Trace metals of concern are arsenic, cadmium, chromium, lead, manganese, mercury, nickel, and vanadium, which are emitted in quantities also reflecting the nature of the combustion technologies and the flue gas controls.

Coal cleansing installations associated with power plants are not widely discussed in the Soviet literature. Moreover, due to the emphasis on increasing the concentration of sulphur for purposes of waste reclamation, it is unlikely that this will be a subject of significant investment in the near future. Coal cleansing technologies can remove significant amounts of sulphur (when it is present at high concentrations in the form of pyrites) prior to the stage of combustion, at costs significantly lower than flue gas treatment.[54]

Under *khozraschet* conditions, enterprises are expected to handle more of the construction work within the confines of their own financial and labour resources. An objective of the *khozraschet* policy is to ensure that the quality of purchased equipment and replacement parts are judged more carefully, since payment for them will come from enterprise funds and be enterprise responsibility. On the negative side, before environmental regulations are strictly enforced, the process of shifting the burden of investment to the enterprise will slow down the pace of environmental improvements. Such an unfortunate pattern may be avoided if deliberate steps are taken to exert pressure on enterprise management to make environmental investment. One way of doing this is so frequently mentioned that it seems to have been accepted amongst economists: it would make workers' bonuses dependent on the extent to which any given plant can demonstrate its contribution to improved environmental conditions.

Goskomgidromet inspections notwithstanding, the performance of pollution control installations is left to enterprise officials. This same situation obtains in respect of repair work, although where work involves substantial reconfiguration of the cleansing installation, the Ministry of Petroleum Machine Building (MPMB) may be contracted to do the work. One difficulty is seen in the fact that the existing process of determining bonuses (seemingly based on power generated) deters such contractual arrangements, as it effectively returns responsibility to the enterprise.

The responsibility for producing gas cleaning equipment rests on the MPMB. The performance standards by which the equipment operates are set jointly by Goskomgidromet, the USSR State Committee on Standards, and the design organisation. In instances where the gas cleaning installation is a new unit within the factory, the responsibility for its installation usually lies with MPMB, which undertakes the work on a turn-key basis. Officials at the power plant where the equipment is installed then take decisions concerning its acceptability based on its performance and design specifications.[55] Usually, the construction of a power plant and the installation of boilers involve the republic's construction ministry, whose work is also subject to certification and inspection.

Dust Trapping

Vestnik statistiki reported in 1987 that energy installations emitted 16.1 million tonnes of dust, ash and particulate matter into the atmosphere.[56] All indications are that most Soviet power stations have in place some of the basic environmental apparatus (usually dust traps and filters).

The emissions of particulate matter in flue gases can be eliminated by using a combination of bag filters and electrostatic precipitators. Thus, even if Soviet officials do not emphasise improving installations to reduce particulate matter, they will achieve a reduction in the emissions of ash, dust, and other particles in exhaust gases by using desulphurisation technologies. Even if the equipment is not operational (and some 20 per cent of emissions occurred for this reason) the level of capital investment needed for desulphurisation far exceeds that of dust traps and filters.[57] The fact that 66 per cent of the dust trapping equipment is over ten years old contributes to poor performance in this area. Some discussion is warranted due to the fact that complaints about dust and ash emissions are so frequent in Soviet journals.

For electric stations (such as those at Kohtla-Jarve and Balti, in Estonia) which are fuelled by shale or shale dust, consisting of about 50 per cent mineral matter, the efficiency of the dust traps is critical. Unfortunately, the installations there are old and frequent stoppages are causing additional, otherwise preventable pollution (presently, one-fifth of all ash is emitted into the air for these reasons). Modernisation of the pollution control apparatus at the electric power stations was envisaged for 1988, when a combination of cyclone and electric filters were to be fitted to curtail emissions by half,[58] but there have been no reports confirming that the investment has been made.

Inasmuch as there has been little change in the efficiency with which equipment for ash extraction operates, the quantity of fly ash, dust and particulate matter emitted into the atmosphere grows at least proportionately to the change in the ash content of coal. This is expected because extraction equipment is set for emissions in line with the PDK, so that when fuel with inferior characteristics is used, the PDK for ground-level air would be exceeded; to meet the health requirements, reconstruction of the dust traps is mandatory.[59]

Larger particles are more easily trapped by dust extraction technologies. Thus, a regulatory concern must be that environmental protection should not be measured solely on the basis of the volume of extracted materials. The dispersion of ash depends both on the nature of the fuel, and on the technological processes of fuel processing and combustion. Fuels containing rock waste, which is difficult to pulverise, form a greater amount of large particles in fly ash as a result of crushing and burning than fuels taken from deposits associated with clay strata. Low ash fuels, as a rule, have smaller ash particles than high ash fuels; similarly, the size of ash particles also depends on the extent of fuel pulverisation. Thus, the practice of combining anthracite coal dust with high ash fuels to improve combustion often increases the emissions of small particles.[60]

The most commonly used gas cleaning technologies are described in Soviet literature as vertical and horizontal electrostatic filters; cloth filters including large volume bag filters suitable for high temperature gases; cyclones; and Venturi Tubes.[61] There is some information available as to the efficiency of Soviet gas cleaning technologies, but most suggests that the general optimism of the late 1970s (when much of the dust trapping equipment was installed) was unsuccessful in operating conditions. The equipment has not functioned properly because of technological designs faults, poor quality of domestic replacement filters, and the lack of subsequent repair and replacement work. *Voprosy ekonomiki* indicated that electric filters cost between 100,000–300,000 rubles each, while cyclones are about 1,000 rubles, exclusive of operating costs.[62]

Flue Gas Desulphurisation

Sulphur gas is the primary target of environmental policies in many countries due to its implications for health and environment, and in the Soviet Union probably because it is an eminently controllable toxin that draws a lot of unwelcome attention due to its severe transboundary impact. Sulphurous emissions can be reduced by the use of low sulphur fuels, fuel cleansing, and flue gas desulphurisation. The latter installations can achieve 99 per cent removal of sulphur from waste gases, although this level of success is only reported in respect of non-Soviet technologies.[63] Advanced sulphur abatement technologies, such as limestone injection in special combustion chambers, and chemical coal cleaning, are being developed.

The desulphurisation technologies are known as 'dry' or 'wet' processes, and can further be identified as those with or without arrangements for reclaiming sulphur. Economic and technical calculations show that as the sulphur content of the fuel increases (along with the corresponding concentration of sulphur dioxide in the flue gases), it becomes more expedient to apply methods to extract the sulphur. Conversely, when a relatively small amount of sulphur is contained in the fuel but which treatment of flue gases is still required, there is more economic justification in treating the gases without extracting sulphur. Thus, even if the volume of gaseous emissions remains constant, the amount of sulphur varies. In this context, the capital outlay in sulphur extraction equipment and the operating costs for gas treatment vary little in real terms, but the returns are reduced. Thus, it is likely that methods of extracting sulphur from flue gases for purposes of recycling will be confined to power stations burning coal with high sulphur content, for example, from basins like the Moscow and Kizelovskii coalfields.[64]

Dry scrubbers, which are efficient for low sulphur fuels, have been developed in several forms that introduce limestone or dolomite at different stages. One method uses a spray dryer or absorber in which hot flue gas containing sulphur dioxide is brought into contact with lime slurry, producing a dry solid mass that can be reprocessed or discarded. Another method adds limestone or dolomite to the solid fuel that is to be burned prior to its being crushed. This process removes most of the sulphur in the form of calcium sulphate, the remainder being handled with electrostatic filters. This is regarded as the cheapest and simplest of the methods, but leads to the formation of scale on the heating surfaces that inhibits heat exchange and reduces output of steam. The dry scrubbing method is not regarded as efficient in respect of oil shale, because of the damage that the residues cause to the boilers.[65] Interestingly, a goal of gas development construction in Astrakhan is to transform sulphurous compounds chemically into less toxic and more easily handled substances. There, most of the hydrogen sulphide naturally found in the gas is removed at the preparation stage, but flue gas scrubbers are still essential due to the presence of hydrogen sulphide in the gas, which is toxic even in very small dosages.[66]

Wet scrubbing processes use lime or limestone as a reagent in a scrubbing vessel; its wastes (in the form of gypsum) can be thrown away or recycled. A particular problem associated with wet scrubbing is the dispersion of gaseous emissions, because the process involves lowering the temperature of the gases and thus increasing the concentrations of pollutants in the immediate vicinity of the power station. To counter this, significant amounts of energy are expended to reheat the gases which raises the costs of cleansing. The simplicity of the technology, the fact that there is no need to use expensive acid-resistant materials in producing the apparatus which need not be operated under increased or reduced pressure, means that there is lower capital investment in the limestone method for sulphur extraction, than in those using technology to reclaim the sulphur dioxide.[67]

Soviet authorities hold the somewhat unusual view that removing the sulphur prior to combustion is not necessarily a good thing, as the higher the concentration of sulphur in the fuel, the higher the concentration of extracted sulphur, a factor which enhances its commercial value. Since this approach is taken in response to the government's emphasis on recycling waste by-products, it supports the supposition above that wet scrubbing is the preferred technology for European plants using high sulphur coal. It should be noted that the basins currently being extensively developed (for example, Kansk-Achinsk, Ekibastuz, and Kuznetsk) are reported to have a sulphur content of 0.2, 0.1, and 0.2 per cent × 1000 kcal/kg respectively, which is three to ten times lower than that of coal from the Donetsk and Moscow Basins.[68]

Nitrogen Oxides

Nitrogen oxides (also known as NOx) are also emitted in substantial volumes from coal fired plants. The levels of nitrogen oxides depend on the amount of nitrogen present both in the combustion chamber and in the fuel itself. Regulating NOx emissions constitutes a considerable difficulty for power stations dependent on Kansk-Achinsk and Ekibastuz coal, which release high volumes of ash and nitrogen oxides. The reduction of nitrogen oxides is primarily dependent on improvements in combustion technology. But while a fluidised bed system with limestone injection and particulate controls can reduce the emissions, no combustion technology presently available in the Soviet Union or in the West has satisfactorily resolved the problem of nitrogen oxide emissions, the best only reducing emissions by 60 per cent. Soviet standards for removal of nitrogen oxides are higher than what they can achieve on a broad scale in the absence of recapitalisation, although it is sometimes claimed that nitrogen oxide emissions could be reduced by 2–2.5 times without incurring significant additional costs.[69]

Carbon Dioxide

Carbon gases are formed in decreasing quantities when burning coal, oil and gas respectively, with the volume of emission dependent on the efficiency of combustion technology. The techniques for preventing or controlling releases of carbon dioxide are costly in materials and energy and are not presently considered economically justifiable. Marginal reductions in emissions may occur with the use of new combustion technologies.

Alternative combustion technologies

Sulphur gases are the inevitable result of oxidizing sulphur borne in fuel and ore. Preventing the generation of these gases during the processes of burning fuel is virtually impossible. In a few cases, such as Baltic shale and some deep deposits from Kansk-Achinsk, the limestone contained in the coal absorbs a high percentage of the sulphur. Nitrogen and carbon dioxides are also generated in the process of combustion; however, the presence of these components can be lessened by adjusting combustion technologies to neutralise them.[70]

The most commonly discussed new combustion technologies are fluidised bed combustion and limestone injection burners. Although this technology increases the amount of toxic dust emitted by thermal power stations,[71] on the positive side it permits high levels of sulphur to be transformed into compounds during the combustion process without allowing them to come into contact with the heating surfaces (where oxides of sulphur become actively corrosive), thereby inhibiting their release into exhaust gases. The fluidised bed technology creates conditions for reduced temperature levels in the combustion zone, causing less nitrogen oxide to be formed. Fluidised bed combustion can be configured to respond to the type of fuel (solid, liquid or gas). However, the use of fluidised bed combustion and limestone injection produces a larger quantity of solid waste that must be removed from the area of the power station. In connection with the use of such technologies, it was noted in 1979 that they were considered appropriate only for new power stations, and that reconstruction of power stations was not deemed feasible.[72] Further, these combustion units may not be available in the sizes needed in the Soviet electric power industry.[73]

Similar to the situation confronted by other sectors of the Soviet economy, the electric power industry must eventually contend with chronic shortages of replacement parts or whole systems for pollution control. The shortages obtain also in respect of automated management instruments. Possible solutions involve the following: allocating equipment and replacement parts on a priority basis; reducing stockpiles of these materials; expanding the manufacturing capacity; increasing the rate at which old power plants are replaced by more efficient combustion units and pollution controls; and import purchases. So far, of these alternatives, there is evidence of interest, based on limited numbers of purchases, in foreign manufactured boilers, while delegations from several countries (including Great Britain, Finland, and the United States) have made proposals in areas such as management of capital stock, financing and provision of automated systems and other equipment purchases, as well as pollution controls.

Future Investments

In several years of research, only one estimate of the cost of desulphurisation was found, in an article written in 1984 by M A Styrikovich and A K Vnukov, as follows:[74]

> In the opinion of experts, equipping thermal power stations with sulphur catching installations entails specific capital outlays (and the reconstruction of some stations) of about 100 rubles per kilowatt and subsequently an expenditure of 15 kopeks per kilowatt hour. Inasmuch as the general capacity of electric power stations in the country that burn waste oil or coal comes to about 180 million kilowatts (180,000 MW), and produces electric power in such furnaces amounting to about 800 billion kilowatt hours, then cleansing sulphur gases ... requires a one-time capital investment of about 18 billion rubles, and operating costs of more than 1 billion rubles annually. This value exceeds total capital investment to build electric power stations in the Ministry of Energy system over the past two five-year periods.

The estimates refer only to desulphurisation, and do not seem to include expenditure associated with dust trapping or elimination of nitrogen or carbon oxides from waste gases. If Western experience of a 3:1 cost ratio of desulphurisation to dust extraction are borne out in Soviet experience,[75] it is likely that the authors could have anticipated the need for several billion rubles on boiler renovations.

The Styrikovich estimate can be supplemented by a second set of data provided by N G Zalogin, who noted that 99.5 per cent extraction of ash from flue gases by power plants using Ekibastuz coal costs 8.8 million rubles per 500 MW unit. This is calculated on the basis of two ash extractors per 500 MW units at a cost of 4.4 million rubles per device,[76] for four extractors this is 17.7 million rubles per 1000 MW. This totals about 3.2 billion rubles for 180,000 MW or oil- and coal-fired capacity. The estimate increases according to the number of extractors used, but may decrease with the use of higher quality coal.

When 'Western experience' of the 3:1 ratio of desulphurisation to dust extraction costs are used alongside Styrikovich's estimate of capacity and Zalogin's profiles of waste gas emissions, data found in *Voprosy ekonomiki* article result in an estimate similar to Zalogin's. The Zalogin profile is as follows:[77]

A thermal electric power station, rated at 2400 MW, burning 1,060 tonnes per hour of anthracite dust coal, will remove 34.5 tonnes per hour of slag from the boilers, 193.5 tonnes per hour of ash from the electrostatic precipitators (set to clean exhaust gases at 99 per cent), and emit 10 million cubic metres per hour of flue gases. The emissions contain, apart from nitrogen and a residue of oxygen, 2,350 tonnes per hour of carbon dioxide, 251 tonnes per hour of water vapour, 34 tonnes per hour of sulphur dioxide, 9.34 tonnes per hour of oxides of nitrogen (converted to units of NO_2), and 2.0 tonnes per hour of fly ash not extracted by the ash extractor.

Assuming the profile represents emissions by a typical Soviet power station, the total exhaust gas comes to 10 million cubic metres per hour for a 2400 MW station. Therefore, the calculation is made by multiplying the ruble cost of extraction (at 5 rubles per cubic metre according to a table in *Voprosy ekonomiki* on capital outlays to reduce air pollution) times the total gaseous emissions by power stations, and adjusting the calculation to include emissions for the estimated 180,000 MW capacity of oil- and coal-fired stations. The resulting estimate for electric filtering devices is 3.75 billion rubles.[78] Since this information was based on actual investments calculated for the reported amount of gas purified each hour, the estimate represents the levels of efficiency or inefficiency of the technologies in use, as well as the accuracy of estimated gaseous emissions.

A third source of information comes from T S Khachaturov, who provides a table outlining the costs of desulphurisation.[79] The importance of Khachaturov's estimate is that he demonstrates both that investment for desulphurisation declines parallel to the size of the electric power plant, and that it varies according to the type of coal. Further, the amount of investment decreases according to the nature of the desulphurisation technology used relative to the size of the plant. Khachaturov's data generally confirm Styrikovich's estimate. The above estimates clearly demonstrate two facts: the importance of the reconstruction budget for pollution abatement, and the insignificance of present allocations for pollution controls relative to need. It will be interesting to see how the electric power industry proceeds.

Notes

1   *Narodnoe khozyaistvo SSSR za 1988* g, Moscow: Finansy i Statistika, 1989, p. 379.
2   Ekonomika strany: itogi goda, *Izvestiya*, 28 January 1990, pp. 1–4.
3   A P Banin, *Effektivnost' okhrany okruzhayushchei sredy v kapital' nom stroitel'stve*, Moscow: Stroizdat, 1982, p. 12.
4   I M Smirnov, Vklad Instituta Energoset'proekt v uskorenie nauchno-technicheskogo progressa v elektroenergetike strany, *Elektricheskie stantsii*, no. 6, 1987, pp. 2–7; N G Zalogin, L I Kropp, and Yu M Kostrikin, *Energetika i okhrana okruzhayushchei sredy*, Moscow: Energiya, 1979, p. 179.
5   Smirnov, ibid.
6   R Caron Cooper, Petroleum Displacement in the Soviet Economy: the Case of Electric Power Plants, *Soviet Geography*, vol. 27, no. 6, 1986, pp. 377–97; see also, N I Ryzhkov, O gosudarstvennom plane ekonomicheskogo sotsial'nogo razvitiya SSSR na 1986–1990 gg, *Pravda*, 19 June 1986, pp. 1–5.
7   A S Gorshkov, Povyshenie effektivnosti ispol'zovaniya topliova na elektrostantsiyakh i v energosistemakh vazhneishaya otraslevaya i narodnokhozyaistvennaya zadacha, *Elektricheskie stantsii*, no. 5, 1987, pp. 6–10. Gorshkov indicated the following costs per tonne: Ekibastuz coal = 4.5 rubles; Kansk-Achinsk = 5.3 rubles; Donets coal = 28.4 rubles; L'vov-Volynsky = 34.5 rubles; Moscow coal = 30.3 rubles. Fuel oil with less than 2 per cent sulphur content is 23–8 rubles per tonne; gas from the Urengoy station is 5 rubles per tonne, but in Rostov, Krasnodar *oblast*, Moldavia, it is 25.6 rubles per ton. He indicated that 'what is required is an economic stimulus to move to less expensive energy supplies. It may be possible to introduce some sort of unitary economic valuation, reflecting the value of solid fuels and promoting the conservation of fuel oil.'
8   V V Rabotnov, Resursosberegayushchaya politika v neftepererabotke i neftekhimii, *Khimicheskaya promyshlennost'*, no. 7, 1987, pp. 3–5.
9   Ryzhkov, *Pravda*, 19 June 1986, op cit.
10   *Soviet Power Engineering: Problems and Prospects*, Moscow: Novosti, 1988, p. 80.
11   A Sh Reznikovskii and I I Fishman, Sovremennoe sostoyanie i osnovnye napravleniya razvitiya gidroenergetiki SSSR, *Vodnye resursy*, no. 6, 1986, pp. 162–7.
12   *USSR: The 12th Five Year Plan*, Moscow: Novosti, 1986, pp. 41–2. The booklet summarised the 1986–1990 programme in the following way: 'More thermal and hydropower stations will be built in the east of the country, and large nuclear power stations, from 4 million to 6 million kW each will be constructed. Giant thermal stations will be built east of the Ural mountains: four 4 million kW stations in the area of the Ekibastuz coal field in North Kazashstan, two 6.4 million kW stations at

Berezovka in the Kansk-Achinsk coal field, and large stations at Surgut and Urengoi in West Siberia. Large hydropower stations will continue to be built in the east of the country and in Central Asia: the Boguchansk on the Angara river, at the confluence of the Angara and the Yenisei, on the Bureya (a tributary of the Amur river), the Shulbinsk in Kazakhstan, and at the Tash-Kumyr and Samaldy-Sai in Kirgizia. Two large hydropower projects in Central Asia will be the Rogunsk and Sangtudsk stations. Other hydropower stations will be built inside the Arctic Circle and in the Caucasus, and hydroelectric pumped storage power stations will be constructed in the country's European part. The commissioning of that many hydropower stations will help to economise large amounts of fuel and will make the country's Integrated Power Grid more flexible and effective, because stations of this kind can just as easily be switched off, depending on loads. In addition to these advantages, hydropower stations cause no pollution.'

13 Ryzhkov, *Pravda*, 19 June 1986, op cit.
14 T S Khachaturov, N G Fetel'man, N V Bazilev, *Investitsionnaya politika prirodopol'zovaniya*, Moscow: Nauka, 1989, pp. 169–86, argues that in the future, as the raw materials for power generation are exhausted, the main option will be nuclear power. The authors present data showing that the costs of alternatives such as hydro power and solar energy are much higher than nuclear facilities. They do not discuss the 'risk factor' associated with public preferences and fear of the industry.
15 Ryzhkov, *Pravda*, 19 June 1986, op cit.
16 According to Cooper, *Soviet Geography*, op cit the fuel structure at fossil-fuelled electric power stations in 1980 (in per cent of fuel use) was oil – 35.7; natural gas – 24.2, and coal – 40.1. Cooper's data are from A M Nekrasov and A A Troitsky, *Energetika SSSR v 1981–1985 gg*, Moscow: Energoizdat, 1981, pp. 221–3.
17 *Narodnoe khozyaistvo SSSR v 1988 g*, Moscow: Finansy i statistika, 1989, p. 381.
18 A S Nekrasov et al, Effektivnost' primeneniya novykh tekhnologii szhiganiya topliva na teplovykh elektrostantsiyakh, *Elektricheskie stantsii*, no. 9, 1987, pp. 11–13. *Narodnoe khozyaistvo v 1988 g*, ibid, indicates that in 1988, about 22 per cent of total coal production (as opposed to consumption by the energy sector) was in the form of brown coal.
19 S A Demin, *Zakon na strazhe prirody*, Moscow: Yuridicheskaya Literatura, 1987, pp. 37–44.
20 Zalogin, op cit, p. 35.
21 Z M Lazarev, F F Daitov, Kompleksnoe reshenie voprosov okhrany okruzhayushchei sredy na neftekhimicheskom predpriyatii, *Gigiena i sanitariya*, no. 1, 1987, pp. 61–2.
22 Zalogin, *supra*.
23 Demin, op cit.
24 Zalogin, op cit, p. 36. The 1988 environmental protection decree specified that 'regular inspections of the performance of cleansing installations will be made by an impartial organisation'. This provision creates some uncertainty in respect of USSR Goskomgidromet's role and that of USSR Goskompriroda.
25 V Tsentral' nom Komitete KPSS i Sovete Ministrov, *Pravda*, 17 January 1988, pp. 1–2 (translated in *Current Digest*).
26 Environmental Protection. Rules of Air Quality Control in Populated Areas, cited in *Environmental Management Abstracts*, vol. 2, no. 1, 1988, p. 20: 'GOST (the State Standard of the USSR) 17.2.3.01.86 was elaborated by the State Committee of the USSR for Hydrometeorology and Environmental Control and the USSR Ministry of Public Health, and was enacted on 1 January 1987 by the Decree of the State Committee of the USSR for Standards on 10 November 1986, instead of GOST 17.2.3.01.77. The Standard consists of the following sections: (1) organisation of control, (2) arrangement and number of stations, (3) programme and periods of

observation, (4) sampling, and (5) characteristics of atmospheric pollution. Observation stations have been assigned to three categories: stationary, route and mobile (under the plume). The number of stationary stations depends on the number of population: 1 station – population up to 50,000; 2 stations – up to 200,000; 3–5 stations – from 200,000 to 500,000; 5–10 stations – over 500,000; 10–20 stations (stationary and route) – over 1 million. There are four observation programmes to be performed by stationary stations: complete, incomplete, reduced, and daily'.

27   Zalogin, ibid, p. 47.

28   I I Kal'tman, V M Galchikhin, P A Korkytis, V P Dichuvene, V Ulyatskas, and L Kryazhdis, Programma ozdorovleniya vozdushnogo basseina g Kalaipedy, *Elektricheskie stantsii*, no. 5, 1987, pp. 40–4.

29   Regional estimates of air quality are made under the authority of SN 369–74. A collection of air pollution laws is in N I Malyshko, *Gosudarstvennyi kontrol' za okhranoi atmosfernogo vozdukha*, Kiev, Naukova Dumka, 1982; *Okhrana okruzhayushchei sredy v gorodakh*, Kiev: Naukova Dumka, 1981, pp. 153–72; I I Kal'tman, ibid.

30   V Bartov, Politiko-ekonomicheskie voprosy vzaimodeistviya obshchestva i prirody, *Voprosy ekonomiki*, no. 10, 1984, pp. 3–11.

31   M A Stryrikovich and A K Vnukov, Kachestvo vozdukha v gorodakh. Issledovaniya i normirovanie, *Vestnik Akademiya Nauk SSSR*, no. 1, 1984, pp. 45–51. A similar article published in 1979 said that normatives were established for 114 substances; Zalogin, op cit, p. 38; O S Kolbasov, *Pravovaya okhrana prirody*, Moscow: Znanie, 1984, pp. 99–112; Demina, op cit.

32   Zalogin, ibid, p. 47.

33   'Dispersion' may be understood as the result of a combination of transport and turbulence. The plume of pollutants is transported by wind, while the turbulence diffuses the plume or increases its size. Turbulence can be mechanical or thermal, the effect of which distributes the pollutants at various altitudes. Smoke and other emissions that have been cleaned still contain contaminants, and tall chimneys are built in order to reduce their concentrations. The tall smoke stacks increase the vertical velocity of the emissions, the height to which the emissions are dispersed, as well as the radius and area of dispersion, thus reducing the local ground-level concentration of harmful substances.

34   A P Banin, *Effektivnost' okhrany okruzhayushchei sredy v kapital' nom stroitel' stve*, op cit, p. 23.

35   N V Talyzin, O gosudarstvennom plane ekonomicheskogo i sotsial'nogo razvitiya SSSR na 1987 g i o okhode vypolneniya plana v 1986 g, *Pravda*, 18 November 1986, pp. 1–3 (abstracted in *Current Digest*).

36   N A Popovich, Nekotorye gigienicheskie voprosy melioratsii v sel'skom khozyaistve, *Gigiena i sanitariya*, no. 1, 1986, pp. 69–70.

37   Banin, op cit, p. 24.

38   *Okhrana okruzhayushchei sredy v gorodakh*, op cit, p. 24.

39   Zalogin, op cit, p. 42.

40   Richard H Rowland, Changes in the Metropolitan and Large City Populations in the USSR, 1979–1985, *Soviet Geography*, vol. 27, 1986, pp. 638–58.

41   V Gubarev, Ekologiya bez kosmetiki, *Pravda*, 7 September 1987, p. 4, for an interview with Yu Izrael, Director of the USSR State Committee on Hydrometeorology. See also, O Frantsen, Formula zdorov'ya, *Pravda*, 13 April 1987, p. 3; and P Poletaev, V otvete pered prirodoi, *Pravda*, 5 June 1987, p. 2, who indicated that 50 cities have problems with organic and inorganic compounds in the air.

42   I I Kal'tman, et al, *Elektricheskie stantsii*, no. 5, 1987, op cit.

43   P N Burgasov, E M Saak'iants, G I Kutsenko, XXVII S'ezd KPSS i zadachi sanitarno-epidemiologicheskoi sluzhby strany, *Gigiena i sanitariya*, no. 7, 1986, pp. 4–6.

44   News Notes, *Soviet Geography*, vol. 27, 1986, p. 276.

45 *Environmental Effects of Electricity Generation*, Paris: OECD, 1985, p. 135, cites from Western experience that heat and hot water can be transmitted 20–30 kilometres. However, such distances are feasible only in the cases of large power stations; the distance may be somewhat greater with supplies originating with nuclear installations. See also *US/USSR Joint Seminar on External Utilities Systems in Populated Areas*, US Department of Housing and Urban Development, c 1983, p. 170.

46 A S Nekrasov et al, *Elektricheskie stantsii*, no. 9, 1987, op cit.

47 *Soviet Power Engineering: Problems and Prospects*, op cit, p. 59.

48 E G Gribov, G K Kyatbaev, cited in *Environmental Management Abstracts*, vol. 2, no. 3, 1988, p. 25.

49 Zalogin, ibid, p. 191. Sulphurous *mazut* can also be subjected to a process of gasification using steam generators and wet scrubbing. This combination is largely experimental, although it could become more important if recovery of sulphur at power plants is developed. However, considering the low probability of equipping new power stations to be fired with *mazut* and the impossibility of implementing a method of gasification of *mazut* at existing power stations, it is anticipated that this method will probably not be broadly applied in the energy sector.

50 OECD, op cit, p. 62.

51 Zalogin, op cit, p. 183.

52 Ibid.

53 OECD, op cit, p. 68.

54 Zalogin, op cit, p. 213.

55 V Krasovskii, Sovremennye prioritety investitsionnogo kompleksa, *Voprosy ekonomiki*, no. 5, 1985, pp. 103–12 (translated in *Problems of Economics*).

56 *Vestnik statistiki*, no. 6, 1988, p. 77.

57 OECD, op cit, p. 82.

58 Paul Vesiloo, Tostatatud kusimustele vastab ensev rikliku atmosfaariuhu kaitse inspeksiooni ulema asetaitja Roomet Egon Hirvesee, *Esti Loodus*, no. 11, 1987, pp. 258–9. Similar levels of ash are found in coal produced at Ekibastuz, see *Soviet Geography*, vol. 27, 1986, pp. 268, 277, and 382–4.

59 Zalogin, op cit, p. 42.

60 Ibid, pp. 73–4.

61 Banin, op cit, p. 17.

62 S Khodorkovskaya, Effektivnost' okhrany vozdushnogo basseina, *Voprosy ekonomiki*, no. 6, 1984, pp. 89–97.

63 Okhrana okruzhayushchei sredy – Aktual'naya zadacha, *Ekonomicheskaya gazeta*, no. 18, April 1987, pp. 4–7.

64 Zalogin, op cit, p. 193.

65 Zalogin, Ibid.

66 M Umanskii, Rentabel'no li sinee nebo? *Gazovaya promyshlennost'*, no. 3, 1987, pp. 36–9; S Nekrasov, Spasite del'tu, *Sel'skaya molodozh*, no. 10, 1987, p. 13.

67 Zalogin, *supra*.

68 Zalogin, ibid, p. 180, 201, 208–209. Soviet sources also discuss other wet scrubbing methods, using ammonia and magnesium, neither of which is ideal in respect of wear and tear on the boilers and scrubbing units, and for the environment in respect of secondary pollution from waste. The Wellman Lord process, developed in the United States, is also acknowledged in the Soviet literature. This process is analogous to that of the ammonia cycle method, but uses sodium sulphate in the process rather than ammonia salts. The process forms more stable compounds with sulphur dioxide and is more efficient at removing sulphur in the flue gases. The drawback is high energy consumption and the evaporation of water in the separation of sulphur dioxide which causes the precipitation of sodium and sulphite crystals.

69 Zalogin, ibid, p. 180.

70   M A Styrikovich, A K Vnukov, *Vestnik Akademiya Nauk SSSR*, no. 1, 1984, op cit.
71   Zalogin, *supra*, p. 191.
72   Zalogin, ibid, p. 188.
73   OECD, op cit, p. 76.
74   M A Styrikovich, A K Vnukov,*Vestnik Akademiya Nauk SSSR*, no. 1, 1984, op cit.
75   OECD, op cit, p. 82.
76   Zalogin, op cit, p. 127, table 5.8. (Zalogin does not provide for ash extractors at gas-fired power plants.)
77   Ibid, p. 14.
78   S Khodorkovskaya, op cit.
79   T S Khachaturov, *Ekonomika prirodopol'zovaniya*, Moscow: Nauka, 1987, p. 210, citing *Promyshlennaya i sanitarnaya ochistka gazov*, no. 3, 1979, p. 21, and *Teploenergetika*, no. 11, 1980, p. 3.

6 Environmental Prospects for the Soviet Metallurgical Industries

Introduction

The metallurgical complex in the Soviet Union consists of two ministries for ferrous and non-ferrous metallurgical production, whose environmental goals are the complete elimination of contaminated effluent and the reduction of gaseous emissions to prescribed levels by the year 2005. A major addition to the industry's environmental goals since 1986 is the resource conservation mandate. The investment strategy being pursued in the Soviet economy generally and by the metallurgical industry in particular offers a unique opportunity widely to apply and integrate both pollution-reducing and re-source-conserving features into technologies during the reconstruction and retooling initiatives.

The industry will probably not keep to its environmental protection schedule for several reasons. Amongst them is the fact that the environmental budget is insufficient in respect of allocations for air pollution controls. It appears that such investment will occur mainly after renovation of the production technologies which is proceeding very slowly. Also, the environmental budget for protection of water resources is inadequate at its present level fully to provide for effluent treatment, and existing gaps in capacity will be aggravated in the context of any expansion of metallurgical production. Solid waste management and land reclamation do not yet figure amongst the industry's environmental priorities.

To date, environmental investment has been primarily in waste water treatment and recycling, but no locational priorities have been reflected in related expenditure. The pattern seems to be changing – the non-ferrous

127

metallurgical industry will concentrate its environmental resources, at least until the year 1995, on a small number of sites, primarily in Kazakhstan and Siberia, where air and water pollution are particularly serious. The new programme represents a positive step to ensure that investment is directed to where it is most needed. By thus concentrating expenditure, however, it is unlikely that anything other than planning can take place at other mills which also badly need ecological investment.

Development Background

The metallurgical industries are (and will continue for the foreseeable future to be) amongst the most significant sources of pollution in the Soviet Union. Environmental disruption caused by the metallurgical industries is the legacy of governmental decisions relating to extraction, industrial siting, growth in production, and capital investment. Of course, the fact that some raw material resources are mined and manufactured in remote, sparsely populated areas is unavoidable. The disruption new construction engenders will not be automatically curtailed under *khozraschet* conditions if siting options, that are ecologically less unsatisfactory, are eliminated because of the financial gain to be accrued by having raw materials and energy near to hand.

Over the years, Soviet metallurgy has expanded production by building new plants, albeit (as in the relatively recent case of Kazakhstan) without deploying technologies to lessen environmental damage; nor has there been much subsequent attention to environmental management.[1] The ecological impact is made worse by housing that overflows into the 'sanitary zones' of the metallurgical plants.[2] While new construction has slowed down considerably, a central policy conflict – between environmental preservation and economic interests – has not been eliminated. Such choices are clearly in evidence in the discussions concerning the mining of Soviet Far Eastern iron ore and coking coal deposits that are scheduled to receive investment and may already have.

Soviet practice is to locate metal-based industries within the framework of mining-metallurgical centres (MMC), where machine-building and metal-working industries, chemical plants, and electric power stations are situated in the vicinity as well.[3] For the future, metallurgy may attempt to 'rationalise' the distribution of production capacity within the context of territorial production complexes (TPC).[4] Both approaches take advantage of the proximity of mineral resources to energy supplies, transportation, and/or consumers, although the TPC approach seeks to integrate industrial capacity over a larger geographic unit. Already, complaints have emerged within the Ukrainian metallurgical industry over the lack of coordination amongst TPC-based planning for contiguous areas.[5] If each territory is to be self-sufficient in respect of metallurgical production and/or if their divisions are to be optimally distributed within the TPCs, additional investment for construction of new capacity will be required to achieve the desired industrial balances.[6] Construction for such purposes will extend the ecological impact of metallurgy. Industrial and other economic planning within the context of the TPCs and that which may eventually take place within Environmental Protection Regions (EPRs) are not the same. EPRs may be used for purposes of environmental planning and administration, but their configuration has not been announced.

Investment Background

The main direction of investment by the metallurgical sector originated before 1985, but President Gorbachev's strategy of industrial renewal appears to be 'tailor-made' for metallurgy, where retooling and reconstruction of plant and equipment can no longer be delayed. It is not surprising that the priorities remain unaltered since the industry has a very long planning/ construction/commissioning cycle. Meanwhile, the legacy from inadequate investment in advanced production technologies, in addition to the concentrated development of metallurgy and related industries in some locales, is extraordinary ecological disruption. A typical case is the Lipet'sk *oblast* where '90 per cent of all pollution is caused by ferrous metallurgy'.[7]

Official data concerning the metallurgical sector are not plentiful; in particular, they do not facilitate an examination of the funds available to ferrous and non-ferrous metallurgy by branch activities which would be useful in an examination of environmental priorities. Metallurgy does not appear to be financially impoverished. Although the following table indicates that metallurgy commands a decreasing share of total capital investment within the Soviet economy, the industry consistently receives larger capital budgets.

6.1 Capital Investment in the Soviet Economy

	1976–80	1981–85	1986–90[1]	1986–1988
Total (rubles 10^9)	717.7	843.2	1030	618.0
of which:				
Metallurgy	28.9	30.0	34.3	20.6
as % of total	4.0	3.6	5.5	3.3

[1] projected on the basis of three years.
Source: Narodnoe khozyaistvo SSSR v 1988 g, p. 555.

Unofficial evidence in the case of ferrous metallurgy is that one-third of capital investment funds are designated for the iron ore and coke-chemical branches. That being the case, there is an institutionalised constraint on the funds available to the iron and steel manufacturing branches for whatever purpose. Further, about 18 per cent of the iron and steel budgets are directed to social construction (that is, housing and other non-industrial infrastructure).[8]

In general, the national drive to decentralise financial responsibility means that managers in metallurgy have a stronger basis from which to object to investment out of enterprise funds that will not enhance production or profits.[9] The following table illustrates the direction of capital investment in the metallurgical industry during 1988, as well as metallurgy's whole hearted commitment to Gorbachev's reinvestment strategy.

6.2 Structure of the State Capital Budget for the Metallurgical Industry in 1988

	Billion Rubles	Per cent
Total Budget	6.0	100
of which expended on:		
Retooling and Reconstruction of Enterprises	3.8	64.0
Expansion of Enterprises	0.7	12.4
New Construction	1.4	22.7
Other	0.1	0.9

Source: Narodnoe khozyaistvo SSSR v 1988 g, p. 266.

Return on Investment

In a situation where money is not money and capital and raw materials are not adequately valued, it is virtually impossible to know what is profitable and what is not. Westerners must rely on *perceptions* of profits and losses expressed by Soviet economists. Here it is useful to note that the usual Soviet method to ensure 'profitability' of investment is simply to direct resources to areas that produce saleable goods and income. In the past, at least, this practice has ensured that expenditure on nature protection could not be an investment priority. Even so, judging by official accounts, metallurgical managers should be alarmed about the dramatic downturn in their fortunes since the 1970s.

Previously, returns fell due to the age of production units, outdated technologies, condition of equipment, incomplete construction, and delayed commissioning of basic plant and equipment. These factors still obtain, and

6.3 Return on Investment by Branch of Industry in the Period 1970–1986
(output of commodity products per 1 ruble
of the average annual value of capital assets)
(1970=100)

	1975	1980	1985	1986
All Industry	95	81	69	69
Heavy Industry	102	91	80	80
Metallurgical Complex	91	72	59	59

Source: Narodnoe khozyaistvo SSSR za 70 let, p. 155.

a further downturn is expected for various reasons: as production is inter-rupted for reconstruction and repair work; due to higher costs in non-productive spheres (for example, to improve labour conditions and nature protection); and because of price increases for construction and installation work. Additionally, Soviet valuations of capital assets usually do not reflect changes accruing from the retooling and reconstruction of depreciated plant and equipment.[10] So, if a higher quality of capital is taken into account, the return on investment, expressed in relation to capital, will be even less favourable.

By official accounts, the return on investment within industry and in the metallurgical complex did not look quite as bad in 1988 compared to 1980, although the overall pattern remained negative and that for metallurgy was still lower than for industry as a whole.[11] In comparison to 1985, which is significant in respect of Gorbachev's ascent to power, metallurgy's profitability deteriorated in line with the economy as a whole.

6.4 Return on Investment for Branches of Industry
(output of commodity products per 1 ruble
of the average annual value of capital assets,
in per cents)

	1980 = 100				1985 = 100		
	1985	1986	1987	1988	1986	1987	1988
All Industry	85	84	83	82	99	97	97
Heavy Industry	87	87	87	86	99.3	99.2	99
Metallurgy	82	82	80	80	99.9	98	97

Source: Narodnoe khozyaistvo SSSR v 1988 g, p. 364.

Industrial sources do not paint a better picture. Between 1981 and 1987, profits fell by a quarter, of which 4.3 per cent occurred between 1986 and 1987. While the losses were mainly caused by past failures to renew the industrial base, they now also reflect the rising value of non-production expenditure, such as that for nature protection, which is demonstrated in the following table.

6.5   Dynamics of the Basic Fund, Commodity Output, and Return on Investment in Non-ferrous Metallurgy
(in per cents)

	1980	1985	1987
Return on Investment	100	78.15	74.8
Cost to Fund for			
Nature Protection	7.6	8.7	9.6
Cost of Maintenance	7.4	19.2	23.3
Value of Active Part of			
the Basic Fund	35.6	36.2	36.2
Profits	26.8	17.5	17.3

Source: B G Kiselev, et al, Fondootdacha v tsvetnoi metallurgii, *Tsvetnye metally*, no. 12, 1988, pp. 88–92.

Thus, Kiselev pointed out the three main loss-generating areas in non-ferrous metallurgy: nature protection, maintenance, and unassimilated capacity.

Use of Productive Capacity

The use of productive capacity is important to environmental protection in a number of ways, but primarily as a criterion against which the industry judges the necessity of new, environmentally disruptive, construction. The term 'use of productive capacity' refers to expectations for quantity of output, raw materials processed, intensity of use of equipment and labour, and other physical and economic considerations. Such expectations are expressed in normatives which differ for each type of equipment and input. The normatives periodically change, so that an aggregate figure on an industry-wide basis offers no insight into the sub-branches where capacity is idle. The terms 'removing from use' and 'retiring basic plant and equipment' are understood to mean 'in the course of modernisation and repair, not necessarily as a permanent condition'.[12]

In ferrous metallurgy, the use of productive capacity is high – over 95 per cent in 1987 – and is the main factor underlying the metallurgical industry's unwillingness to retire outdated technologies for environmental reasons.[13] For example, the use of coke-chemical production capacity is oversubscribed; this is the reason the old coking batteries at Kemerov and Nizhni Tagil were not retired when new batteries came on-stream (eventualities which prompted public demonstrations over intensified local pollution).[14]

Little direct information exists about the use of productive capacity in the non-ferrous metallurgical industry, although there appear to be bottlenecks in several branches, including copper and nickel, that have caused some idle capacity.[15] Unused production capacity and sluggish performance create the temptation to extend the industry into new locales (with all the attendant ecological disruptions) or to expand production in areas already suffering from pollution. For example, there are plans to expand the Bakyrchiksk MMC, the Kairaktinsk tungsten combine, the Koktenkol'sk molybdenum combine, and the Boshchekul'sk copper MMC to remedy such imbalances.

Modernisation

All the signs are that modernisation by means of reconstruction and retooling is the foremost priority within the sector, although a central feature of the metallurgical industry is its slowness to replace inefficient production technologies.[16] The term 'retooling and reconstruction' means a significant increase in production capacity at existing mills, brought about by installing up-to-date technology and measured by improvements in the most important indicators of operation. This is of interest because progress in environmental management can be achieved as a spin-off to the introduction, for instance, of continuous casting, oxygen converters in larger metallurgical plants, and electric furnaces in the smaller capacity units. Of course, it cannot be forgotten that recapitalisation is a long-term investment strategy, and the need for environmental protection can only be satisfied by an approach that also guarantees that pollution generated in the national economy is reduced in the aggregate.

Soviet Geography reported that the plan for 1990 was to have oxygen converters for 45 per cent of steel-making capacity, electric furnaces for 12 per cent, and the proportion of open-hearth furnaces reduced to 43 per cent. By 1986, oxygen converters accounted for 32.7 per cent of steel-making capacity, electric furnaces for 13.0 per cent, and open-hearth technologies for 54.3 per cent.[17] The state plan also called for continuous casting to be used in 30 per cent of all steel production by 1990, including commissioning of advanced units in 15 continuous casting centres (of which 7 were put into service between 1986 and 1988).[18] Another source anticipated that 3 modern rolling mills may be commissioned by 1990,[19] although it is not clear whether these will be new or reconstructed units.

Amongst the metallurgical combines targeted for reconstruction commencing in the 12th plan period were: Kuznetsk metallurgical combine,

Rustavsk metallurgical plant in Georgia, various enterprises of ferrous metals in the Ukraine, the Sarkanais metallurgical plant in Latvia, and some enterprises of non-ferrous metallurgy in Armenia. Large-scale reconstruction is presently on-going at Magnitogorsk MMC (with the ultimate provision of the 'largest European' oxygen converter sector with continuous casting of steel and a capacity of 9 million tons of high quality steel and products). Some of the reconstruction will be very costly; for example, that at the Magnitki plant is valued at 1 billion rubles, inclusive of environmentally related construc-- tion.[20]

A reliable and efficient repair and maintenance programme is essential for environmental protection for two reasons: firstly, it ensures that production does not cause more pollution than was set out in the operating licences for a given enterprise. Secondly, it ensures that pollution control equipment operates efficiently (that is, barring other, non-mechanical, obstacles). The term 'repair and maintenance' means that equipment and machinery at existing sites are kept to standards that will not allow reductions in the basic performance indicators. Proportionately little investment within industry as a whole has been directed to repair and maintenance, although there appears to be a slow increase in this area of expenditure. The funding for repair and maintenance work can appear in either the operating or the capital budgets; but when it is provided through the operating budgets, relevant decisions can sometimes be taken at the discretion of local managers rather than requiring a central directive. In this respect, the Soviet journal, *Metallurg'*, published the following observation in 1984:[21]

> Theoretically, an increase in amortisation deductions for recapitalisation should stimulate a more rapid replacement of capital assets. However, this does not happen in practice. This apparent discrepancy is largely due to the difference

6.6   Technological Structure of the Capital Budget
(as per cent of total capital budget)

Period	Total	Construction Budget and Installation Work	Equipment, Instruments, Inventory	Design Work	Repairs and Maintenance
9th FYP	100	64	29	2	5
10th FYP	100	57	34	2	7
11th FYP	100	52	37	2	9
1986	100	51	37	1	11
1987	100	51	36	–	13

Source: Narodnoe khozyaistvo SSSR za 70 let, p. 326; *Narodnoe khozyaistvo SSSR v 1987 g*, p. 292.

between the funding for renovation and the material resources required to replace outdated equipment. That is, an increase in amortisation deductions makes it financially feasible to retool; it does not speed up the actual process of renovation.

The metallurgical industry's environmental outlook depends on the modernisation of existing basic plant and pollution abatement installations.[22] But a warning has appeared in *Voprosy ekonomiki* that 'in practice, a large percentage of resources allocated for reconstruction is used to expand existing enterprises'[23] – in effect, for new construction on or near existing sites. If such practices still obtain, and a further complaint registered in *Ekonomicheskaya gazeta* suggests that they do,[24] then the gains to environmental protection from reconstruction investment in operating production units will be jeopardised. Investment funds are officially distributed as shown below.

6.7   Structure of the State Capital Budget for Metallurgy in 1988
(in comparable prices)

	Total Budget	Retooling & Reconstruction	Expansion	New Construction	Other
Billion Rubles	6.0	3.8	0.7	1.4	0.1
Per cent	100	64.0	12.4	22.7	0.9

Source: Narodnoe khozyaistvo v 1988 g, p. 266.

The task confronting the metallurgical industry is formidable. Approximately 22 per cent of total equipment in non-ferrous metallurgical production enterprises is described as outdated and wornout. But the situation is much worse in some branches. In the mining and ore-concentration industries, for instance, it has been pointed out that 40–60 per cent of equipment productivity is lost after four to five years in use, which means that retooling, reconstruction, repair and maintenance should be sustained at a high rate.[25] Another example is ferrous metallurgy's pipe-producing sector, where as much as 70 per cent of the value of basic production equipment has been depreciated.[26] At present, however, being 'fully depreciated' does not trigger investment, although given the rate at which equipment wears out, perhaps it should.

Commissioning and Decommissioning of Capital Assets

Another way to anticipate the need for ecological investment is by the rate at which new industrial capacity is brought on-stream. The commissioning of fixed capital assets by the metallurgical industry has been sluggish in comparison to industry as a whole, though there has also been a steady deceleration of the rate at which obsolete equipment is retired in the national economy. Some areas have been especially hard-pressed. For example, V I Lapin, from the Sverdlovsk *oblast* party committee, described the impact of low rates of retiring capital assets on the *oblast*'s environmental situation as follows:[27]

> There is a negative ecological situation in the oblast that affects us all. One reason is the low coefficient for renewing equipment, which in the oblast's non-ferrous enterprises occurs at 2 per cent overall, in comparison to 4 per cent in non-ferrous metallurgy across the Soviet Union, and also because the coefficient of retiring the old equipment is 0.8 per cent against 1.7 per cent in the Ministry at large.

A complicating factor in the investment programme is that future construction is to be undertaken mainly to ensure regionally 'balanced' metallurgical production (for example, an argument for additional Central Asian steel production capacity is to reduce transportation costs).[28] In the Ukraine, new construction of water-consuming industries is prohibited in principle, and there are many uncertainties about construction for the purpose of 'rationalising the distribution of industry'.[29]

The commissioning and decommissioning of basic production funds were about 66 per cent and 83 per cent, respectively, of the levels achieved by industry as a whole in 1988. This represents a sharp downturn of the rate at which installations were commissioned in 1988 compared to the years since 1970, and a somewhat lesser improvement in the rate of decommissioning.[30]

6.8   Commissioning and Decommissioning of Capital Assets by Type, in 1988
(as percentages of the overall value of assets)

Year	Total	Buildings & Installations	Machinery & Equipment	Other
Commissioned				
All Industry	6.6	6.0	7.3	6.8
Metallurgy	4.4	3.6	5.1	5.6
Decommissioned				
All Industry	1.8	0.8	2.9	2.2
Metallurgy	1.5	0.7	2.3	2.5

Source: Narodnoe khozyaistvo SSSR v 1988 g, p. 361.

In 1986, metallurgy as a whole commissioned 83 per cent of installations due in that year, with ferrous metallurgy at 82 per cent and non-ferrous showing 84 per cent commissioned. The 1986 result was an improvement (111 per cent) over 1985, with non-ferrous metallurgy performing much better than ferrous metallurgy (114 and 107 per cent, respectively). In 1986, the reason for a shortfall in commissioned new installations cannot be attributed solely to shortages of investment funds, which reportedly were 108 per cent of 1985 level, and the full allocation appears to have been expended. Rather, the data reaffirm that there continues to be a large backlog of projects queuing for investment,[31] which increases competition for scarce material and labour sources. *Pravda* reported that one-third of the 127 planned facilities of all types were not commissioned in 1987;[32] while *Ekonomicheskaya gazeta* reported delayed commissioning of 31 from a total of 79 installations in 1988.[33]

According to the 12th plan documents, by 1990 ferrous metallurgy is supposed to have retired from service 14 obsolete blast furnaces and reconstructed 70, as well as discontinued the use of 38 rolling stations. According to *Vestnik Akademiya Nauk SSSR*, these goals meant that 'open-hearth furnaces with a capacity of 15 million tons will have been withdrawn from service by 1990'.[34] So far, no progress has been observed.

A further indicator of the poor performance of metallurgical construction is reflected in the availability of uninstalled equipment. In any country, the presence of a large inventory represents potential wastage. However, the lack of warehouse facilities in the Soviet Union is well known, and under such circumstances equipment deteriorates rapidly. According to G Mishin, the value of the equipment inventory was 1.2 billion rubles in 1988, and expected to increase to 1.5 billion to 1989. Imported equipment was roughly one-third of the total stock in 1988, and slightly more in 1989. Ferrous metallurgy's uninstalled stocks were roughly two-thirds of the metallurgical inventory. The situation will not improve, as inventory levels and the rate at which installations are commissioned are dependent on the number of construction sites and, as Mishin pointed out, the policy to modernise Soviet industry means the number of sites has proliferated.[35]

Environmental Consequences of Modernisation

Judging by the above general investment picture, an environmental strategy appears to have emerged in the metallurgical industries. The major thrust involves the programme to install technologies which generate less waste. A somewhat lesser element depends on investment in pollution controls. The programme has several drawbacks requiring specific compensatory investment, some of which may take advantage of the nature protection budget, which is discussed below.

The reservations are these. Replacement and modernisation of production equipment and the application of waste recovery and recyling activities do not eliminate the need for pollution controls. Such changes simply shift the emphasis of ecological investment within the metallurgical industry and, significantly, to other sectors of the economy. The use of electric furnaces, for example, transfers part of the pollution burden away from metallurgy to the electric power industry, as the latter must produce the energy that is needed for production. Thus, sulphur gases and dust, that are associated with the use of coke, oil, and gas fuels in metallurgical furnaces, are significantly reduced; but they reappear if the electric power industry has had to use more low quality coal or *mazut*. Some Soviet economists state outright that a shift to electric power will generate even more ecological damage than open-hearth furnaces.[36] In this respect, some compensation may occur if the power plant emissions do not contain all of the contaminants characteristic of metallurgical production. However, toxic emissions are not eliminated by the technologies being installed at the metallurgical plants. In non-ferrous metallurgy, for example, oxygen and autogenous smelting processes increase the concentration of sulphur. This may make investment in recycling and recovery technologies more attractive, while any failure to do so (or to apply pollution controls) will multiply the ecological impact of production even after modernisation.

When selecting modern production technologies, their environmental features, the size of the required additional investment for environmental controls, and operating costs will each have significance for the final decision. N A Kharitonov, from the Magnitogorsk Mining-Metallurgical Institute, indicated that there are considerable cost differentials in respect of the

6.9   The Share of Costs Attributable to Protection of Water and Air Basins for Different Types of Ferrous Metallurgical Products
(in per cents)

	Water Basin		Air Basin	
	capital	operating	capital	operating
Ore Concentration	1.5	4.5	5.0	2.0
Coke	3.1	7.4	3.2	1.5
Iron	2.2	7.0	10.0	3.7
Steel Produced by				
Converter	3.5	10.3	11.7	3.0
Open hearth	2.6	8.5	5.5	2.5
Electric	3.0	7.2	4.6	2.0
Rolled metals				
Special kinds	2.9	7.5	6.0	3.4
Sheet metal	2.7	7.0	7.5	3.1
Refractories	0.5	1.0	10.6	5.2

Source: N A Kharitonov, Voprosy organizatsii bukhgalterskogo ucheta zatrat po okhrane okruzhayushchei sredy na predpriyatiyakh otrasli, *Stal'*, no. 11, 1988, pp. 97–100.

environmental features for different ferrous metallurgical production technologies. He illustrated these differences in Table 6.9 that is based on normative costs that were used for purposes of budget formation during the first half of the 1980s.

The table shows that the most expensive production process in respect of pollution controls for both the capital and operating budgets is the converter furnace. The size of the differential should raise very serious questions concerning the long-term impact of the retooling programme in the metallurgy since the current trend to converter technologies represents a significantly higher burden on the operating budget.

Automation

A feature of the metallurgical industry is its difficulty in translating the flow of investment funds into output capacity, yielding higher quality and greater variety of products. This is related to the choice of production technologies themselves and to the regulations that fix the raw material content of each product. In both respects, the lack of computing, measuring, regulating, and laboratory equipment is a factor underlying significant wastage.

6.10 Structure of BIPF

(by enterprises, compared to independent balances, in per cents)

	All Industry			Metallurgy		
	1986	1988	1989	1986	1988	1989
Total	100	100	100	100	100	100
Buildings	27.6	27.2	27.1	30.1	30.2	30.3
Installation	19.0	19.3	19.5	19.7	19.4	19.4
Transmission Equipment	10.6	10.5	10.4	7.4	7.2	7.2
Power Machinery and Equipment	7.5	7.6	7.5	3.8	3.8	3.8
Operating Machinery and Equipment	29.3	29.0	29.2	33.2	33.3	33.4
Measuring, Regulating and Laboratory Devices	1.6	1.7	1.8	1.1	1.1	1.1
Computers	1.1	1.1	1.2	0.6	0.6	0.7
Transport	2.2	2.3	2.3	3.5	3.5	3.5
Other	0.7	0.9	1.0	0.4	0.6	0.6

Source: Narodnoe khozyaistvo SSSR v 1985 g, pp. 118–19; *Narodnoe khozyaistvo SSSR v 1987 g*, pp. 102–103; *Narodnoe khozyaistvo SSSR v 1988 g*, pp. 352–353.

Computing, regulating, and monitoring equipment are also essential to rapid, continuous, complex, and accurate analysis of industrial wastes, the inadequacy of investment in this area being well illustrated by the practice of manual testing of industrial effluent. Between 1981 and 1987, an additional 81 'divisions, sectors, production units, or enterprises' at 18 enterprises were fully automated, or received some mechanisation and automation.[37]

Production Output

The level and nature of commodity output are important considerations in respect of nature protection because these two factors largely determine the scope of ecological damage due to raw material extraction, water consumption, and toxic wastes. For example, it is thought that by installing continuous casting technologies, there will be improvements in 'efficiency'. Efficiency, to environmentalists, could be interpreted as the potential to reduce air pollution, as continuous casting technologies can eliminate the need for some furnace capacity and facilitate energy savings.[38] In 1987, about 15 per cent of the total volume of smelted steel was produced in plants having continuous casting,[39] although the slow introduction of such progressive technologies has been roundly criticised.[40]

The quantity of ferrous metallurgical production showed some growth in 1986, although was virtually static in 1987 and 1988. This performance is unsurprising if the industry has indeed decided to emphasise the quality and diversity of current output rather than quantitative growth.[41]

6.11   Production of Important Types of Products
(in tons)

	1970	1980	1985	1986	1987	1988
Iron	86	107	110	114	114	115
Steel	116	148	155	161	162	163
Rolled Products of Ferrous Metals	93	18	128	134	135	136
of which:						
Finished products	81	103	108	112	114	116
Steel pipe	12	18	19	20	20	21

Source: Vestnik statistiki, no. 5, 1987, p. 63; Narodnoe khozyaistvo SSSR za 70 let, p. 164; SSSR v tsifrakh v 1987, pp. 88–89; Ekonomicheskaya gazeta, no. 5, 1988, p. 11; Narodnoe khozyaistvo SSSR v 1988 g, p. 382. Tonnes rounded to nearest whole number.

In fact, however, Soviet planners do envisage that reconstruction and retooling of enterprises will eventually yield increased quantities of produced commodities. One, perhaps extreme, example is given in the Urals, where 17 old plants currently produce 2.5 million tonnes of iron and 4 million tonnes of steel; after the reconstruction process is completed, output will be 20 million tonnes of metal products.[42] Such production increases will intensify pollution, unless appropriate abatement technologies are simultaneously installed.

Resource Conservation

Over the years, growth in production has been achieved by the consumption of increasing and uncontrolled quantities of raw materials a factor which has particularly intensified pressures on the environment. Resource conservation is commonly practised under conditions of resource scarcity or when raw material prices are sufficiently high to discourage industrial wastage. In general, it is not clear why Soviet metallurgy is motivated to integrate and sustain resource conserving practices unless steps are being taken by the central authorities artificially to create resource scarcity or to raise raw material prices so as to reduce profitability.

It is certain that some Soviet managers are counting on the modernisation of basic industrial production units to curtail the volume of raw materials required by the metallurgical sector. They take the view that introduction of resource conserving technologies should reduce the long-term costs of environmental protection. As elsewhere in the Soviet economy, the metallurgical industry is mandated to reduce water, fuel, and energy used in production as measured in total consumption and per unit of output, and to recover and recycle waste products from industrial activities. Non-ferrous metallurgy, for example, has an on-going resource conservation programme involving specific productivity targets for ore refining, solid waste recovery and recycling, use of waste heat, and reducing raw materials consumption per unit of output.[43] In the short term, some resource savings can probably be achieved by adhering to state regulations for inputs into a given commodity. In the long-term, the pace of raw material conservation can only be sustained at the rate operational normatives are changed in respect of a given metallurgical product, changes that are themselves dependent in many instances on future scientific research or adaptation of existing theoretical knowledge.

The immediate targets for raw materials conservation in respect of metallurgical production are clear. In 1988, 61 per cent of operating funds were expended on raw materials, and 11.5 per cent for fuel and energy.[44] Reductions in the quantity of raw materials consumed per unit of output could create greater financial flexibility in the metallurgical industry's operating budget, for instance, to accelerate repairs to plant and equipment. However, under present circumstances, if resource conservation releases significant funds within the operating budgets, they will probably stimulate upward revisions of commodity prices, since this could be done without affecting the total value of production funds available to the industry. Offsetting price increases of metallurgical products will in turn, be reflected in higher prices of pollution control equipment, which for the most part is metal-intensive.

On the other hand, improvements in environmental management will occur as waste recovery and recycling technologies are put in place. In the national economy generally, investment in processing of secondary raw materials is said to have accounted for '0.34 per cent of total capital expenditure in industry during the 11th FYP period', an amount characterised as inadequate.[45] So, while one may be sceptical about the prospects for great leaps forward in resource conservation, it is clear that recent examples, such as the reprocessing of waste metal in mini-mills, do represent progress.[46]

Environmental Investment

The metallurgical industry's environmental priorities are to:
- curtail releases of polluted waste water by means of water recycling technologies and effluent treatment. In the past, the industry has not made large-scale progress in treatment technologies for waste water that is not then recycled. The emphasis on expansion of circulating water systems and recycling means that, in the interim of putting the systems in place, large volumes of liquid effluent containing potentially higher than usual concentrations of toxic substances will continue to cause environmental damage.
- reduce air pollution by means of dust trapping. Here, the application of desulphurisation technologies is the exception to the trend, but attention to desulphurisation is so far mainly in the European part of the country, not USSR-wide. It is unlikely that there will be a general effort to equip 'outdated' plants with installations to neutralise gaseous emissions or liquid effluent. In the past, the industry has tended to ignore local pressures to change the direction of its investment programme, and the present strategy seems to underscore a delay in the application of air pollution controls until after the basic production technologies have been changed,[47] while land reclamation is not an investment concern at present.
- engage in resource conservation in respect of water, raw materials, fuel and energy, and to reprocess scrap metal from inside and outside the industry. This section reviews environmental investment as it is outlined in the industry's literature. It is assumed that the cost of resource conservation, perhaps with the exception of that relating to water recycling, are external to the environmental budget.

Ferrous metallurgy   Information about nature protection expenditure by ferrous metallurgy is at best indicative. Industry sources say that the amount totalled about 800 million rubles *on average per year*.[48] This is distributed as 150–200 million rubles on capital construction (66 per cent of total capital

6.12 State Capital Budget for Nature Protection and Rational Use of Natural Resources
(millions of rubles)

	1981–85	1986–1990*	1986	1987	1988
Metallurgy	1695	2073	431	401	412
Water	1095	1182	237	220	252
Air	430	513	107	104	97
Land	15	22	2	6	5

Source: Okhrana okruzhayushchei sredy i ratsional' noe ispol' zovanie prirodnykh resursov v SSSR, pp. 148–50.

investment for nature protection), 80 million rubles for capital repairs (34 per cent) and more than 500 million rubles in operating costs (62 per cent of total environmental protection allocations).[49] Thus, from industry sources it is estimated that about 230 million rubles (150 million + 80 million) are available on average per year for capital investment in environmental protection for ferrous metallurgy. Thus, industry sources imply 1.1 billion rubles would be made available over a five year period. The industry reports are generally in line with the preceding table and Appendix 1 which reflect official accounts.

It is important to note that the investment data are inflated to the extent that the construction or modernisation of cleansing installations have not proceeded as scheduled. In this respect, for ferrous metallurgy, only 90 per cent of the planned construction of cleansing installations was completed, while a third of the expected installations were not commissioned as scheduled in 1987.[50] For the national economy, F Morgun noted that by mid-1988, commissioning of waste water treatment systems was at 49 per cent of plan, and water recycling systems was fulfilled by 61 per cent.[51]

Non-ferrous metallurgy In the five years of the 11th plan period, 880 million rubles were provided (854 million rubles were expended) by non-ferrous metallurgy for nature protection work, of which 700 million (79 per cent) were designated for construction-installation work.[52] In 1986, of 230.4 million rubles available for nature protection investments by the Ministry of Non-Ferrous Metallurgy, 189.6 million rubles (82 per cent) were expended on construction-installation work. Of the total, 130.4 million (57 per cent) were invested in water pollution controls, of which 113.8 million (87 per cent) was for construction-installation work.[53] At the 1986 rate of expenditure, 1.1 billion rubles would be made available by non-ferrous metallurgy for capital investment in nature protection during the 12th plan period.[54] In other words, ferrous and non-ferrous metallurgy divvy up the resources designated for the metallurgical sector on a 50:50 basis.

Air pollution controls   The portion of the capital budget allocated to investment in air pollution controls within all sectors of the national economy increased in 1988 to 317 million rubles from 263 million in 1986, and 234 million rubles in 1985. The important factor here is that the allocations were miniscule in the first instance. Meanwhile, the level at which the funds were actually used fell to 81 per cent in 1987 from 84 per cent in 1985, and there was no improvement in 1988. Also falling was the rate at which air pollution control installations were commissioned in the national economy: in 1985 it was 83 per cent, 1986 – 81 per cent, 1987 – 73 per cent of that planned.[55]

In the 11th plan period, roughly 25 per cent of investment by metallurgy in air pollution controls, with the same relative proportion was planned for the 12th plan period. Of total funds (215 million rubles) available to non-ferrous metallurgy in 1986, 75.6 million were expended on air pollution controls, of which 56.7 million (three-quarters) were for construction and installation work.[56]

Characteristics of Pollution

Ferrous and non-ferrous metallurgy generate solid, liquid, gaseous, and sludge wastes. This section briefly characterises waste management as it is discussed in the industry's literature: thus, it attempts to illustrate major categories of an environmental programme which will require budgetary and material resources.

Solid Wastes

The mountains of solid wastes generated each year by the metallurgical industry are *environmental concerns* because the toxic components contaminate land, air, and water and in some instances are absorbed into the food chain or by humans and animals. They are *economic concerns* because the wastes can have value as raw materials in industrial production; because, it is expensive to correct damage to public health and environment;[57] and because losses in agricultural production due to pollution or displaced land are not retrievable.

'Solid waste management' includes the accumulation, storage, transportation, disposal, and post-disposal monitoring of designated wastes produced during the manufacturing of ferrous and non-ferrous metals. It is understood also to include interim storage of non-gaseous and non-liquid wastes produced by the industry that are destined for recycling by metallurgical enterprises or other consumers.

There are no official accounts of solid waste generation or investment for purposes of solid waste management. The metallurgical industry has five operations that generate most of the solid wastes: coke-chemical production, ore concentration, blast furnaces, rolling mills, and foundaries. Khachaturov indicated that if the wastes from ore concentration and coke-chemical production are included, the total solid wastes from mining and metallurgy come to about 200 million tonnes on average in a given year.[58] Kolosov estimated that about 75 per cent of all solid wastes in the Soviet Union are generated by the mining industry.[59] In addition, where fossil fuelled electric power is generated at the site of a metallurgical combine, it poses a solid waste disposal task that probably must be taken into account relative to the future investment responsibility of the metallurgical sector. A similar circumstance for the future may be confronted in the form of coal desulphurisation installations.[60]

Solid waste disposal   Sold waste disposal is not an investment priority. Current practices are unmanaged dumps or burial of all slime, rock, slag, ash, and cinder that is not recycled. Research on the toxic effects of such wastes and waste disposal practices appears to have been stepped up and health regulations promulgated for a number of substances.[61]

Solid waste resource recovery   There is no agreement in the literature as to the nature, quantity, or origin of solid waste currently produced. A recent article indicated that 'resources' of secondary raw materials of non-ferrous metallurgy total over 1.4 billion tonnes annually, including 85 per cent overburden rock, 11 per cent (169 million tonnes) of tailings, 1.5 per cent (17.8 million tonnes) of metallurgical slag, 1.3 per cent (15.0 million tonnes) of aluminous slag, and 1.0 per cent (11.7 million tonnes) of metallurgical cake. From these resources, 190 million tonnes of secondary raw materials (or 14 per cent of total raw materials used by the sector) account for 20 per cent of total non-ferrous metallurgical production.[62]

6.13   Use of Secondary Raw Materials in the National Economy
(million tonnes)

	1981	1985	1986	1987
Slag from Blast Furnace Production	35.9	43.3	49.9	53.6
Scrap and Wastes of Ferrous Metallurgy	88	93	98	102
Slag from Steel Production	6.8	9.4	11.4	11.3

Source: *SSSR v tsifrakh v 1987*, p. 73.

Resource conservation affects the metallurgical industry in another way, as national policy is also concerned with metallurgical wastes that can be used, for example, by construction-related enterprises. Again, the literature is only indicative. For example, between 70 and 84 per cent of an estimated 50 million tonnes of blast furnace slag produced each year at ferrous metallurgical mills are recycled; such statements imply that a substantial volume is not used.[63]

A special category of solid wastes, scrap metals, are particularly valuable as a secondary raw material in metallurgical production. It is claimed that by using scrap metal there are lower expenditures for coking coal and electric power, as well as 86 per cent reductions in atmospheric emissions, 76 per cent in waste water, and 97 per cent in solid wastes.[64] Scrap metals form a substantial part of the waste disposal task for the metals manufacturing industry.[65] No official account exists of the quantity or nature of scrap metal that needs to be processed.

Liquid Wastes

The Soviet metallurgical industry does not measure its effluent by means of automated equipment.[66] The following calculations of the required investment for waste water treatment were based on estimated water usage.[67] The following terminologies may be helpful.

- 'Water supply' is equal to the volume of external water intake plus circulating water *plus* recycled waste water from metallurgical plants. Apparently, as much as 97 per cent of water supplies can be met by its repeated use and circulation systems.[68]
- 'Circulating water' includes all water that is maintained within the water supply system for technological uses; it is always less than the total volume of water consumption by a given enterprise of combine. It may require interim cleansing, but in Soviet practice periodic flushing is more common. In optimal conditions, circulating water is cleansed and replenished, but is not released.
- 'Recycled water' refers to retained waste water from metallurgical production that is subsequently reused. It is not always cleansed prior to reuse, and in this instance is sometimes called 'repeat use water'. In Soviet practice, recycled water that does not flow into an isolated circulation system will eventually be released, and will probably bear increased concentrations of toxic wastes. In optimal circumstances, however, recycling means there is substantially less waste water, or none at all. The value of the technologies for circulating water and for recycling or repeat-use water in combination is not in respect of the quality of effluent, but of the quantity of effluent and the quantity of water withdrawn from natural resources. Clearly, without waste water

treatment, ecological gains in respect of quantity are lost since toxic concentrations in the effluent are higher.

• 'External water' intake includes fresh water drawn from surface and groundwater sources, sewage, and rainwater. External water replaces water consumed during the production processes and other water losses, or meets new consumption requirements. In optimal circumstances, once the technological water supply is initially plenished, the volume of external water intake is far less than recycled water.

Water supply purification capacity is developed for (a) fresh water and rainwater; (b) recycled water from internal sources, and (c) waste water intake from external sources, including urban sewage. In most metallurgical processes, a low standard of purification is sought.[69]

Estimate 1. In 1982, the industry journal, *Stal'*, reported that the volume of water supply for technological uses in *ferrous metallurgy* totalled 36.2 cubic kilometres, of which 85 per cent was in circulating systems, while 5.3 cubic kilometres came from external water sources.[70] If the 1982 iron and steel output are added together, then 254 million tonnes of ferrous metals required 142.5 cubic metres of water per tonne of produced metal. Using a calculation of 143 cubic metres per tonne, 277 million tonnes of iron and steel in 1988 required about 39.6 cubic kilometres of water, of which at 87 per cent circulating water, 5.1 cubic kilometres were from external sources.

Estimate 2. T S Khachaturov indicated in 1987 that while the normative for water consumption per tonne of steel was about 115 cubic metres, in reality the level of consumption was 250 cubic metres.[71] Khachaturov apparently excluded water used in the production of iron. In 1982, 147.1 million tonnes of steel were produced; at 250 cubic metres of water per tonne, this would require 36.7 billion cubic metres of water. At 85 per cent circulating water, this volume would include external water withdrawals of 5.5 cubic kilometres. However, if the production of iron also required 250 cubic metres of water per tonne of produced metal, then the 107 million tonnes of iron produced in that year would have required an additional 26.7 cubic kilometres of water; and with 85 per cent circulating water, 4.0 cubic kilometres would have been needed from all external sources. Thus in 1982, production of iron and steel together used a total of 63.4 cubic kilometres, of which 9.5 were from all external sources.

Estimate 3. Applying Khachaturov's approach to 1987 data, it can be seen that 250 cubic metres/tonne of steel implies that production of 162 million tonnes of steel required the use of 40.5 cubic kilometres of water, of which at 87 per cent circulating water 5.3 cubic kilometres would have been from all external water resources. In 1988, there was little change: production of 163 million tonnes of steel required the use of about 41 cubic kilometres of water, of which (at the 1987 level of 87 per cent circulating water) 5.3 cubic kilometres would have been from all external water sources. The 1987 use of water for iron production would have been configured as follows: 114 million tonnes of iron required 28.5 cubic kilometres/year of water; at 87 per cent circulating water, 3.7 cubic kilometres would have been needed from external sources. Together, iron and steel production required about 9 cubic kilometres from all external sources.

The 1982 *Stal'* presentation, mentioned in estimate 1, did not specify whether municipal and domestic sewage was considered part of 5.3 cubic kilometres of water from external sources, although in light of Khachaturov's statements, it is unlikely. The *Stal'* article went on to say that the expenditure of fresh water and sewage water in 1982 were 38.6 and 30.2 cubic metres per tonne of steel, respectively.[72] This suggests that 10 cubic kilometres would have come from *all* external sources, rather than the 5.3 cubic kilometres calculated in example 1 above.

These estimates tend to discredit suggestions that the ferrous metallurgical industry has significantly curtailed fresh water consumption in the aggregate.

Estimate 4.   The amount of water used in non-ferrous metallurgical production can be only roughly estimated. In a 1985 *Tsvetnye Metally* article, it was stated that 'by the end of the 11th plan period, 81 per cent (40 cubic kilometres) of the water supply would be saved by recycling'.[73] This is an unfortunately ambiguous statement, and may reflect either a cumulative multi-year or an annual figure. If it is the latter, it suggests that in 1985, the non-ferrous metallurgical sector required about 50 cubic kilometres of water, of which 10 cubic kilometres were from all external sources. However, it may mean that the industry recycled about 8 cubic kilometres per year, and only needed an additional 2 cubic kilometres of fresh water. Since the Soviet Union does not publish statistics for non-ferrous metallurgical production, the statement cannot be evaluated on the basis of tonnage produced. In either case, since 1985, two factors might have increased or decreased consumption of fresh water: expanded requirements for water due to the commissioning of new production units, and the degree to which additional consumption was offset by expansion of recycling.

There are important regional differentials for the consumption of fresh water by metallurgical industries. For example, in Kazakhstan, non-ferrous metallurgical industries required external water for 75 per cent of water used in production, which contrasts sharply with the industry average of 20 per cent or less.[74] Due to the serious water supply problems in the Central Asian region, it seems appropriate that the metallurgical industry in Kazakhstan has achieved priority status in the allocation of capital investment funds for water conservation and waste water treatment.

Recycled water is equal to water supply *less* circulating water, *less* the volume that is lost, consumed, or released, and *less* external water intake. The goal of the metallurgical industry is 'effluentless' production, and the industry's water management programme emphasises repeated use of water, water recycling, elimination of water losses, and use of domestic and municipal sewage.[75] Recycling is regarded in Soviet industry as a way to avoid the expense of deep cleansing of polluted waste water, as recycled water in metallurgy can be used in a heavily contaminated condition.[76]

With continued growth in metallurgical production capacity and the installation of gas cleansing technologies, the volumes of potentially recyclable waste water will increase.

The importance of the above calculations, however approximate, is that they suggest the ferrous metallurgical sector has been able to stabilise its overall requirements for external water supplies for technological uses by expanding recycling capacity and repeated use systems. However, since there is also no information concerning water consumed by the industry in addition to 'technological' water, progress towards the goal of reducing on expenditure of water by 30–40 per cent per tonne of produced metal cannot be confirmed.[77]

Soviet statements about the increased use of circulating water systems are borne out in the official statistics, as follows. Noteworthy is the fact that the rate of commissioning during the period 1986–90 is likely to be lower by one-quarter of that in the previous five years.

6.14 Commissioning of Systems for Circulating Water Supplies and Waste Water Treatment in the Metallurgical Complex
(thousand cubic metres/day)

	1981–85	1986–1990*	1986	1987	1988
Circulating Capacity	12805	9955	2548	1750	1675
Waste Water Treatment	2065	2628	294	158	1125

* estimated on the basis of three years.
Source: Okhrana okruzhayushchei sredy..., p. 151.

The industry's journals did publish information about progress in non-ferrous metallurgy, but no comparable information was in evidence about ferrous metallurgy. Unfortunately, the following data drawn from the industrial journals show results very different from official figures.

For example, during the 11th plan period, non-ferrous metallurgy commissioned waste water treatment capacity of 892,000 cubic metres/day (325 million cubic metres/year), and recycling systems having a capacity of 3.65 million cubic metres/day (1.3 cubic kilometres/year).[78] The data on waste water treatment capacity are roughly what might be expected for two industries having the same financial means. However, the industry account implies that ferrous metallurgy must have commissioned three times the capacity achieved by non-ferrous metallurgy if the data in table 6.14 are correct, unless there is another category of construction not delineated in the industry data.

In 1986, 70 nature protection installations were commissioned by non-ferrous metallurgy with an increase in waste water treatment of 189,500 cubic metres/day, and in recirculating water of 713,400 cubic metres/day.[79] Again, the waste water treatment figures are approximate to the official data, but not those for recirculating capacity.

The 1987 plan for non-ferrous metallurgy was to raise the share of circulating water to 85.6 per cent of water supplies (per estimate 4 above, 50 cubic kilometres of water supply in 1985). *Stal'* reported that on average in the 10th plan period, the annual increase in water consumption equalled 3 per cent per annum.[80] Given the current national emphasis on increasing the output of non-ferrous metals, it is assumed that the same rate of increase would obtain during the 12th plan period; in 1987, then, the water supply would be about 52 cubic kilometres, of which as much as 44 cubic kilometres could be in circulation systems.

The 12th plan targets are to reduce fresh water consumption by 100 million cubic metres, to increase circulating water to 87.6 per cent of total water consumption, and to curtail releases of waste water by a factor of two. Based on 1985 water supplies, an additional 3 cubic kilometres in circulating capacity would be required to meet that goal. However, the industry's targets only envisaged a very modest increase in waste water treatment capacity, and virtually the same amount of capacity in water circulation systems in comparison to the 11th plan, which is far below that needed. There are further reasons why the state plan will not be achieved: the reported under-expenditure of capital funds for environmental protection, and shortfalls in commissioned capacity during the years 1986–88.

Waste water is equal to the volume of water supply *less* that portion lost, consumed, maintained in circulation, and/or recycled. Using the 'Khachaturov' figure of 69 cubic kilometres of water supply less 87 per cent as circulating water, the amount of ferrous metallurgical waste water requiring treatment prior to reuse or release in 1987 would have been in the neighbourhood of 9 cubic kilometres annually. In non-ferrous metallurgy, another 9 cubic kilometres would need treatment annually, assuming that all effluent is subject to environmental regulation.

One difficulty is to ascertain whether additional capacities in waste water treatment are for purposes of treating water that is to be recycled or for treating wastes prior to release. Soviet industry sources do not clarify the point, but given the priority of reducing fresh water consumption by recycling waste water, it is most likely that additional waste water treatment capacity has been used for purposes of treating water to be recycled and that most effluent is untreated.

Waste water treatment systems must cope with waste water flows that are contaminated to different degrees, meet a range of cleansing standards, and deal with a variety of solid and liquid toxic substances. In 1982, it was reported that water used for cleansing blast and open-hearth furnaces, converters, electric steel smelting, and tempering constituted 80 per cent of polluted waste water in ferrous metallurgy.[81] Treatment capacity has been developed for:

- *waste water that is to be recycled*. Waste water that is to be recycled is precipitated and treated (for example, by electrolytic and chemical neutralisation) to standards required by both the water circulation and production technologies.[82] The degree to which waste water is cleansed prior to recycling should reflect the uses to which it will be put. For example, some Soviet scientists now urge the use of chemically contaminated waste water to cool metallurgical slag so as to reduce the use of technological water (that is purified to some standard).[83]
- *waste water prior to release*. Waste water is supposed to be filtered and neutralised to the degree specified in the terms of an enterprise's operating licence for protection of public health and nature; then, it is called 'normatively cleansed waste water'.
- *storm water*. Such water is not addressed at all by Soviet metallurgical installations.
- *soil 'washing' effluent*. Although the technique is frequently mentioned in the literature, no cases have been cited where soil washing activities have taken place.[84]

Finally, the 'coefficient of use' of waste water treatment installations in the Ministry of Non-ferrous Metallurgy was 0.7 in 1987, a term which indicates that 30 per cent of capacity was not used. This factor may be explained by a need for reserve capacity to cover peak flows and decommissioning for purposes of maintenance and repair. However, it is reported that the efficiency of these installations is 0.47. This lends itself to a negative interpretation: that over half of the time the treatment is inadequate, even when it complies with existing design standards. An alternative possibility is that the installations are in operation less than half the time; such a situation would improve the picture of effluent quality for waste water that *is* processed, but it is negative in suggesting that over half of the time waste water is not processed at all.

Estimated Investment Requirements

The following calculations are essentially speculative. The approach used is that of Academician Khachaturov, and the data on which they are based are drawn from the two previous sections that discussed investment and estimated the volume of effluent. It is assumed that the investment priority will be effluent that is not recycled which, in 1987, was equal to about 13 per cent of water supplies. No attempt is made to quantify investment that is needed to improve treatment for effluent that is inadequately treated; such investment well beyond the resources of the industry within the next three plan periods.

Water Protection

Here, the assumption is that the ultimate goal for total effluent in metallurgy is equal to 3 per cent of external water intake, as industry sources say that 97 per cent of water supplies can be met from circulating and recycling systems. (This percentage seems rather high on the supply side, given the level of water losses reported elsewhere in the economy; but no adjustments have been made.) It was estimated above that external water intake for 1985 was 18 cubic kilometres, less 3 per cent as indicated, leaving 17.4 cubic kilometres annually to be recycled or treated prior to release. This comes to about 48 million cubic metres of water daily.[85]

Water Recycling and Circulation Schemes

Estimate 1.   Here it is assumed that ferrous and non-ferrous metallurgy proceed at the same rates for a planned total within a 5 year period of 7 million cubic metres/day, and that at least 90 per cent of planned capacity will be completed and commissioned. Thus, three five-year plan periods will be needed to provide capacity for 48 million cubic metres/day in recycling systems.

Here, two difficulties emerge: the share of capital investment in water protection that is absorbed by waste water treatment, and construction cost increases. From industry sources, it appears that the ratio of construction of waste water treatment to water recirculation capacity is 1:4, although official data do not bear this out. Industry sources indicate that the relative cost differential is roughly 4:1.[86] The assumption here is that the capital budget for water protection is expended on a 50:50 basis between the two types of systems. The capital budget for nature protection has suffered from inflation along with the rest of the Soviet economy, so that a planned increase of some 15 per cent in the 12th plan period as a whole was not expected, from the outset, to realise significantly greater capacity than in the previous five years. The inflationary pressure has not abated, and the budget in 1988 was 10 per cent over that of 1986, which is more or less in line with inflation.

If allocations are increased at a rate of 15 per cent within each of the next three five-year plan periods, then *2.7 billion rubles will be required for water recirculating systems alone*. If a 10 per cent rate of increase is sustained, then *2.4 billion rubles will be needed*. (In neither instance, of course, is the inflationary effect of price rises expected after 1990 taken into account.) If it is estimated that 50 per cent of all capital investments in water protection are designated for recirculating systems, then the present rate of expenditure will provide about 2 billion rubles over three five-year plan periods. *Here, the shortfall is between 0.4 and 0.7 billion rubles over current spending levels*.

A final difficulty is that this calculation does not take into account growth in water consumption. Such growth will occur due to anti-pollution measures and to new capacity coming on-stream for coke-chemical and non-ferrous metallurgical production, albeit at a somewhat reduced rate due to the higher allocations of capital investment to repair and maintenance. In the 10th FYP, it was reported that ferrous metallurgy required a 3 per cent annual increase in water supplies. But given the shift in investments from new construction to retooling/reconstruction, water consumption may grow at a lower rate of increase – here estimated to be about 1.5 per cent annual growth for both ferrous and non-ferrous metallurgy.

A 1.5 per cent increase in water consumption will move the metallurgical industries from a total of 119 cubic kilometres annually in 1987 (of which 105 cubic kilometres or 87 per cent was in recirculation systems) to a total demand by the year 2000 of 144.6 cubic kilometres, and by the year 2005 to 155.8 cubic kilometres of water. By the year 2000, construction of new recirculating capacity will provide an additional 21 cubic kilometres, which would leave a shortfall in capacity of 18 cubic kilometres, that will increase to 22 cubic kilometres by 2005. *By the year 2000, therefore, the shortfall in investment for recirculating/repeat use capacity will be 2.8–3.4 billion rubles*.

Estimate 2. In the national economy during 1986, the cost of one cubic metre capacity for recirculating water was 34 rubles, and that for waste water treatment capacity was 156 rubles. In comparison, the metallurgical industry appeared to show costs of 94 rubles per cubic metre of daily capacity for recirculating water, and 356 rubles for waste water purification. In this instance, capacity to handle 48 million cubic metres/day of recirculating water would mean a *capital outlay of 4.5 billion rubles at current costs, exclusive of inflation. Here, the shortfall by the year 2000 will be 2.5 billion rubles at present consumption levels and investment, and 4.2 billion rubles at 1 1/2 per cent annual increase in consumption, less anticipated investment at current levels.*

Estimate 3. In 1984, according to industry sources, the capital costs of water purification were 13.1 kopeks per cubic metre, while operating costs were 2.2

kopeks. Capital costs of recirculating water were 3.3 kopeks per cubic metre and operating costs only 0.6 kopeks,[87] which probably is sufficient only for pipe but not treatment installations.

Here, the data reflect capital costs in the middle of the 11th FYP, and inflationary increases in construction costs (about 15 per cent) must be added. Thus, the capital costs of water purification installations would be 15 kopeks per cubic metre of capacity by 1990, 17 kopeks by 1995, and about 20 kopeks by 2000; and for recirculating water systems would be 4 kopeks per cubic metre of capacity by 1990, nearer to 5 by 1995, and to 6 by 2000.

Because the type of capacity (hourly, daily, annual) to which the costs refer was not specified, the data are less reliable. If the costs refer to annual throughput of water, the resulting costs approximates those given above. That is, by the year 2000, 17.4 billion cubic metres of water multiplied by (an average of) 5 kopeks per cubic metre would require *870 million rubles for water recirculation systems, exclusive of increased consumption, and 1.7 billion rubles at a 1.25 rate of increase in consumption. The current capital budget appears sufficient at this level of expenditure.*

Waste Water Treatment

Estimate 1.   New waste water treatment capacity is required for the difference between total water supply and that in repeat use and recirculating systems, less current waste water treatment capacity. At present rates of consumption and construction, metallurgy should achieve 97 per cent recycling by the year 2000. This would leave a volume equal to 3 per cent of the water supply subject to treatment. However, given anticipated growth in water consumption, recirculating capacity will not be sufficient at present rates of construction to achieve effluentless production by the year 2005. This means that waste water treatment capacity for an equal amount of effluent will be required.

Unfortunately, there is no reliable indicator of the availability of treatment capacity in the aggregate, or even if the purpose of existing capacity is to treat waste water prior to release. Construction over the 11th and 12th FYPs was in the order of 1.8 million cubic metres daily capacity per plan period, at an implied cost of 356 rubles per cubic metre of daily capacity. *If this rate is sustained until 2005 (3 plan periods), then nearly 5.4 million cubic metres daily capacity (2 cubic kilometres annual flow-through) will be made available at a cost of 2 billion rubles.*

Estimate 2.   Again, the same questions impose themselves: the rate of growth of water supplies, how much capacity is represented by existing waste water treatment installations, and the purpose of the capacity (to treat water before recycling or to treat effluent prior to release). None of these questions can be answered definitively, so the following represents a range of possible developments:

If the growth in consumption of water is in the order of 1.5 per cent per annum, given that development of new production capacity will be slower due to the shift of investment funds to renewal and reconstruction of existing plant and equipment, this means that by the year 2005, total water supplies would be 25 per cent over the 1987 level (from 119 to 155 cubic kilometres). If all the new recirculating and repeat use systems are installed, as planned, to treat 17.4 cubic kilometres, then by the year 2000 total water supplies will reach 144 cubic kilometres annually, of which only 119 cubic kilometres or 82 per cent could be handled by recirculation and repeat use systems. By the year 2005, 126 out of 155 cubic kilometres would be recirculated water. The rough difference is 25–29 cubic kilometres of water intake annually. Assuming that all waste water treatment installations existing in 1990 are for purposes of cleansing water prior to recycling, then new construction of 2 cubic kilometres in new waste water treatment capacity by the year 2005 would still leave about 22 cubic kilometres of effluent (less unrecoverable consumption and other losses) that are not handled either by waste water treatment or recirculation schemes. *To treat such a volume of effluent, the capital budget for effluent treatment systems would have to cover the shortfall of over 20 billion rubles.* Obviously, it is cheaper to provide additional recycling capacity.

Gaseous Wastes

Acidic and metal-bearing steam are characteristic features of the metallurgical industry. The regulations to govern metallurgical emissions are still being developed. It is expected that within the context of integrated environmental assessments, exhaust gases from such enterprises will present special problems because of the variety of contaminants that are contained in them. The main difficulty associated with metallurgy is that its raw materials – metal ores and acids – are usually toxic in small quantities and, stable by nature, they retain their toxicity when deposited downstream.[88] Metallurgical exhausts most frequently cited as causing the greatest harm are compounds of sulphur, fluorine, and chlorine, nitrogen and carbon oxides; aerosols and arsenic, while nickel, lead, and other metals are discussed in respect of pollution in the specific locales where plants are located. Amongst these, the national priority is retention of particulate matter and reduction of sulphurous emissions, whereas local investment priorities must eventually address other regulated substances.

The air pollution policy currently being followed by the Ministry of Ferrous Metallurgy was established in GOST 17.2.3.02–78 – a state regulation requiring that urban enterprises work out measures to ensure that ground-level concentrations of pollutants in their exhausts do not exceed those specified in their operating licences. Such pollution control standards are supposed to take into account pollution from other enterprises, as well as the quantity and toxicity of the metallurgical plant's emissions and the conditions of their release into the atmosphere (height and diameter of smoke stacks, speed of released gases, locational factors) that dictate the rate and distance of dispersion of the pollutants.[89]

By 1986, emissions criteria had been established for 200 separate substances in respect of pollutants released in urban areas.[90] It was reported about that time that 95 per cent of pollutants released into the atmosphere were sulphur, nitrogen, ash, and dust of light dissolved alkaline materials, while 3–4 per cent consist of 'more exotic' types such as phenols, halogens, ammonia, and the like.[91] There is some controversy in the Soviet Union over whether the emphasis in air pollution control investments should be placed on the very few pollutants that comprise the bulk of regulated substances contained in gaseous emissions (since the regulations are established and in most instances the technologies are also known) or on a more blanket approach. The concern is that, by 1989, air pollution control regulations had been promulgated for over 600 substances, most of which occur only as small tonnages and comprise less than 1 per cent of pollution as a whole. M A Styrikovich raised the point that greater return on investment in respect of air quality might be achieved by giving attention to high tonnage pollutants.[92] He noted that for these pollutants, such as sulphur, regulatory criteria have not been formulated for 'natural areas'. This creates a special problem for enterprises located in such remote regions as the Kola North, 'where most of the sulphur and all of the nickel originates within the metallurgical sector'.[93] Noteworthy also is a statement by a newly elected member of the Council of People's Deputies to the effect that 'what isn't being done at Nizhni Tagil is hair-raising, and the annual total emissions are approaching 4 tonnes per resident.[94]

One answer to the dilemma may eventually be mandatory assessments of economic damage and economic benefits associated with different levels of prevention and technologies.[95] For example, non-ferrous metallurgy is experimenting with a cost-benefit methodology for evaluating alternative controls, types, and sources of pollution. The methodology takes into account two types of 'damage': breaches of licensing requirements and damage to nature. It does not consider related social costs, such as impairment of human health. At the moment, investment decisions are generally based on assessments of local capital costs at different levels of pollution control efficiencies. Other economic damage and benefit analyses are not pursued except to acknowledge population density and perhaps the potential for resource recovery.[96]

Approaches to Air Pollution Control

The metallurgical industry is taking three main approaches to reduce air pollution. The first is the selection of basic production technologies that generate less pollution. The second is the application of pollution controls and resource recovery practices. A third is the creation of sanitary zones around the metallurgical enterprises, perhaps eventually moving the living quarters of nearby communities some distance from the plants or vice versa.

The second approach is of great interest, as aside from pollution control technologies discussed below, the industry is experimenting with a number of low technology options. The most 'popular' are sealing furnaces, cupolas, bunkers, and pipes to reduce the intake of external air and purposefully direct exhaust gases. Along these lines, loading and unloading of dry materials inside of enclosures, and elimination of powdered materials below prescribed sizes are thought to be low-cost approaches to avoidance of air pollution by particulate substances.

In the main, the discussions in respect of air pollution controls refer to several classes of technologies:

Pollution control category no. 1 – to contain matter such as dust, ash, and cinder at the smoke stack. Over the period of the 12th FYP, the Ministry of Non-ferrous Metallurgy planned to increase the trapping of particulate matter by 3.3 million tonnes, and reduce emissions by 1.1 million tonnes or 16.2 per cent per annum.[97] The following table provides data on the commissioning of capacity to trap or neutralise harmful substances generated by metallurgical enterprises. However, as the industry's literature expresses its goals in different units of measure (such as, in tonnes trapped), it is impossible to say from data about the capacity commissioned to what extent progress has been made.

6.15   Commissioning of Installations
for the Trapping or Neutralisation of Harmful Substances
from Waste Gases at Metallurgical Enterprises
(thousand cubic metres of gas/hour)

	1981–85	1986–1990*	1986	1987	1988
Total Economy	200000	188085	38796	48235	25820
Metallurgical Complex	77960	77728	16262	21633	8742

* calculated on the basis of three years.
Source: Okhrana okruzhayushchei sredy..., p. 152.

Ferrous Metallurgy.   *Vestnik statistiki* indicated in 1987 that total emissions by all industrial sources was 64.1 million tonnes, of which 10.9 million tonnes were 'harmful substances' emitted by ferrous metallurgical enterprises. A figure of 64 million tonnes of 'harmful substances' within the national economy is often cited, but it is uncertain from the characterisation what these numbers actually represent.

Of total ferrous metallurgical emissions, 300,000 tonnes were released by gas-cleaning installations that operated inefficiently.[98] *Vestnik statistiki* also cited a survey by the State Committee on Hydrometeorology (Goskomgidromet) which indicated that 60 per cent of gas-cleaning installations surveyed has been in use for ten years or more (in comparison with the normative of 8–12 years), and 13 per cent of inspected installations operated inefficiently due to 'infringements of operating regime'.

In the 12th FYP, the industry's goal is to lower the emissions of harmful substances into the air by 30 per cent in the coke-chemical sector.[99] In 1987, only 80 per cent of the gas-cleansing installations for ferrous metallurgical enterprises anticipated in that year were actually commissioned.[100] It is most likely that the reduced emissions of substances other than dust are the result of dust trapping, during which there is coincidental containment of sulphur, nitrogen, and carbon oxides. For example, industry sources indicate that at three open-hearth furnaces where dust trapping was at 99 per cent efficiency, there was coincidental removal of 26 per cent of nitrogen oxides, 80–90 per cent of fluorine, and 15–23 per cent of sulphur dioxide.[101]

Non-ferrous Metallurgy.   In 1987, of the 64.1 million tonnes of harmful substances released by industry, non-ferrous metallurgy emitted 6.2 million tonnes, of which 900,000 tonnes were due to faulty installations. 55 per cent of all gas filtering apparatus had been in use for 10 years or longer; and, according to Goskomgidromet, 26 per cent of surveyed installations operated inefficiently due to 'infringements of the operating regime'. *Tsvetnye metally* indicated that in 1988, enterprises of non-ferrous metallurgy released 6 million tonnes of pollutants, including 4.5 million of sulphurous anhydrides (achieving 44 per cent sulphur removal by the end of 1988), 580,000 tonnes of oxides of carbon, and 15,800 tonnes of hydrogen fluoride.[102]

The non-ferrous metallurgical industry is candid about the sources of, and substances in, the greatest volumes of its emissions, stating that 95 per cent of polluted substances released into the atmosphere are caused by six sub-branches: nickel – 54 per cent, copper – 18.6 per cent, aluminium – 16.4 per cent, polymetals, rare metals, and tungsten-molybdenum – 11 per cent.[103] It was reported that eight sites are responsible for two-thirds of the total volume discharged into the atmosphere by non-ferrous metallurgy; these are Achinsk Alumina, Almalyk, Balkhash, Noril'sk MMC and Ust'-Kamenogorsk lead-zinc combines, Bratsk Alumina, and the Severonikel' and the Pechenganikel' combines.[104]

Tsvetnye metally also indicated that during 1988, the authorities in the Chimkent, Zaporozh'e, Eastern Kazakhstan, Murmansk, Chelyabinsk, and Sverdlovsk *oblasts* and in the cities of Bratsk and Noril'sk 'worked on questions of nature protection'. Apparently, this led to the decision to concentrate ecological investment from 1989 until 1995 in Eastern Kazakhstan (370 million rubles) and Sverdlovsk *oblasts* (400 million rubles), and the city of Zaporozhe (200 million rubles). At current budget levels, this decision means that these three targets will absorb 86 per cent of the budgetary allocations for non-ferrous metallurgy at least until 1995. In addition, between 1991 and the year 2000, Noril'sk may receive an injection of some 1,850 million rubles – although the financing will be primarily from the capital budget for reconstruction and retooling of industry.

During the 11th plan period, non-ferrous metallurgy commissioned gas purification installations with a capacity of 34.9 million cubic metres/hour.[105] Over the years of the 11th FYP, equipment for purification of waste gases was commissioned with a capacity of 30.2 million cubic metres/hour; the industry claimed that this represented a 300,000 tonne reduction in gaseous pollutants, and that existing capacity then covered 40 per cent of total exhaust gases.[106]

The non-ferrous metallurgical programme for air protection in the 1986–1990 plan was expressed differently: it envisaged increasing the trapping of harmful substances from waste gases by 3.3 million tonnes, and reducing emissions to the air by 1.1 million tonnes/year, leading to 87.4 per cent trapping by 1990.[107] Other information translated the plan objectives into terms comparable with the 11th plan results: in 1986, with 70 nature protection installations commissioned, 4.3 million cubic metres/hour of gas cleansing were brought into service (at that rate, 21.5 million cubic metres/hour of new capacity would be built over five years). In 1987, the plan was to raise the level of trapping to 85.4 per cent efficiency. This implies a regressive posture due either to increased emissions or sluggish performance of existing equipment. Barring new investment activity, it appears that new air pollution control capacity in the 12th plan period will be commissioned at roughly two-thirds the rate of the 11th plan period.

Category 1 pollution is handled by applying cyclones and Venturi tubes, or electrostatic precipitators. There are numerous domestic and foreign designs available to Soviet industry. To date, about three-fourths of expenditure on air pollution controls reportedly relate to dust-trapping apparatus.[108] *Tsvetnye metally*, as above, reported 97.7 per cent of dust could be trapped; but while most metallurgical plants have dust traps, a very large number of the installations clearly need to be repaired or replaced because they are old and worn out, or have broken down.

Pollution control category no. 2 – for exhaust gases containing substances *not* designated for recycling. Process gases of non-ferrous metallurgical plants that are not subject to recycling are supposed to be handled by high-speed electric filters.[109] Soviet industry also uses a combination of Venturi tubes and electric filters to trap fluorine, for which 87 per cent efficiency has been achieved.[110] Such a level has probably not been reached for the metallurgical industry as a whole, as indicated by an article in *Metallurg'*, in which the gas cleaning of the sintering area at Kommunarsk MMC was described as between 75–80 per cent efficient.[111] Fluorine is used in aluminium manufacturing, and the Bratsk and Krasnoyarsk plants are most often mentioned as sources of pollution in this context.

The main source of pollution by the iron producing industry is the open-hearth furnace, most of which are reported to lack adequate pollution controls. Carbon monoxide, released by the furnaces, is estimated to total about 50 per cent of the dangerous gases emitted by the industry, and can be found in concentrations up to 10 per cent by volume. At present, the industry relies on the injection of oxygen to reduce harmful emissions. In the 12th FYP, the main effort by iron producers will be to work out the pollution control normatives and technological designs that will eventually be implemented to avert air pollution. Meanwhile, it is hoped to reduce the emissions of harmful substances by 25,000 tonnes – a volume that is insignificant relative to the national tonnage of emissions, but will be important in one or two locales.[112]

Pollution control category no. 3 – dispersal methods. Here, and in both categories 1 and 2, tall smoke stacks are still being used by some plants to disperse contaminants over distances and thereby reduce the need for pollution treatment capacity. This method is no longer considered desirable. Data cited for an integrated iron and steel works in Samarkand indicate that tall stacks spread the toxic metals for the most part within a radius of 4–5 miles from the point of emission, but that toxins from the plants are found up to 40 kilometres away in fruit, and in the organs and tissues of children.[113]

All nickel production plants supposedly rely on tall stacks to disperse gases bearing low concentrations of sulphur. The air basin of the Kola North is mainly polluted by enterprises of copper-nickel production which account for 70–90 per cent of sulphur dioxide emissions and 100 per cent of those containing copper and nickel. Studies of the nickel content of atmospheric air show that the metal remains close to the plant in the form of aerosols of soluble sulphates and oxides. Nickel compounds are completely stable and, when they settle, poison land and water.[114]

Treatment capacity no. 4 – for the thermal content of exhaust gases. This is often not handled at all, although recycling of the heat within and external to the production site is an increasingly sought after option. Most investment in this category will be outside the environmental budget.[115]

Resource Conservation

Certain emissions present a substantial threat to the environment if they are released, but the potential for recovery is so great that resource conservation is one of the main air pollution control priorities for the industry. For example, ferrous and non-ferrous metallurgy generate about half of the total tonnage of sulphur emitted in the Soviet Union. This is one reason that the primary area for resource conservation in the medium-term will be in respect of the sulphur content of exhaust gases, although whether sulphur is the most damaging pollutant in non-ferrous metallurgical emissions at local levels is somewhat contentious. That this is the most common pollutant is generally agreed, and non-ferrous industry sources indicate that up to 83 per cent of emissions are sulphur-bearing gases.[116]

Of the total 64.1 million tonnes of emissions from stationary sources in 1987, Yuri Izrael indicated that one-third (21 million tonnes) were comprised of sulphurous substances.[117] As noted above in the section on dust trapping, total emissions of harmful substances by metallurgy were reported as 17.1 million tonnes in 1987, of which 6.2 million were released by non-ferrous metallurgy. This suggests that the quantity of sulphurous emissions is increasing rapidly: in 1985, *Tsvetnye metally* placed total sulphur emissions at over 83 per cent of pollutants released by non-ferrous metallurgy, of which 5.1 million tonnes were sulphurous materials.[118] Soviet economists claim that it can be economically advantageous to attempt to recover sulphur in exhaust gases when it reaches 3 per cent concentration.[119] Although not uniformly the case, emissions from metallurgical plants routinely have concentrations of sulphur dioxide ranging between 10 and 20 per cent by volume.

The USSR Ministry of Non-ferrous Metallurgy has adopted a general policy that stresses the retention of sulphur. For the period to 1990, the industry plans to reduce its emissions of sulphur by 950,000 tonnes. While much of the discussion centres on efforts by the aluminium sector, three other branches (copper, nickel and polymetals) were also ordered to produce plans for sulphur recovery by the end of 1987 covering the period to 1995; these reports have not been publicly discussed as yet.[120] In general, most sources emphasise that substantial reductions in the emissions of sulphur dioxide can only be achieved by replacing the existing technologies of copper, nickel, and lead production (reverberatory, ore-thermic, and shaft-furnace smelting) in which large amounts of gases are formed that contain low concentrations of sulphur. Amongst the recommended changes are progressive semi-autonomous and autogenous flowsheets, oxygen flash smelting, and electric furnaces.[121]

Future Investment

The Soviet objective is to curtail emissions of dust and particular matter entirely, and to reduce emissions of sulphurous gases to prescribed levels. Over the period 1986–1990, Soviet metallurgy will have had access to about 500 million rubles for the construction of air pollution controls, with about 75 per cent apparently designated for dust controls. *Over the period to the year 2005, at the same rate of financing, it can be expected that 1.1 billion rubles will be made available for dust controls.* Unfortunately, there is no indication that funding for dust controls will be sustained at such levels, although apparently it will be needed.

In the 12th plan period, non-ferrous metallurgy will have access to 250 million rubles (about 50 per cent of investment resources for air pollution controls), of which 192 million will be allotted to dust controls. Non-ferrous metallurgy indicates that its plans provide capacity that will retain 3.3 million tonnes of harmful substances during this period, at an implied cost of 58 rubles per tonne of trapped substance.

A 1988 article in *Metallurg'* provided a range of capital costs for ten different sintering plants of ferrous metallurgy. It took into account capital costs of buildings and aspiration systems, flues, housing of dust collecting equipment, indicating devices, hydraulic and pneumatic conveyors, controls and measuring equipment, as well as the equipment of gas cleaning, aspiration, and draft systems, and the environmental laboratory. The plants employ one or a combination of battery cyclones, electrostatic precipitators, battery cyclones with centrifugal scrubbers, and Venturi scrubbers. Capital costs in rubles were not identical for enterprises using the same types or combinations of systems, ranging between 37 and 235 rubles per tonne of collected dust. The article implied that the highest cost was probably an anomaly, calculating an average range of capital costs between 37 and 163 rubles per tonne of collected dust.

Of the 17.1 million tonnes of harmful substances that need to be retained, probably 10 million tonnes relate to sulphurous substances. The remaining 7 million tonnes include dust and solid particles, but also other substances which will be partly constrained by dust traps. Having no other figure with which to work, it is assumed that the target is 7 million tonnes, inclusive of any increase in emissions.

To provide installations to retain the remaining 7 million tonnes of harmful substances annually, the construction costs would be 2.6 billion rubles at 37 rubles per tonne collected, and 4 billion at 58 rubles per tonne collected: it does not seem likely that the maximum estimate of 163 rubles per tonne collected will be expended on average. By the year 2005, it can be expected that 1.1 billion rubles will be provided at current budget levels. This would mean a shortfall of 1.6 billion at the low rate of expenditure, and 3 billion at the middle level of expenditure.

Sulphurous gases.　An important issue is the degree of desulphurisation to be achieved. This will be accomplished partly by converting furnace technologies, partly by switching fuels, partly by sulphur reclamation technologies, and partly by desulphurisation technologies at the smoke stack. No estimates are possible without cost data. Unquestionably there will be a gaping shortfall in investment financing.

Notes

1   B Kotlyakov, Mozhno li spasti more? *Pravda*, 14 April 1988, p. 3.

2   I N Grigor'ev, I I Drogomiretski, Ekologicheskiya faktor v otsenke ekonomicheskoi effektivnosti meropriyatii nauchno-tekhnicheskogo progressa v gorno-khimicheskoi promyshlennosti, *Vestnik Leningradskogo Universiteta*, series 5, no. 19, 1987, pp. 110–13; Kol'skii poluostrov: problemy ekologii, *Sever'*, no. 1, 1988, pp. 84–99. Sanitary zones are 'areas exclusive of housing because of the risks to public health and safety'.

3   V E Ziberov, Sostoyanie i perspektivy okhrany okruzhayushchei sredy v usloviyakh perestroiki khozyaistvennoi deyatel'nosti predpriyatii otrasli, *Tsvetnye metally*, no. 12, 1987, pp. 9–16; T Shabad, *Basic Industrial Resources of the USSR*, New York: Columbia University Press, 1969, chapter 3.

4   Ekonomicheskie problemy resursobrezheniya, *Voprosy ekonomiki*, no. 4, 1986, pp. 87–115 (translated in *Problems of Economics*).

5   K Nosov, Strukturnye izmeneniya v chernoi metallurgii regiona, *Planovoe khozyaistvo*, no. 8, 1988, pp. 44–50.

6   For purposes of environmental regulation, it is likely that in the near future there will be designations of environmental protection regions.

7   T G Pyl'nev, *Tsentral' noe chernozem' e*, Izd: Voronezhskogo Universiteta, 1986, pp. 38–42.

8   L L Zusman, in *Voprosy ekonomiki*, no. 4, 1986, op cit.

9   S V Kolpakov, Zadachi otrasli po vypolneniui plana 1988 goda v usloviyakh polnogo khozrascheta i samofinansirovaniya predpriyatii, *Stal'*, no. 2, 1988, pp. 1–5.

10   N I Mityaev, et al, Amortization Deductions for Complete Renovation and Their Use in Metallurgy, *Soviet Metallurgist*, (translated from *Metallurg'*), no. 7, 1984, pp. 41–3.

11   See also, *SSSR v tsifrakh v 1987*, p. 70.

12   K Nosov, *Planovoe khozyaistvo*, no. 8, 1988, op cit.

13   *Narodnoe khozyaistvo SSSR za 70 let*, p. 156.

14   M Styrikovich and A Vnukov, Razmyshleniya o chistom vozdukhe, *Ekonomicheskaya gazeta*, no. 50, 1988, p. 16; Yu Shatalov, Plomba na ... bezotvetstvennosti, *Ekonomicheskaya gazeta*, no. 16, 1988, p. 20.

15   B G Kiselev, et al, Fondootdacha v tsvetnoi metallurgii, *Tsvetnye metally*, no. 12, 1988, pp. 88–92; I K Komarov, *Novaya investitsionnaya politika i stroitel' stvo*, Moscow: Mysl', 1988, p. 26.

16   *Narodnoe khozyaistvo SSSR za 70 let*, p. 157.

17   News Notes, *Soviet Geography*, no. 3, 1987, p. 363. S Kheinman, Resursosbrezhenie – v osnovy khozyaistvovaniya, *Planovoe khozyaistvo*, no. 10, 1988, pp. 19–29.

18   Razvitie promyshlennosti SSSR, *Vestnik statistiki*, no. 5, 1987, p. 63, presumably to increase beyond that by the year 2000; L B Vid, 1989– i: orientiry rosta, *Ekonomicheskaya gazeta*, no. 37, 1988, pp. 4–5.

19   *Voprosy ekonomiki*, no. 4, 1986, op cit.

20   I K Komarov, *Novaya investitsionnaya politika i stroitel' stvo*, op cit, pp. 27–8.

21   N I Mityaev, et al, *Soviet Metallurgist*, translation from *Metallurg'*, no. 7, 1984, op cit.

22   N G Boitsov, Okhrana vodnykh ob'ektov ot zagryazheniya v zone deistviya predpriyatii tsvetnoi metallurgii, *Tsvetnye metally*, no. 12, 1987, pp. 15–18; V Prokuratura Soyuza SSR, *Izvestiya*, 26 November 1987, p. 6.

23   V Kamaev, Intensifikatsiya i kachestvo ekonomicheskogo rosta, *Voprosy ekonomiki*, no. 3, 1985, pp. 14–25 (translated in *Problems of Economics*); I K Komarov, op cit, pp. 76–94; discussed at length the reconstruction and retooling aspects of the capital

investment programme in the context of the national economy. He also appeared to distinguish between capital investment to expand an existing enterprise and that for reconstruction of an existing enterprise (where increased production by means of modernisation of the plant also occurs). Komarov also mentioned that the retooling portion of the reconstruction-retooling capital budget is about 8 per cent of the total, and it is this notation that prompts the question whether 'reconstruction' should be understood as another term for 'expansion'.

24   G Mishin, Zamorozhennyi rubl', *Ekonomicheskaya gazeta*, no. 17, 1989, p. 6.

25   B G Kiselev et al, *Tzvetnye metally*, no. 12, 1988, op cit.

26   S E Gershgorin, et al, Analiz ispol'zovaniya amortizatsionnykh otchislenii na kapital'nye remonty trubnykh tsekhov, *Stal'*, no. 12, 1988, pp. 81–2.

27   Comment by V I Lapin, in M P Rybin, Uluchshenie ekologicheskoi obstanovki – vazhneishaya narodokhozyaistvennaya zadacha, *Tsvetnye metally*, no. 4, 1989, pp. 15–19; V Kamaev, *Voprosy ekonomiki*, no. 3, 1985, pp. 14–25, op cit.

28   K Nosov, *Planovoe khozyaistvo*, no. 8, 1988, op cit.

29   P F Lomako, An Appropriate Welcome to the 27th Congress of the CPSU, *Tsvetnye metally – Nonferrous Metals*, no. 3, 1985, pp. 1–11 (translation from *Tsvetnye metally*, no. 3, 1985).

30   *Narodnoe khozyaistvo SSSR v 1985 g*, p. 123.

31   Perestroika nabiraet silu, *Izvestiya*, 19 January 1987, pp. 1–3.

32   Na putyakh radikal'noe reformy, *Pravda*, 24 January 1988, pp. 1–3.

33   *Ekonomicheskaya gazeta*, no. 5, 1988, p. 12.

34   K Ts Petrosyan, *Uskorenie i perestroika: Voprosy i otvety*, Moscow: *Sovetskaya Rossiya*, 1988, p. 201; and Osnovnye napravleniya nauchno-tekhnicheskogo progressa v chernoi metallurgii i zadachi nauki, *Vestnik Akademiya Nauk SSSR*, no. 10, 1986, pp. 17–29.

35   G Mishin, *Ekonomicheskaya gazeta*, no. 17, 1989, op cit.

36   K Nosov, *Planovoe khozyaistvo*, no. 8, 1988, op cit; A Arbatov, S Bogolyubov, L Sobolev, *Ecology*, Moscow: Novosti, 1989, p. 56.

37   *Narodnoe khozyaistvo SSSR v 1987 g*, p. 46.

38   Ekonomika material'nykh resursov, *Vestnik statistiki*, no. 6, 1988, pp. 72–3. It is stated that 20 tonnes of standard fuel per 1000 tonnes of steel (that is, a 2 per cent savings in total fuel consumption) are saved by plants that employ the technology.

39   *Vestnik statistiki*, no. 5, 1987, op cit.

40   *Izvestiya*, 19 January 1987, op cit.

41   *Pravda*, 24 January 1988, op cit.

42   I K Komarov, op cit, p. 28.

43   P F Lomako, The Main Direction, *Tsvetnye metally/Non-ferrous metals*, no. 10, 1985, pp. 1–15.

44   *Narodnoe khozyaistvo SSSR v 1988 g*, pp. 246–7. Gosplan's handbook on elaboration of the planning balances in the national economy indicates that fuel, energy, and raw materials represent 88.1 per cent of prime costs for metallurgical products, which is higher than the 83 per cent of prime costs for industry as a whole.

45   V A Berezin and T V Zhadanov, Economic Aspects of the Rational Management of Secondary Raw Materials Resources in the Region, abstracted in *Environmental Management Abstracts*, no. 4, 1988, p. 21.

46   *Vestnik statistiki* regularly provides data of savings on energy, fuel, sulphur and metals.

47   M Styrikovich and A Vnukov, *Ekonomicheskaya gazeta*, no. 50, 1988, op cit; V V Kryuchkov, Scientific and Technical Progress and Changes in the Natural Environment of the Kola North, cited in *Environmental Management Abstracts*, no. 4, 1988, p. 59; V Gubarev, Ekologiya bez kosmetiki, *Pravda*, 7 September 1988, p. 4.

48 I V Kalenskii and B E Tarasov, O korennoi perestroike dela okhrany prirody v otrasli, *Stal'*, no. 7, 1988, pp. 1–4.

49 Ibid.

50 Ibid.

51 F Morgun, Ekologiya v sisteme planirovaniya, *Planovoe khozyaistvo*, no. 12, 1988, pp. 53–63.

52 V E Ziberov, *Tsvetnye metally*, no. 12, 1987, op cit; V E Ziberov, Scientific Technical Progress – The Basis for Solving Questions Related to Nature Protection at Nonferrous Metallurgical Plants in the 12th FYP, *Tsvetnye metally/Non-ferrous metals*, no. 12, 1985, pp. 1–5.

53 Ibid.

54 5 times 230 million = 1.15 billion rubles.

55 Ob effektivnosti ispol'zovaniya pylegazoochistnogo oborudovaniya na promyshlennykh predpriyatiyakh, *Vestnik statistiki*, no. 6, 1988, pp. 77–8; and V E Ziberov, *Tsvetnye metally*, no. 12, 1987, pp. 9–16, *supra*.

56 V E Ziberov, *Tsvetnye metally*, no. 12, 1987, ibid.

57 A D Vybarets, Ispol'zovanie otkhodov proizvodstva predpriyatii chernoi metallurgii urala, *Izvestiya VUZ, Chernaya metallurgiya*, no. 4, 1988, pp. 131–. V E Ziberov, *Tsvetnye metally*, no. 12, 1987, op cit. The article indicated that the state plan for recultivation of land in 1986 was fulfilled by 122.6 per cent. 6,049.6 hectares were reclaimed against the planned 4,934 hectares. M Lemeshev, Ekologo-ekonomicheskaya otsenka nauchno-tekhnicheskogo progressa, *Voprosy ekonomiki*, no. 3, 1987, pp. 31–9, indicated that 'at present, the reuse of top soil represents additional outlays for extractive industries. Industry bothers with recultivation only under administrative pressure.'

58 T S Khachaturov, *Ekonomika prirodopol'zovaniya*, Moscow: Nauka, 1987, p. 132. There are a number of stages involved in metals manufacturing. Two such stages – ore separation and machine building and metalworking (MBMW) – are primarily associated with economic activities that will be assessed in subsequent studies (for example, mining and MBMW), and for the most part are excluded from consideration here. Large volumes of dirt and rock are associated with the separation and beneficiation of ore that takes place at the mine site, such waste management being the responsibility of the mining industry. To a lesser extent, metal-bearing dust and particulate matter, along with metal scrap, are also produced during these stages. The difficulty is in classifying similar wastes as originating with either the metallurgical or mining industry, since they are often formed on sites having both mines and metallurgical production units, and ore beneficiation can be a function of either industrial sector.

59 A Kolosov, Okhrana okruzhayushchei sredy v usloviyakh intensifikatsii ekonomiki, *Voprosy ekonomiki*, no. 12, 1985, pp. 90–8 (translated in *Problems of Economics*).

60 *Pravda*, 24 January 1988, op cit.

61 V G Hadeenko, E A Borzunov, Gigienicheskaya otsenka khvostokhranilishch, shlamootstoinikov i nakopitelei stochnykh'vod, *Gigiena i sanitariya*, no. 1, 1989, pp. 10–12, indicated that the regulations governing these facilities are not fully developed at present; V M Perelygin, Pervoocherednye zadachi v oblasti gigieny pochvy v dvenadtsatoi pyatiletke, *Gigiena i sanitariya*, no. 1, 1988, pp. 4–5.

62 V I Chalov and O P Kravchino, Rational Management of Secondary Raw Materials Resources is an Important Reserve for Improving the Efficiency of Production and Environmental Protection, abstracted in *Environmental Management Abstracts*, no. 41, 1988, p. 21.

63 A D Vybarets, *Izvestiya VUZ, Chernaya Metallurgiya*, no. 4, 1988, op cit. The average of blast furnace slag that is used by the USSR Ministry of Ferrous Metallurgy is 84 per cent, but in the Urals, it is 67 per cent. See also A Kolosov, *Voprosy ekonomiki*, no. 12, 1985, pp. 90–98; and Arbatov, et al, *Ecology*, op cit, p. 55. Arbatov also

mentioned that a waste-free technology of reprocessing nephaline raw materials is being used at the Volkhov Aluminium Works near Leningrad. A N Lyusov, Resource Savings as one of the Lines of Scientific Technical Progress, *Environmental Management Abstracts*, no. 1, 1988, p. 56, indicates that the building materials industry is a primary consumer of metallurgical wastes, the following amounts of solid wastes supposedly recycled by that industry: 160 million tonnes of mining waste; 20 million tonnes of blast furnace slag; 3.5 million tonnes of nephaline slime; 3.1 million tonnes of pyrite cinder; and 3 million tons of ash and cinder. The source indicated that 27 per cent of steel-making and ferro-alloy slags, and 4 per cent of ferrous metallurgy slags are also used. Here, problems with terminology obscure the situation.

64   *Uskorenie i perestroika: voprosy i otvety*, op cit, p. 216; Khachaturov, 1987, op cit, p. 133.

65   *Vestnik statistiki*, no. 6, 1988, p. 72: 30 per cent of rolling mill metal products go to waste. A V Antskaitis, N V Krasnov, Major Problems of Setting up Cooperative Systems for the Sale of Usable Wastes, abstracted in *Environmental Management Abstracts*, no. 2, 1988, p. 20, indicates that in the Soviet Union a quarterly catalogue of the wastes of ferrous metals and metal products is commonly published. However, this has been found to be insufficient for purposes of introducing the wastes into the national economy, while storage costs have been very high.

66   V A Grenbentsov, Reshaet li problemu limit na vodu? *Zhilishchnoe i kommunal' noe khozyaistvo*, no. 6, 1986, p. 11. This example is not from the metallurgical industry, but the general approach, appropriately modified, would apply:

- According to normative uses for canteens, washing floors, watering green spaces as indicated in SNiP 11.34.76 and SNiP 11.30.76.
- According to the approved design specifications developed for the intake of water at the cooling plant in operating hours.
- As a percentage of the overall consumption of water circulating in the system for the intake of water to replenish the recycling system.
- According to formula contained in 'The Recommendations for Optimising Galvanising Processes,' dated 1979, for the volume of water intake for electric machines and apparatus used in galvanising processes, by each bath.
- By direct measurement (without consumption standards) for the intake of water for flushing, replenishing cisterns, or preparing solutions.
- According to design standards for the water necessary for air conditioning, and adjustments according to 'real experience'.
- By individual estimations in cases of unmetered boilers for the amount of water to top up boilers and to flush the filters, taking into account the hardness of the water and quality of material with which the filter is charged.
- As a percentage of holding capacity, for the intake of water for replenishing heating systems.

67   G S Pantelyat, L V Kosovtsev, N I Streshin, Prognozirovanie razvitiya vodnogo khozyaistva chernoi metallurgii na osnove 'dereva tselei', *Vodnye resursy*, no. 3, 1987, pp. 167–9.

68   D D Myagkii, et al, Otsenka tekhniko-ekonomicheskikh pokazatelei i ekologicheskoi nadezhnosti sistem vodosnabzheniya metallurgicheskikh zavodov, *Stal'*, no. 12, 1982, pp. 29–31. This is the only estimate that was found of the volume of water that can be recycled as a percentage of total water requirements.

69   V Petrikeev, Okhrana okruzhayushchei sredy v chernoi metallurgii, *Stal'*, no. 12, 1982, pp. 23–5. According to Frank Sebastian, a member of our Advisory Panel, it was indicated to him by Soviet industry representatives in September 1989, that the efficiency of waste water treatment in metallurgical industries is measured against permissible quantities of specific contaminants contained in the effluent after it has been treated and diluted, and has been released and subsequently rediluted by river

flows. The measurement apparently takes place at a designated point downstream of the actual point of release. If so, Soviet environmental practice, if not actual regulations, envisages the continuation of pollution within a given distance of an enterprise.

70   V Petrikeev, *Stal'*, no. 12, 1982, ibid.

71   T S Khachaturov, 1987, op cit., p. 111.

72   V Petrikeev, *Stal'*, no. 12, 1982, op cit.

73   V E Ziberov, *Tsvetnye metally – Non-ferrous Metals*, no. 6, 1985, op cit.

74   N G Boitsov, *Tsvetnye metally*, no. 12, 1987, op cit.

75   V I Petrikeev, *Stal'*, no. 12, 1982, op cit.

76   N G Boitsov, *Tsvetnye metally*, no. 12, 1987, op cit.

77   V I Petrikeev, *Stal'*, no. 12, 1982, pp. 23–25, op cit.

78   The figures in the text are from V E Ziberov, *Tsvetnye metally/Non-ferrous Metals*, no. 12, 1985, op cit. However, in *Tsvetnye metally*, no. 12, 1987, pp. 9–16, op cit Ziberov indicated that during the period of the 11th plan, there were constructed and commissioned installations for cleansing sewage water at 900,000 cubic metres/day (328 million cubic metres/year), and systems of recirculating water supply with a capacity of 3.7 million cubic metres/day (1.35 billion cubic metres/year).

79   V E Ziberov, *Tsvetnye metally*, no. 12, 1987, ibid.

80   V I Petrikeev, *Stal'*, no. 12, 1983, op cit.

81   A I Tolochko, S G Pantelyat and V A Kholodnyi, Sozdanie zamknutykh sistem vodosnabzheniya osnovnykh proizvodstv metallurgicheskikh predpriyatii, *Stal'*, no. 12, 1982, pp. 26–7.

82   V Ya Poznyakov, Environmental Protection – An Important Goal of the Combine, *Tsvetnye metally/Non-ferrous metals*, no. 2, 1979, pp. 16–18.

83   Tekhnologiya pererabotki domennykh shlakov ispol'zovaniem khimicheski zagryaznennykh stokov, *Metallurg'*, no. 4, 1988, p. 34.

84   M K Baibekov, A Course for Waste-Free Technology, *Tsvetnye metally/Non-ferrous metals*, no. 2, 1986, pp. 4–6, translated from *Tsvetnye metally*, no. 2, 1986. *Tsvetnye metally* noted that for the Ust'-Kamenogorsk Titanium Magnesium Combine it had been decided not to invest in soil washing or domestic sewage cleansing equipment during the 12th plan period; it was decided that such expenditure was 'not financially justifiable at present' and would be included in 'a second round' of expansion and reconstruction investment at the combine.

85   Soviet sources do not indicate whether the rate at which water recirculation systems are built is dictated by the rate of reconstruction and retooling of the basic production technologies, although it is assumed that in setting targets, planners will have taken such a factor into account.

86   V V Borodai, Major Trends in Environmental Protection in Non-ferrous Metallurgy Enterprises, *Tsvetnye metally/Non-ferrous metals*, no. 2, 1984, pp. 1–4.

87   Ibid.

88   N F Plotitsin and T A Golybev, Atmospheric Precipitation as a Source of Pollution of Surface Waters, cited in *Environmental Management Abstracts*, no. 5, 1988, p. 29; and B A Rovich, et al, Experience of the Integrated Biochemical Assessment of the Environmental State in the Neighbourhood of an Integrated Iron and Steel Works, abstracted in *Environmental Management Abstracts*, no. 2, 1988, pp. 50–1.

89   V I Shapritskii, Methodika opredeleniya optimal'noi ocherednosti vnedreniya meropriyatii po zashchite atmosfery, *Stal'*, no. 12, 1982, pp. 28–9. See chapter 5 on the electric power industry, which offers a full description of the methodology.

90   S A Demin, *Zakon na strazhe prirody*, Moscow: Yuridicheskaya Literatura, 1987.

91   M A Styrikovich and A K Vnukov, O proekt 'Metodicheskikh ukazanii po obosnovaniyu predel'no dopustimykh kontsentratsii atmosfernogo vozdukha, *Gigiena i sanitariya*, no. 12, 1988, pp. 59–61.

92   M A Styrikovich and A K Vnukov, ibid, p. 59–61; Yu G Feldman, Po povodu stat'i M A Styrikovicha i A K Vnukova, 'O proekt ...' *Gigiena i sanitariya*, ibid p. 62; and M A Pinigin, Po povodu zakolyucheniya rabochei gruppy po proektam normativnykh dokumentov v oblasti sanitarnoi okhrany atmosfernogo vozdukha, *Gigiena i sanitariya*, no. 12, 1988, pp. 62–6.

93   *Sever'*, no. 1, 1988, op cit.

94   V A Yarin, Vystuplenie tovarishcha! *Pravda*, 1 July 1988, p. 6.

95   Ya I Vaisman, N V Zaitsev and A V Mikhailov, Gigienicheskie kriterii prioritetnosti vybora planiruemykh vozdukho- i vodookhrannykh meropriyatii, *Gigiena i sanitariya*, no. 12, 1988, pp. 7–10.

96   V E Ziberov, *Tsvetnye metally*, no. 12, 1987, op cit.

97   Ibid.

98   *Vestnik statistiki*, no. 6, 1988, pp. 77–8; I V Kalenskii and B E Tarasov, *Stal'*, no. 7, 1988, op cit.

99   I V Kalenskii, Okhrana priroda v chernoi metallurgii, *Stal'*, no. 11, 1988, pp. 108–11.

100   I V Kalenskii and B E Tarasov, *Stal'*, no. 7, 1988, op cit.

101   T A Krivchenko, et al, Ochistka otkhodyashchikh gazov ustanovki polucheniya samoplavkikh shlakov v sisteme mokroi razoochistki martenovskoi pechi, *Stal'*, no. 12, 1982, p. 33.

102   I E Proskurin, Resheniyu ekologicheskikh problem tsvetnoi metallurgii – prioritetnoi vnamanie, *Tsvetnye metally*, no. 5, 1989, pp. 4–9.

103   V E Ziberov, *Tsvetnye metally*, no. 12, 1987, op cit.

104   V E Ziberov, *Tsvetnye metally/Non-ferrous metals*, no. 12, 1985, op cit; V E Ziberov, *Tsvetnye metally/Non-ferrous metals*, no. 6, 1985, op cit.

105   Ibid.

106   L P Lomako, Realising The Resolutions of the 27th Congress of the CPSU, *Tsvetnye metally/Non-ferrous metals*, no. 4, 1986, pp. 1–13. During this period, gas cleansing installations with a capacity of 34.9 million cubic metres/hour were commissioned. In 1985, 84.2 per cent efficiency was achieved. V E Ziberov, *Tsvetnye metally/Non-ferrous metals*, no. 6, 1985, op cit.

107   V E Ziberov, *Tsvetnye metally*, no. 12, 1987, op cit.

108   K B L'vovskaya, O vliyanii sredozashchitnoi strategii na ekologo-ekonomicheskoi razvitie, *Ekonomika i matematicheskie metody*, no. 3, 1988, pp. 438–46. Again, the data are drawn from an article which discusses a theoretical model for distribution of environmental protection funds, where the author is attempting to represent gains to environmental protection from variations in actual practice.

109   O I Kharlamov, Basic Approaches to Nature Conservation by the Soyuztsvetmetgazoochistka Trust, *Tsvetnye metally/Non-ferrous metals*, no. 12, 1985, pp. 7–8. These have been introduced experimentally at Alaverdi Mining Metallurgical Combine by the Soyuztsvetmetgazoochistka Trust (The Union Trust for Non-ferrous Metallurgy Gas Cleaning, which apparently manufactures part of the pollution control equipment used by enterprises of the USSR Ministry of Non-ferrous Metallurgy). Twenty were built in 1984 for the Chimkent Lead Plant, the Ust'-Kamenogorsk Lead-Zinc Combine, Leninogorsk Polymetals, and the Balkhash MMC. During 1985, the Trust planned to produce and install another twelve electric filters and a further twelve in 1986.

110   T A Krivchenko, et al, *Stal'*, no. 12, 1982, op cit.

111   G A Dodik, et al, Modernisation of Gas Cleansing Equipment for the Cooling Zones of Sintering Machines, *Soviet Metallurgist* (translated from *Metallurg'*), no. 1, 1986, pp. 20–1. There, the low reliability of gas cleaning (dust extraction) systems was due in part to the poor performance and inappropriate design-configuration of Venturi tubes, drop separators, and clean gas flues, and the need for high quality circulating water that was not available at Kommunarsk. A radical reconstruction of the equip-

ment was undertaken to achieve improved performance. This suggests that if similar technologies are employed in other metallurgical industries, reconstruction of the gas cleansing systems will be needed.

112   S A Chuchalin, L V Nikolaevskaya, L I Oskolkov, O razrabotke norm predel'no dopustimykh vybrosov v atmosferu na predpriyatiyakh otrasli, *Khimicheskoe i neftyanoe mashinostroenie*, no. 8, 1987, pp. 9–16.

113   Experience of an Integrated Biogeochemical Assessment of the Environmental Conditions in the Neighbourhood of an Integrated Iron and Steel Works, *Environmental Management Abstracts*, no. 2, 1988, pp. 50–1.

114   V V Kryuchkov, V dele okhrany prirody tozhe nuzhna perestroika, *Sever'*, no. 1, 1988, pp. 85–9.

115   S P Sushon, The Present-Day State and Prospects of the Use of Secondary Power Resources in the National Economy, *Environmental Management Abstracts*, no. 4, 1988, p. 21. By 1986, secondary energy resources accounted for 32 and 8 per cent, respectively, of total heat consumption in ferrous and non-ferrous metallurgy. A Lavrishchev, *Economic Resources of the USSR*, Moscow: Progress Publishers, 1969, chapter 7: Ferrous metallurgy is often singled out as having a high potential for recovery of heat that would substitute for consumption of primary fuels and electric power. The potential for recovery of thermal energy is also obvious in non-ferrous metallurgical production. For example, while the zinc industry is considered energy intensive and production of 1 ton of zinc requires about 4 kWh of electricity of 3.5 tons of coal, this is a modest amount in comparison to copper, which needs 1,500 kWh of electric power per ton of produced metal. Aluminium production requires 20,000 kWh to smelt 1 ton of aluminium; for this reason, plants are located as close as possible to hydroelectric power. Production of magnesium requires even greater amounts of electric power. These figures will be outdated where new technologies, consuming smaller amounts of electric power or energy, have been installed. No such data have been found. However, the important point is the potential for recovery of heat and steam, and it is here that Soviet scientific institutes are concentrating their efforts.

116   V E Ziberov, *Tsvetnye metally/Non-ferrous metals*, no. 12, 1985, op cit, indicated that 83.4 per cent of all gaseous discharges are sulphurous gases and V E Ziberov, *Tsvetnye Metally/Non-ferrous metals*, no. 6, 1985, op cit, indicated that for non-ferrous metallurgy, 72 per cent of the emissions are sulphurous gases. The two articles, written by the same author in the same year, reflect the uncertainty of the estimates.

117   V Gubarev, Ekologiya bez kosmetiki, *Pravda*, 7 September 1987, p. 4.

118   V E Ziberov, *Tsvetnye metally/Non-ferrous metals*, no. 12, 1985, op cit.

119   Yu T Skornyakov, O merakh po povysheniyu urovenya utilizatsii sernistogo angidrida, ob uskorennom stroitel'stve prirodookhrannykh ob'ektov v dvenadtsatoi pyatiletke, *Tsvetnye metally*, no. 12, 1987, pp. 10–11.

120   Ibid.

121   V E Ziberov, *Tsvetnye metally/Non-ferrous metals*, no. 12, 1985, op cit. V E Ziberov, *Tsvetnye metally*, no. 12, 1987, op cit. *Sever'*, no. 1, 1988, op cit: The Severonikel' Combine, which emits large amounts of sulphur each year, reported that about 43–4 per cent of sulphur was being reclaimed in 1988, with the plan to reclaim 70 per cent by 1993; achievement of this goal is dependent on the development of new technologies to neutralise salt wastes and is therefore in some doubt. The source indicated that its level of trapping sulphur was greater than in non-ferrous metallurgy as a whole. The Severonikel Combine uses ores with a 25–6 per cent sulphur content, and existing technological capacity could produce up to 386,000 tonnes of sulphuric acid annually. The 12th FYP called for 240,000–250,000 tonnes annually. *Soviet Geography*, no. 6, 1984, p. 466: Soviet production of elemental sulphur in 1980 was 4.43 million metric tonnes, of which 2.6 were native sulphur, 0.27 recovered from petroleum, and 0.23 recovered from other sources. In the same year, Soviet production of sulphuric acid

was 23.03 million metric tonnes, of which 1.3 were from native sulphur, 7.4 from pyrites, and 3.4 from smelter gases. By 1985, industry sources reported an improvement in the production of elemental sulphur and sulphuric acid from recycling technologies, and stated that during the period 1981–84, non-ferrous metallurgical enterprises salvaged 5.4 million tonnes of sulphur from exhaust gases, and produced 13 million tonnes of sulphuric acid and 0.5 million tonnes of elemental sulphur. *Narodnoe khozyaistvo SSSR v 1988 g*, p. 398, reported production of 29.4 million tonnes of sulphuric acid and monohydrate during 1988.

7 Environmental Investment in the Soviet Chemical and Petrochemical Industries

Introduction

Chemical waste management in the Soviet Union, as elsewhere, means the identification, separation, reprocessing, storage, neutralisation, and/or disposal of substances formed during the production process from raw materials or commodities used in production. A chemical waste can take the form of a solid, liquid, gas, or a sludge, bearing substances which must be managed because of the dangers they pose for health, safety, and nature, because it is toxic, corrosive, or combustible; or because in combination with other substances in the environment, these or other such hazards obtain.[1] As it happens, most of the wastes are presented as liquids, with proportionately smaller amounts emitted as gases or solids.[2]

The Soviet chemical industry has a commanding portfolio of scientific achievements, and its products will underpin performance in many areas of the economy in the future. Despite its accomplishments, the industry does not operate within the confines of a formal, identifiable, chemical waste management system; nor have environmental protection priorities been articulated. Moreover, three features on which an environmental management strategy should rely are lacking: a mandatory, chemical waste classification system;[3] a closed-loop, monitored, chemical waste management cycle (or systematic provision of the elements thereof);[4] and sufficient laboratory and testing facilities to cope with critical junctures in the waste management cycle.[5]

Although most industries have not published statements concerning their environmental policies as such, there often exists a sufficient body of literature of a repetitive nature from which priorities can be discerned. This is not the case for the Soviet chemical industry, although in recent years a few articles on technological and scientific topics have included the currently popular buzz-words of 'low-waste and waste-free production', 'resource conservation', and 'nature protection'. In other contexts, such articles have been regarded as expressions of investment priorities or, at least, policy orientations. However, similar articles about the chemical industry usually lack aggregate or unit cost data, suggesting that such technologies have not been applied in operating conditions, which is where and when such calculations are commonly made.

Environmental investment in the sector is made on a 'residual basis', a Soviet term suggesting its low priority. The resulting situation was characterised in stark terms by a leader from the chemical industry's professional union, V K Borodin: "It is indisputable that infringements of production technologies, lack of necessary cleansing and trapping installations at the enterprises, complacency, and in a number of cases ignorance and irresponsibility have led to today's tense ecological situation.[6] And noteworthy, too, is the reliance on future technologies, as expressed by a senior CPSU official, V I Ovchinnikov, 'It is important to work out new processes and to modernise the enterprises in ways that secure nature protection ... which they presently cannot guarantee.'[7]

Until the turn of the next century and probably for some years after, the main concern of all branches within the chemical industry will be to expand and diversify production by means of new construction and to modernise existing plant. In the past, when the production ministries had to decide between intensive investment and extensive development, they opted for new construction. The environment eventually lost out because the older plants were not properly maintained and the new plants did not incorporate appropriate nature protection technologies. A repetition of this pattern can be seen now; an expansion programme is underway, and official Soviet sources report that pollution is worsening.

As in the past, pressure on enterprises to increase production encourages them to take shortcuts in respect of ecology. For such reasons, complaints are appearing in the Soviet press about the slow pace of investment, about wastage due to less-than-optimal technological solutions, about using nature protection funds for other purposes, about the longstanding emphasis on costly, large-scale, experimental units rather than on more mundane efforts of dust-trapping, desulphurisation, water recycling, and so forth. International pressures are considerable (although largely ineffective) in respect of ecological investment to control emissions of chlorine, fluorine, nitrogen oxides (as these affect the integrity of the ozone layer),[8] and sulphur (which is a major component of transboundary acid rain originating in the Soviet Union).

The capital budget for nature protection over the 12th plan period has kept pace with inflation; but, at its present level, resources appear to be insufficient in every respect. A constructive response will occur if, during reconstruction or retooling, resourse-conserving and other environmental features are incorporated within the production technologies. While this would undoubtedly be a positive step, nature protection cannot be secured without simultaneous investment in pollution control technologies.[9] The emphasis of central government's environmental policies is to reduce the volume of wastes and in some cases their toxicity, thereby cutting down the capacity *required* for waste management. But, it emerged during the furious debates over proposals for a new superphosphate plant in Odessa that the oft-mentioned waste-reducing technologies may not be available.[10] Thus, given the dangers inherent in chemical production, coupled with strong pressure from the central leadership on the industry to increase output, environmental authorities should anticipate an expanding quantity and range of unmanaged chemical wastes.

Economic and Social Context

The Soviet Union is one of the world's largest producers of chemicals and chemical products with rapid growth since World War II, especially during the 1960s. An assessment of investment priorities for the chemical industry in the Soviet Union addresses several ministries whose functions are to satisfy the national economic needs for basic chemicals, agricultural chemicals, petrochemicals and textiles, pharmaceuticals, biological products, and similar commodities. Soviet statistics and much of the economic literature concern the industry as a whole; accordingly, reference is made to the branch ministries only where their industrial journals shed light on specific investment priorities.[11]

The Soviet chemical industry is confronted with a mandate to double overall production by the year 2000,[12] of which about one-third was to be achieved during the 12th plan period. The burden has been placed on three chemical production ministries – agricultural fertilisers, basic chemicals, and petrochemicals.[13] The pharmaceutical ministry (microbiology having recently been deleted from the name but not the remit of this ministry) will also expand, although for the interim the commodity shortfall will be offset by imported medicines and related products.[14] The industry operates under the 1985 version of the 'General Guidelines for the Chemicalisation of the National Economy', which has offered shifting investment targets in its several iterations. In this respect, there are few published accounts showing how the decision to achieve these goals mainly by new construction can be economically substantiated. The prevailing attitude seems to be that such analyses are a waste of time since output is more or less immediately absorbed in the domestic economy, and the 'value of chemical products in the national economy at less than 7 per cent' needs to be brought closer to the Western standard of 10–15 per cent.[15]

As elsewhere in the Soviet economy, the 1,071 chemical plants, subsidiary enterprises, and scientific research institutes[16] are adopting cost accounting (*khozraschet*) principles. As a result, there is considerable discussion about the need to rationalise the geographic contribution of industry.[17] Past practice has been to concentrate a large number of chemical plants within relatively constrained geographic areas, selected according to their proximity to raw materials and energy supplies or to the consumer (where the nature of the product represents too great a risk for long-distance transport). No fundamental change in policies governing siting can be discerned;[18] for example, near-term construction of the very large petrochemical and chemical complexes will almost certainly take place in Siberia,[19] and that of the agricultural chemical industry in Central Asia and Kazakhstan.[20] The chemical industries prefer the economies of scale afforded by large-tonnage plants, but do not always employ up-to-date technologies. Taken together, these three factors intensify the ecological risk associated with chemical production.

There is considerable concern about the ability of the existing reconstruction and repair industries to service the reinvestment programme; here, too, a considerable programme of new construction and retooling is envisaged, at least part of which will be funded from the capital budget of the chemical industries. Given the lagging pace of investment in nature protection, it is probable that the Ministry of Chemical and Petroleum Machine Building, in particular, as well as other specialised equipment manufacturers and/or repair trusts, do not have sufficient capacity to produce the pollution control equipment that is fundamental to the success of any environmental programme.[21]

Since the beginning of the 1980s, as environmental investment has increased in the national economy, the impact of chemical products on human health and nature has been the subject of regulatory scrutiny as part of the environmental protection package requiring investment decisions. It is useful to note here that distinction has been made between environmental disruption that is caused by the production of chemicals and chemical products, and that which is the result of their packaging, transport, storage, and use. This separation is somewhat artificial because it is the combined effects of industrial discharges *plus* drainage of agricultural chemicals *and* untreated domestic sewage that have produced an extraordinary incidence of infectious diseases, and infant mortality rates as high as 92–118 per 1000 live births in some areas of Central Asia.[22]

Even though there are scientific authorities external to the chemical ministries with responsibility to test and approve chemical production technologies and products, it appears that the Soviet Union chemical industry is by and large attempting to 'regulate' itself by means of an intra-industry nature protection policy committee and 'in-house' inspectors. Such arrangements have not been successful in other countries. To strike a balance between industrial activities and other national economic interests, F T

Morgun, the past chairman of the USSR State Committee on Nature Protection, announced in 1989 that a series of regional environmental centres and research laboratories will be established.[23] It appears that the new laboratories will be in addition to existing laboratories specialising in water and air quality research. Meanwhile, the inspectors do not have sufficient political clout to exercise their legal authority to constrain enterprise behaviour, and are hard-pressed even to obtain scientific evidence as a basis for prosecution. This can make the present situation outright dangerous. It appears that some banned substances continue to be used in sufficient quantities that it can be assumed they continue to be produced. Most common, however, are reports of pollution caused by inadequately controlled disposal of waste chemicals. One, perhaps controversial, example is that of DDT, which was prohibited in 1970, due to the rate at which it is absorbed into the food chain, and due to the harm that scientists suspect it may cause to wildlife.[24] Public reference to an instance of its use in Azerbaidzhan appeared in 1988, while seemingly it is regularly applied in Siberia to suppress ticks.

The chemical industries are faced with mounting criticism from citizens, local councils, health inspectorates, and the USSR State Committee for Nature Protection.[25] These sources of opposition have considerable nominal influence over local development schemes, but it remains to be seen if, by acting in concert, they will be able to wield decisive influence over ministries that are politically and financially stronger. So far, only a few instances have been reported in which such agencies proved to be an effective obstacle to new construction,[26] although Borodin and others regard such opposition as a factor in the slow rate of new construction starts.[27]

The industry can claim that substantial progress has been made to prevent pollution, by virtue of the fact that many chemical plants have installed isolated and repeat-use water supply systems. Water supplies provided by such means are estimated at 74 per cent overall, and as much as 89 per cent in the petrochemical industry.[28] They also demand credit where thermal, chemical, biochemical, and other advanced waste disposal techniques are used. But the latter are not comprehensive on the one hand, and not necessarily effective on the other. Two further issues, that of technical and occupational safety, have become sore points; in this respect, the concerns are partly due to the unnecessary exposure of workers to toxic chemicals in the workplace, and partly because recurring accidents and explosions intensify the risk posed by chemical plants (for example, in Gur'evsk where lives were lost in 1988). In this respect, many problems associated with plant and worker safety may be eliminated during reconstruction and retooling, while 'others require further scientific substantiation of the specific hazards' and remedial technologies.[29]

There are no industry-wide data concerning the volumes of fresh water intake or effluent, although it is established that not all effluent is environmentally regulated. This is important environmentally and economically, because all industrial effluent should be tested and certified in compliance with environmental standards prior to release. In Soviet practice, liquid wastes associated with cooling water are not environmentally controlled, unless such effluent has been further contaminated by combination with other wastes (for example, in diluting chemical wastes prior to treatment in biological or thermal installations). Thus, even with an overall average of 74 per cent of the water supply guaranteed by some form of recycling, a portion of the remaining effluent is deliberately untreated and recycling, by other means than an isolated system, only offers short-term environmental relief as the waste water is eventually released. The economic advantage of such regulations is demonstrated clearly by the case of the chemical and petroleum machine building enterprises, where 60 per cent of the water supply is used for cooling purposes, and because it is 'practically not polluted', such effluent is exempted from environmental control. In these plants, 74 per cent water recycling would embrace only about 30 per cent of the general water supply. Since 10–15 per cent is consumed during the manufacturing process, treatment capacity is targeted to the remaining 10–15 per cent.[30] In effect, this suggests that low level treatment or recycling installations are needed, albeit not required, for a large volume of waste water.

By the year 2005, the chemical industries, at present levels of production and with current environmental standards, could achieve the maximum economic advantage possible by means of water recycling. The prognosis will change rapidly under two conditions. First, it will increase as production is expanded at existing and new plants; in such circumstances additional investment will be required for water recycling, together with waste water treatment installations and infrastructures. Secondly, it will change when additional classes of effluent are environmentally regulated.

Officially, chemical plants produce about 8 per cent of harmful industrial emissions into the atmosphere, of which oxides of sulphur, carbon and nitrogen comprise some 3–8 per cent.[31] National statistics do not characterise 92 per cent of the chemical industry's emissions. The direction of new environmental investment is confused; but judging by the amount of attention in technical and popular journals to damage associated with emissions, additional expenditure for air pollution controls can be anticipated. If this occurs and if current national air pollution control priorities obtain, the outlays will be on technologies to reduce emissions of dust and sulphur-bearing gases. Current pollution control technologies cannot retain or neutralise many of the 600 substances are presently addressed by air quality regulations.[32]

Finally, the levels of environmental regulation are set in the context of all other pollution in a given geographic area.[33] One review took place in Moscow, where it was found that local chemical plants pollute most heavily within a radius of 3–5 kilometres; while another assessment in Tashkent reported that contaminants originating there have been documented many kilometres downstream.[34] The local impact of chemical production is fully illustrated by environmental difficulties reported in Ufa, where plants currently operate without equipment to neutralise sulphur, benzene, chlorine, mercury, or hydrocarbons, and the industry intends to expand its presence there.[35] Shortages of appropriately trained environmental monitoring personnel will impede the general implementation of this aspect of environmental regulations. The burden might initially be shifted to industry, with the participation of scientists from outside the industry in decisionmaking. Some authorities, such as those in the Western Caucasus Economic Region, indicate they will rely also on the assistance of university faculties to obtain and assess data and to devise regulatory schemes.[36] The matter of the availability of specialised environmental management cadres will become increasingly important inside and outside the chemical industry as nature protection laws are implemented and compliance is monitored.

Investment Background

In the past, investment statistics for the chemical and petrochemical sector were presented in combination with those for the forestry industry; nowadays, official data increasingly identify trends specific to the chemical industry. These data are important in that they express investment priorities and trends; to some extent, they also indicate whether industry can sustain heavy ecological investment.

The chemical-forestry sectors have together commanded a decreasing share of the funds allocated through the state capital budget, both in value terms and as a percentage of total investment allocations since the mid-1970s. These trends must be reversed to meet national economic goals, although data up to 1988 show a declining level of investment allocations in real terms through the state capital budget.

7.1 Capital Budget in Areas of the National Economy
(in comparable prices, billions of rubles)

	1976–80	1981–85	1986–90*	1986–88
All Industry	251.4	300.7	375.8	225.5
of which:				
Chemical-Forestry				
Complex	37.2	34.9	36.1	21.7
Chemical-Petrochemical				
Industry	24.8	22.6	22.0	13.2

* projected on the basis of three years.
Source: Narodnoe khozyaistvo SSSR v 1988 g, p. 356.

The rumours, and they are hardly more than that at present, about the resources to be commanded by the chemical and petrochemical industries in the future are truly wild. One article published during 1989 in *Izvestiya* suggested that, simply to meet production targets, the chemical industry stands to receive an injection of 88 billion rubles by the year 2000, supposedly exclusive of costs related to the new Tyumen *oblast* complex.[37] The most credible interpretation is that this 88 billion rubles represents a potential increase of 25 per cent over the level of the capital budget in the 12th plan period. That is a relatively modest vision. But there are additional plans for 200 high volume production complexes (involving an unspecified number of factories) related to agricultural chemicals production;[38] while 39 new enterprises are desired by the pharmaceutical industry.[39] Of course, extensive development is proposed for Tyumen, which has been valued at 20 billion rubles (one-quarter for housing, social and infrastructure construction),[40] 41 billion (half for construction-installation work),[41] and 90–100 billion rubles.[42] The difference is that the Tyumen petrochemical works (to use natural gas that is presently burned off) will be substantially funded with foreign capital that is not reflected in the 'state capital budget and enterprise means', while the other projects will be funded within it or at least with less foreign participation. A controversial project of even larger scale than Tyumen, involving somewhere between 30 and 120 billion rubles, has been proposed in respect of Yamal natural gas. A question touted by the opposing economists illustrates the uncertainty surrounding the magnitude of future investment in the chemical and petrochemical industries: 'What should be forfeited to pay for the project – education, chemicals, agriculture, or health care?'[43]

Soviet statistics do not indicate the proportional distribution of capital investment funds amongst the several ministries that make up the chemical sector. A passing comment in one journal indicated that about 60 per cent of capital expenditure associated with the sector as a whole are in four types of production: agricultural chemicals, plastics, chemical fibres, and rubber products. These commodities are manufactured by enterprises of the USSR Ministries of Chemicals, Petrochemicals and Agricultural Chemicals. This breakdown corresponds to an assessment by the Director of the State Committee on Hydrometeorology, who indicated that top national sources of air pollution are enterprises that manufacture chemicals, petrochemicals, and fertilisers.[44]

Environmental Investments

The chemical industries are being strongly pressured to make very large investments for purposes of nature protection and resource conservation for a mounting volume of wastes. The state capital budget for this purpose is noted in the following table for the chemical-forestry complex.

7.2 State Capital Budget for the Chemical-Forestry Complex for Nature Protection and Rational Use of Nature
(billions of rubles)

	1981–85	1986–90*	1986	1987	1988
Chemical-Forestry Complex	1895	2281	381	438	550
of which:					
Waste Water Treatment	1440	1635	296	316	369
Air Pollution Controls	215	395	47	66	124
Land Protection	15	42	7	8	10

* projected on the basis of 1986–88.
Source: Okhrana okruzhayushchei sredy i rational' noe ispolzovanie prirodnykh resursov v SSSR, pp. 149–50.

Elsewhere, some light is shed concerning environmental expenditure for three of the main chemical ministries. The USSR Ministry of the Chemical Industry was allocated 400–500 million rubles in the capital budget covering the 12th plan period.[45] The USSR Ministry of Agricultural Fertilisers got 400 million rubles in the 11th plan period, and received a further budget of 640 million in the 12th plan period.[46] Together, these two ministries absorbed some 70 per cent of all capital funds for nature protection in the chemical-forestry complex during the 12th plan period. Also, the USSR Ministry of the Petrochemical Industry expended around 50 million rubles on capital construction for nature protection during the 11th plan period.[47] The size of the latter investment appears disproportionately small in comparison to the foregoing; this amount may have been devoted to air pollution controls alone, with some additional financing for other nature protection construction.

Without doubt, burden of nature protection expenditure surely falls unequally on new construction, even in the context of the need to maintain or upgrade existing water recycling installations. But in this respect, the two issues of funding and of material resources strike a sour chord. For example, critics of the pollution generated by a plant producing agricultural chemicals using Karatau apatite (from southern Kazakhstan) noted that both the production units and the pollution controls required Soviet designs that had not previously undergone trials under operating conditions.[48] The latter have not only been unsuccessful in preventing harmful emissions, but in some instances were not built. The petrochemical industry, by contrast, can rely heavily on foreign technologies and in respect of the contract with Mitsubishi to design a petrochemical plant at Tyumen, there are explicit requirements for the incorporation of nature protection and resource conserving features. [49] Whether the latter approach ultimately heads off the opposition to petrochemical construction remains to be seen, although some Soviet officials appear to hope that the Mitsubishi project will provide a technological prototype for other similar complexes.

Still, some foreign involvement in other branches of the industry is likely since 8 billion rubles to build 200 agricultural fertiliser complexes is obviously insufficient (at 40 million rubles, on average expenditure per *complex*) to incorporate any sophisticated technologies for production or nature protection. Similarly, 4 billion rubles for construction of 39 new pharmaceutical enterprises, plus reconstruction-retooling of 48 others, implies (at 50:50 distribution of resources) an average outlay per plant of 50 million rubles for green-fields construction. That is, the funding appears to be extremely modest if the cost of agricultural chemical and pharmaceutical plants bears any relation to those in the petrochemical industry. For instance, at Tyumen, even with heavy foreign participation, state capital budget outlays will range between 1.3 and 6.6 billion rubles for each of the 15 plants, depending on whose estimate one prefers.

Commissioning of Capital Assets

In respect of the growth of capital assets, the performance by the chemical-petrochemical industry has improved since 1980, but again in comparison to 1980 the rate of growth has been lower than in industry as a whole. A similar pattern is seen in comparison to 1985, where growth of capital assets was achieved at a slower pace than elsewhere in industry.

7.3   Rate of Growth of Capital Assets

	1980 = 100				1985 = 100		
	1985	1986	1987	1988	1986	1987	1988
All Industry	138	146	152	159	106	111	115
of which:							
Chemical-Forestry							
Complex	136	141	146	150	104	108	110
including							
Chemicals &							
Petrochemicals	138	145	149	153	105	108	111

Source: Narodnoe khozyaistvo SSSR v 1988 g, p. 350.

For purposes of capital budget formation, the chemical-forestry complex uses valuations of construction projects that turn out to be very much lower than actual costs. To some extent, this is usual in long-term planning practice, but one result of undue disproportion between budget allocations and actual costs is the very large backlog of unfinished construction – even though expenditure keeps pace with or at times exceeds budgetary allocations. It may turn out that a precondition for the introduction of *khozraschet* in the chemical industry will be to establish a mechanism to estimate construction costs in a more realistic way.[50] Cost over-runs in construction are common throughout the world; most Western banks have found that an effective key to cost-containment is to intensify their scrutiny during the construction process.

The data indicate that the value of installations commissioned within the 10th plan period was roughly 90 per cent of the value of allocated resources; by contrast, 107 per cent of planned values were commissioned in the 11th plan period. In the three years of the 12th plan period for which there are comparable statistics, the value of installations commissioned show a positive gain, although in percentage of the commissionings in the national economy, the overall negative trend in the sector's share of capital investment funds was reaffirmed.

7.4 Commissioning of Capital Assets
(in comparable prices, billion rubles)

	1976–80	1980	1981–85	1986–90*	1986	1987	1988
National Economy	667.5	148.9	815.8	950.5	182.7	195.1	192.5
of which:							
Chemicals-Forestry	33.7	8.5	36.6	34.0	6.8	6.7	6.9
As % of National Economy	5.1	5.7	4.5	3.6	3.6	3.5	3.6

* projected on the basis of three years.
Source: *Narodnoe khozyaistvo SSSR v 1988 g*, p. 546; *Narodne khozyaistvo SSSR za 70 let*, p. 103.

Apparently, the Soviet chemical industries do not exploit the 500,000 square metres of average usable production space in existing buildings.[51] Excessive over-building occurs for a number of reasons: due to an imbalance in associated production capacity for raw materials input or product output; because designers make an effort to accommodate future expansion at existing plant; because needed equipment and machinery are unavailable for installation; and not least due to political intervention. Alec Nove observed that any drive to reduce new construction starts will inevitably produce additional imbalance. Production based on new construction by different ministries is often linked, but to maintain balanced capacity requires centralised planning and execution; again this flies in the face of current policy that seeks a greater degree of decentralisation.

7.5   Commissioning of Capital Assets
(as per cent of total value of assets at the end of the period)

	1976–80	1981–85	1986	1987	1988
All Industry	37	33	6.9	6.6	6.1
Heavy Industry	38	34	7.1	6.7	6.1
Chemical-Forestry					
Complex	39	32	6.1	5.6	5.4
of which:					
Chemicals &	41	33	6.0	5.2	5.0
Petrochemicals					

Source: Narodnoe khozyaistvo SSSR v 1988 g, p. 357.

Because there is unused space, an important area of capital expenditure should be in equipment and machinery, and to some extent this is reflected in data concerning the commissioning of the active part of capital assets. Interestingly, despite the opportunities afforded by near-term use of existing space, the rate at which such commissionings took place was significantly lower than that which occurred in the economy at large, and again the data indicate a continuing slowdown of performance in the chemical industry as a whole.

7.6   Commissioning of the Active Part of the Basic Fund
(excluding Buildings and Installations)
(as per cent of total value of assets at the end of the period)

	1976–80	1981–85	1986	1987	1988
All Industry	41	37	7.8	7.2	6.6
Heavy Industry	42	38	7.9	7.3	6.6
Chemical-Forestry					
Complex	46	38	7.3	6.6	6.4
of which:					
Chemicals					
Petrochemicals	46	36	6.8	5.9	5.6

Source: Narodnoe khozyaistvo SSSR v 1988 g, p. 358.

A controversial issue underlying the entire investment programme concerns the degree to which productive capacity is used. Official statistics are sparse, but those available indicate that a significant part of capacity in three production areas remains unassimilated. Unused capacity may engender economic losses for both the national economy and the enterprise, so the reasons for not using space and capacity are important. On the one hand, the 'idle' plant and equipment may not exist; but assuming they do, the idle capacity may only be theoretical, because after running thirty or forty years, maximum (indeed any) output may be unsustainable. Other logical reasons are numerous: capacity can be idle because of routine repair and maintenance, lack of raw materials to process, problems with fuel and energy supplies, labour shortages, and so forth. The concern is that the chemical industry apparently has installations in place where, with a few dials turned and a few screws tightened, needed commodities could be produced without embarking on more environmentally disruptive construction. The difficulty is to know, from such few indicators, where the excess capacity might be found and whether it represents useful products in today's market.

7.7   Use of Productive Capacity
(in per cents)

	1975	1980	1985	1986	1987	1988
Sulphuric Acids in						
Monohydrate	91	83	81	83	85	85
Mineral Fertiliser	91	77	81	82	85	86
Chemical fibres &						
Threads	93	93	90	90	92	95

Source: Narodnoe khozyaistvo SSSR v 1988, p. 365.

Completion of Construction

The rate at which construction was completed and certified in the national economy was in the order of 13 per cent of the value of that planned in 1980. There appears to be steady improvement, so that by 1987, 23 per cent was actually completed and certified, although it fell again in 1988. This trend was also reflected in the experience of the chemical and petrochemical industries, where uncertified construction was 171 per cent of the volume of the capital budget in 1980, whereas it was 133 per cent in 1986. Despite such relative improvements, the overall picture is very poor indeed; in 1988, the volume of uncertified capital construction climbed to 151 per cent of the volume of the capital budget.

7.8   Uncertified Construction in State and Cooperative
Enterprises and Organisations
(at year end, in per cent of volume of capital budget)

	1980	1985	1986	1987	1988
Total in National Economy	87	78	79	78	83
including:					
Chemical & Petrochemical Industries	171	133	133	145	151

Source: Narodnoe khozyaistvo SSSR v 1988 g, p. 558.

Significantly, the pace of commissioning does not appear to pick up when there is foreign technology involved. At least, this appears to be the conclusion reached in an *Ekonomicheskaya gazeta* article published in 1989 concerning the overly large inventory of uninstalled equipment: about 16 per cent of that for all heavy industry was designated for the chemical industry, of which roughly 50 per cent was imported.[52]

A successful outcome of the construction programme for the Ministry of Mineral Fertilisers seems doubtful, judging by recent performance. For example, planned construction during the 11th FYP of 32 new plants to produce pesticides and herbicides resulted in completion of 5 enterprises. Between 1986 and 1987, it was reported that the Ministry was 'unable to use 800 million rubles of capital budget allocations, including 344 million rubles on construction-installation work; the Ministry would need to spend more than 70 per cent of budget allocations for the 12th plan period between 1988 and 1990.'[53] This suggests that the capital budget for the Ministry was under 3 billion rubles for the 12th plan period, whereas to keep pace with construction plans, the 'capital budget for the Ministry will increase in 13th plan period by more than 1.5 times'.[54]

Structure of the State Capital Budget

Given that the chemical industry's priorities are set nationally and politically, and that some new construction will not be funded through the national capital budget, it follows that the state capital budget was intended largely for expenditure to upgrade existing enterprises. In 1986, industry sources stated that over the 12th plan period, it was planned that 'reconstruction and retooling will secure 82 per cent of expanded capacity at a cost of 45 per cent of the capital budget, while 47 per cent of the capital budget would be expended to expand enterprises, thereby securing an 18 per cent growth in capacity'.[55] To derive production increases largely by reconstruction and retooling represents a striking change in policy from the 10th and 11th plan periods when labour productivity accounted for 75 and 89 per cent respectively of the growth of production, and from 1986 and 1988 when labour productivity accounted for virtually all production increases.[56]

The Gorbachev investment policies can be seen in the following table, which shows a slight budgetary bias towards retooling and reconstruction and away from expansion of existing enterprises. The shift towards reconstruction was supposedly to continue until such activities claimed over 50 per cent of the state capital budget;[57] that level was surpassed in 1988. Despite the statistical returns, there are suggestions that the budgetary picture obscures actual practice; as in other industries, much of the financial means officially designated for reconstruction and retooling in fact goes for new construction at existing enterprises.[58]

7.9 Structure of the State Capital Budget on Objects of Production in the Chemical-Forestry Complex
(in comparable prices, billions of rubles)

	Rubles		Per cent	
	1987	1988	1987	1988
Capital budget total on which:	6.7	6.7	100	100
On technical retooling & reconstruction of enterprises	3.2	3.6	47.4	54.1
On expansion of various enterprises	2.6	2.0	38.4	29.6
On new construction	0.8	1.0	12.2	14.5
On various installations of different enterprises	0.1	0.1	2.0	1.8

Source: Narodnoe khozyaistvo SSSR v 1987 g, p. 58, and *Narodnoe khozyaistvo SSSR v 1988 g*, p. 266.

Gorbachev's drive for reconstruction and retooling of basic plant stems partly from a need to encourage sparing use of raw materials and manufactured resources and partly from a desire to use existing production units that can be operated cost-efficiently only after modernisation. For a while, this was regarded as a least-cost way to obtain production increases in the near-term, but as enterprises confront the actual task, they are finding that the 'degree of difficulty of reconstruction and retooling often exceeds that of new construction'.[59] During preparations for the 12th plan budget, assessments of the condition of operating technologies were undertaken – a common-sense approach that is recommended but often ignored in practice.[60]

We approached the drafting of the 12th plan in a new way. First, work was carried out on the basis of the results of rating and certification of job sites, in which technical inspectors participated. Suggestions regarding the need to close or rebuild plants that do not meet standards for technical safety were obtained beforehand by inspectors. These proposals were analysed by the ministries and made the basis of the comprehensive plan for the 12th plan period.

Elsewhere, it was pointed out that about half of these assessments were made while the equipment and machinery were in operation which, in the opinion of the author, 'significantly decreased their reliability'.[61] A difficulty for economists and policymakers, of course, is not just incorporating the results of such an inventory within the official planning document. There is also an increasing uncertainty whether the investment emphasis is to be placed on expansion or recapitalisation, which serves to undermine the credibility of any investment plans for this industrial sector. The following table shows that the investment programme has not yielded especially significant movement in the outlays for machinery and equipment, in spite of expectations.

7.10   Expenditure on Repairs of Capital Assets
(million rubles)

	1985		1986		1987		1988	
	total	mach & eqmt[1]	total	mach & eqmt[1]	total	mach & eqmt[1]	total	mach & eqmt[1]
All Industry	17942	9667	18733	10171	19447	10402	20900	11339
Heavy Industry	15332	8256	16022	8670	16565	8830	17724	9586
Chemical-Forestry Complex	2895	1631	2990	1699	3165	1794	3287	1940
of which: Chemicals & Petrochemicals	1961	1166	2042	1229	2172	1289	2281	1370

[1] Machines and equipment
Source: Narodnoe khozyaistvo SSSR v 1988 g, p. 354.

Here, the investment picture gets a bit murky, as there is also the issue of repair and maintenance, the definition for which is 'work to secure the working order of equipment, including repairs of machinery during use, storage and transport, and primarily covers preventative measures necessary to secure reliable performance of equipment between schedules repairs.'[62] In theory, the cost of repair and maintenance is included in the operating budget of an enterprise, but often such funds are simply pooled with those for reconstruction and retooling in the capital budget.[63] In the chemical industry as a whole, more than 50 per cent of all assets suffer from excessive wear and tear; this problem has been recognised for a number of years. In such circumstances, perhaps only accountants and budget analysts distinguish between repair and maintenance work and retooling. This point is well illustrated by an article concerning the status of existing pharmaceutical enterprises. There, well over half and in some cases all of the equipment was in 'poor repair', but of 4 billion rubles in investment capital that are anticipated by the author, most will be spent to construct 39 enterprises and only the residual, if there is any, to 'upgrade' 48 operating enterprises.[64]

7.11   Wear and Tear of Capital Assets
(as per cent of total value of capital assets at the end of the year)

	1980	1985	1986	1987	1988
All Industry	36	41	42	43	44
Heavy Industry	36	42	43	44	45
Chemical-Forestry Complex	36	44	45	47	48
of which:					
Chemicals					
& Petrochemicals	35	44	45	48	50

Source: Narodnoe khozyaistvo SSSR v 1988 g, p. 355.

In 1987, the Environmental Commission of the Supreme Soviet expressed alarm that enterprises manufacturing mineral fertilisers continued to be a 'main source of pollution'. Even as an industry spokesman claimed, 'The picture is disquieting, but not a cause for alarm', the Ministry responded by announcing an ambitious programme covering the period to the year 2000, for technical retooling of related enterprises.[65] It claimed that 'by 1990, there will be 25–30 per cent reductions in the quantity of old machinery requiring replacement'. However, the programme is only a start, because if the Ministry does achieve a 25–30 per cent reduction, it will still leave around 40 per cent of the basic plant and equipment in the worn out and obsolete category.

Elsewhere, concerns have been expressed about special difficulties due to the regional concentration of chemical plants. For example, in the Ukraine, retirement of capital assets amounts to 1–2 per cent per annum, but on average[66]

40 per cent of the basic technological installations are technically obsolete or physically worn out. In some areas the situation is especially poor, and in factories at Svema, Krastel, Odessa, and Vnit'sk about 70 per cent of the installations have been used for more than 20 years, and at the Slavyansk chemical plant installations have been used for more than 40 years. The situation is compounded by the lack of an adequate repair industry... .

Perhaps as worrisome are indications that some equipment is being 'renewed' with obsolete designs. One economic argument, of course, is that production can be secured in this way. However, from the combined perspective of environmental protection and investment economics, the use of obsolete technologies aborts an early opportunity to ensure that existing enterprises respond to requirements for ecological safety.[67] It also means the loss of any economies that might have occurred by integrating nature protection technologies during the retooling and reconstruction process, and it eventually forces enterprises to accept the environmental technologies as supplemental costs. Where the add-on costs of nature protection are more expensive than they would be if nature protection features were included in 'cleaner' production technologies, there is a disincentive for the enterprise to make supplementary environmental investment once the plant has been retooled. This negative situation can only be compounded if the enterprise is then forced to make the investment from funds that would otherwise accrue as profits (a point that is addressed below).

The pattern of investment for repairs by the chemical industry is discussed by O G Oganov, who published two articles (in *EKO* and *Khimicheskaya promyshlennost'* on the topic. He, too, suggested that repair-and-maintenance and retooling-and-reconstruction cannot be fully distinguished. Leading from this, Oganov argued that even though the Soviet economy expends far too much of its capital budget for repairs, there is little to show for it. In his view, the repair base is overly large and requires extensive reorganisation. Still, the relative poverty of the investment programme seems evident in his discussion of the resources available to the Ministry of Chemical Fertilisers, which Oganov reported was investing at a rate of 3 per cent of capital assets on average per year for repairs to passive and operating assets, plus current repairs and technical services. At this rate, which he suggested is less than half of that by large US companies, Oganov argued no important gains will occur in production capacity, especially in the context of equipment shortages.[68] From an environmental perspective, this situation has serious implications indeed: existing capacity can be expected to generate more pollution as it continues to deteriorate, and near-term gains in resource conservation will be delayed.

An acid test of the programme for reconstruction and retooling relates to the commissioning of production capacity. According to the annual statistical yearbook, performance in respect of five key areas of the chemical industry was uneven. For example, during 1988, most of the new capacity for sulphuric acid production was due to reconstruction of enterprises, while roughly 75 per cent of new capacity for chemical fibres and filaments was from reconstruction and retooling taken together. By contrast, most of the new capacity for production of synthetic plastics and resins was the result of new construction.[69] In 1989, capacity was commissioned to produce 740,000 tonnes of sulphuric acid, and 200,000 tonnes of synthetic detergents.[70]

During the Spring 1989 debates concerning the new construction programme at Tyumen, a question was raised concerning the capacity of the
Soviet Union to absorb its financial and other costs of Tyumen concurrent to
the reconstruction and retooling that is being (or, more likely, should be)
undertaken at existing sites. A group of leading academicians stated in an
open letter that general shortages of labour and equipment alone dictated that
a choice must be made between new large-scale construction and reconstruction
and retooling. Further, in their view, if the balance weighed in favour of new
construction, the environment would lose out, first, because of 'highly
suspect' provisions for environmental technologies at the new enterprises
and, second, because of the widescale damage that would take place during
the protracted construction process.[71] Of course, any hope for improvements
in environmental protection at existing enterprises centres on the retooling

7.12   Commissioning and Decommissioning of BIBF in 1988
(at enterprises, formed by independent balances)
(in per cents)

	All Industry	Heavy Industry	Chemical-Forestry Complex	Chemicals and Petrochemicals
Relation of Commissioned Assets to General Value of Assets at year end				
Total, of which:	6.6	6.6	5.9	5.5
Buildings & Installations	6.0	6.1	4.7	4.7
Machinery & Equipment	7.3	7.3	6.9	6.1
Other assets	6.8	6.7	6.9	5.9
Relation of Decommissioned Assets to General Value of Assets at start of year				
Total, of which:	1.8	1.8	2.2	1.6
Buildings & Installations	0.8	0.8	0.8	0.4
Machinery & Equipment	2.9	2.8	3.5	2.8
Other assets	2.2	2.0	3.0	1.6

Source: Narodnoe khozyaistvo SSSR v 1988 g, p. 361.

and reconstruction programme; this will be delayed indefinitely if Tyumen, or another project(s) of comparable scale, is pursued.

Decommissioning of Capital Assets

The other side of the coin relates to the removal of plant and equipment. It might be expected, that since reconstruction and retooling are assuming increasing importance, this rate would be on an upswing. In the estimate of industry officials, about 10–15 per cent of equipment should be renewed each year, but official data show a much different reality. As in other industrial sectors, a great part of the problem lies with the machine building industry which – after retooling of its *own* plants – will only be able to replace chemical industrial equipment at two-thirds the rate that is needed.[72]

The rate at which production equipment was retired increased considerably in the first two years of the 12th plan period, although it remained at roughly three-quarters the rate at which retirement took place in heavy industry as a whole. Thus, it can be seen that in 1986, 1987, and 1988, 2.8, 3.8, and 3.7 per cent, respectively, of total active production technologies were removed.

7.13   Removing the Active Part of Capital Assets
(as per cent of total value of assets at the beginning of the period)

	1981–85		1986		1987		1988	
	total	number obsolete	total	number obsolete	total	number obsolete	total	number obsolete
All Industry	20	12	4.3	2.8	5.1	3.2	4.8	2.7
Heavy Industry	19	12	4.2	2.7	5.0	3.1	4.7	2.6
Chemical-Forestry Complex								
of which:	20	15	4.0	2.9	5.2	4.0	5.7	3.4
Chemicals &								
Petrochemicals	13	10	2.8	2.1	3.8	3.0	3.7	2.5

Source: Narodnoe khozyaistvo SSSR v 1988 g, p. 360.

Automation

The structure of basic plant and equipment is important for nature protection since the technological level, including that of automated processes, establishes the ability of the industry to protect nature and conserve resources. Two areas draw immediate attention – those for laboratory, measuring, and regulating devices and for computers. In these instances, the chemical industry (with 2.5 per cent of capital assets in this area) appears to have more capacity than is the case for the industry as a whole. Also, the chemical industry is significantly better off than forestry, pulp and paper (the latter being known as amongst the worst in Soviet manufacturing).

In the area of automation and computers, the chemical industry is again better off than the forestry, pulp and paper industry; but the value of capital assets is less than 1 per cent, and being 'better off' is, simply, insignificant relative to need. Industry officials say that 30 per cent of the main production activities are handled by manual labour, [73] perhaps even more in the production of domestic chemicals, plastics, and chlorine. Amongst the investment priorities are 'instrumentation for control of explosions and toxic admixtures, simulators for operator training, and technical safety'. There is virtually no information concerning the degree to which pollution control installations are automated, but in respect of waste water, the manual testing techniques depicted in the literature are as dangerous to the environmental worker as they are inadequate in respect of the need for continuous monitoring of pollutants in waste streams.

7.14   Structure of Capital Assets*
(by enterprise, compared to independent balances, in per cents)

	All Industry	of which Chemical-Forestry Complex	including Chemicals & Petrochemicals
Buildings	27.1	31.3	30.9
Installations	19.5	14.8	14.2
Transmission Equipment	10.4	9.0	10.9
Power Machines & Equipment	7.5	3.5	3.0
Operating Machinery & Equipment	29.2	34.9	34.9
Measuring, Regulating & Laboratory devices	1.8	1.9	2.5
Computers	1.2	0.8	0.9
Transport	2.3	3.2	2.1
Other	1.0	0.6	0.6

* *On 1 January 1989.*
Source: *Narodnoe khozyaistvo SSSR v 1988 g*, pp. 352–353.

Waste Management

It seems appropriate to inject here a brief discussion about waste identification and classification, since the success of such endeavours is more or less dependent on automation and computers. A key figure within the chemical industry who is agitating for a more scientific approach to waste management is I P Narkevich, who acknowledged that 'one of the most difficult questions in the system of collecting, processing, reusing, or removal of industrial wastes is the question of their classification'.[74] Up to mid-1988, when a particularly relevant article by Narkevich was published, state standards (GOST) had not been set for industrial wastes and residues as 'they do not fit into the classification systems for finished products or raw materials', and as far as could be ascertained they have not been issued subsequently. There are a number of approaches, as follows:

- Classification according to aggregate status (that is, solid, liquid, or gas) is grossly inadequate as it does not provide sufficient information about the sources of wastes or their chemical compositions on which to base judgements about safe methods of removal or appropriate uses. Many Soviet presentations concerning chemical waste management seem to have stopped at this level of analysis, insofar as they are primarily concerned with the disposal and/or recycling of large-volume wastes. B N Lishchin, for instance, mentioned solids, liquids, and gaseous wastes, but ignored sludges which constitute an extremely serious waste disposal problem for all chemical plants.
- A second method approaches wastes according to potential methods of use or removal. Industrial wastes are divided into three groups: those that are to be recycled; those requiring preliminary treatment; and those that can be discharged without treatment.[75] One critical shortcoming of this method is that while information about existing methods of use, decontamination, or disposal may be designated, the approach does not facilitate judgements based on the specific nature of the wastes, their composition, or 'physicochemical' properties. When Lishchin discussed thermal and biological-chemical disposal alternatives, he stated that 'stereotypical approaches' are taken to the disposal of liquid chemical wastes and he questioned the appropriateness of such decision-making.
- A third and preferred method is based on classification according to the nature and composition of the wastes. This facilitates a thorough determination of the safe methods of storage, treatment, reuse, and disposal.[76] V A Kirillov pointed out that this approach would also facilitate investment decisions when the choice was between restructuring and retooling of enterprises or building new waste management installations. The practical obstacles to implementating this classification method are the shortages of laboratory, testing, and monitoring equipment; of

course, the physical absence of corresponding waste management installations could make having the data somewhat irrelevant.

Profitability

A shift to *khozraschet* management practices is supposedly underway in the chemical industry, with the expected effect of reinforcing enterprise autonomy, since enterprises will have funds at their disposal to devote to a variety of purposes including workers' incentives, extending and reconstructing enterprises, and other uses. Profits are understood by the chemical industry as 'that part of income which remains after fulfilling obligations to the budget and the ministry', whereas income is considered as the combined total of the fund for development of production, science and technology, the fund for social and cultural measures including housing construction, the fund for material incentives, plus grants and loans.

A A Astakhov, the Head of the Main Administration for Financing the Chemical Industry at the USSR Ministry of Finance, wrote one of the very few articles that has appeared on the topic of *khozraschet* management in the chemical industry as a whole.[77] Astakhov suggested that large-scale expenditure for nature protection and resource conservation are to be obtained from the appropriate ministry, and not generated within the enterprise. In effect, this could mean that enterprise autonomy may be severely restricted in respect of its ability to set environmental investment priorities. A decision to leave large-scale environmental investment (which is quite possibly beyond the means of individual enterprises) at the ministries suggests that nature protection will not be thoroughly integrated into the system of financial incentives through which enterprises are encouraged both to increase output and to derive greater output per unit of input. An exception to this may occur if an enterprise decides to use its profits to subsidise less profit-generating activities, such as nature protection. But it is widely suggested that a system of financial incentives that are linked specifically to nature protection is necessary to attract the cooperation of many enterprises.[78]

The case of the Astrakhan Gas-Chemical Complex demonstrates the point. There, profits of 50 billion rubles were reported in 1988. Observers suggest that from a national economic perspective the Astrakhan complex actually incurred losses, because accidents, such as releases of hydrogen sulphide which subsequently required evacuations from nearby towns and endangered the nature reserve, have caused severe environmental damage and offsetting social expenditure of 54 billion rubles.[79]

Not all environmental investment is by means of capital construction, and Astakhov pointed out that the operating costs of pollution controls have to be assimilated into the general cost composition at the enterprise level. But elsewhere, in descriptions of how incentive funds are generated and the uses to which the funds for development of production, science and technology in particular can be put, a general impression is given that expenditure for environmental protection will compete with other objectives that fall within the scope of the fund. In this sense, pressures on the enterprise to reduce costs tend to mitigate against environmental measures, whether the initial capital investment or subsequent running costs, and any counter-balance would have to come from the ministry or external organisations. This situation creates an institutional disincentive at least at the enterprise levels to undertake repairs or replace existing flue gas scrubbers, for instance, since to do so will increase operating costs and reduce profits.

7.15   Return on Investment
(output of commodity products per 1 ruble
of the average annual value of capital assets)

	1980 = 100				1985 = 100		
	1985	1986	1987	1988	1986	1987	1988
All Industry	85	84	83	82	99	97	97
Heavy Industry	87	87	87	86	99	99	99
Chemical-Forestry							
Complex	89	90	90	91	101	102	103
of which:							
Chemicals &							
Petrochemicals	90	91	91	92	101	102	103

Source: Narodnoe khozyaistvo SSSR v 1988 g, p. 364.

Retooling and reconstruction has been more profitable in some areas than others. Table 7.16 demonstrates that in 1988, there was a precipitous fall in the level of investment, although that which was made showed handsome returns. It also demonstrates that expenditure for 'progressive technologies' yielded a three-fold leap in profits, outstripping those achieved by modernising operating units. The table also relates that the profitability of automation continued to lose ground. Of special concern to environmental economists is the fact that computers and automated processes, which are as important for environmental protection as for production efficiency, can generate profits, even though such monetary returns may only be marginal.

Resource Conservation and Waste Disposal

Prior to the extensive introduction of resource conservation measures by enterprises, a number of organisational and economic issues remain to be resolved. Generally, these relate to the creation of a market economy, but in

7.16 Introduction of Measures for New Techniques and their Economic Effectiveness in the Chemical-Forestry Complex

	Average/year		1986	1987	1988
	1976–80	1981–85			
Number of Introduced Measures for New Techniques, 10^3	53	57	63	57	50
Actual Expenditures on Introduced Measures (including costs of past years), 10^6 rubles	1510	2035	2058	2227	1430
Results:					
Growth of Profits total 10^6 rubles	408	459	662	648	679
Per ruble Expended on Introduction,	.27	.23	.32	.29	.48
Of which, due to:					
Introduction of Progressive Technologies	.27	.24	.34	.28	.64
Mechanisation of Production	.14	.11	.12	.11	.14
Automation of Production	.18	.11	.18	.15	.13
Modernisation of Various Installations	.32	.32	.27	.38	.42
Period of Covering Costs, years	3.7	4.7	3.1	3.4	2.1

Source: Narodnoe khozyaistvo SSSR v 1988 g, p. 289.

the interim there must be means for enterprises to recover investment. For example, the issue of financial interest might be answered by specifying different prices for primary and secondary raw materials (that is, by raising the prices of primary raw materials well over those for secondary raw materials). A way must also be devised to include secondary raw materials in the nomenclature of products to stimulate trade, which in turn will encourage enterprises to pursue investment in this area.

Judging by the following table concerning the general areas where operating costs have been incurred, the targets for resource conservation in respect of operating budgets are most likely to be in raw materials consumption, closely followed by energy and fuel.

Resource conservation by the chemical industry may become especially important, because opportunities already exist to recover some environmentally damaging wastes that can be reused without costly secondary processing. For example, sulphur, fluorine, and chlorine in exhaust gases are being extensively recovered. There appear to have been some reductions in ex-

7.17　Structure of the Cost of Industrial Production in 1988
(in actual prices, as per cent of total cost)

	All Industry	Heavy Industry	Chemicals-Forestry Complex	of which Chemicals & Petrochemicals
Total Costs	100	100	100	100
Raw Materials	63.2	53.6	52.8	55.7
Supplementary Materials	3.7	3.9	4.8	5.1
Fuel	3.8	5.0	2.4	1.7
Energy	2.7	3.5	6.2	8.7
Amortisation	10.8	13.7	16.2	17.5
Labour & Social Costs	13.8	16.5	14.8	9.9
Miscellaneous	2.9	3.8	2.8	1.4

Source: Narodnoe khozyaistvo SSSR v 1988 g, pp. 346–7.

penditure for raw materials, although whether these were the result of conservation investment is uncertain.

The following table, representing the electric power allocated to and consumed by the chemical industry in several key product areas, holds few surprises. The greatest consumption per ton of output was in the petrochemical industry, exclusive of refining where consumption was relatively modest. Significantly, the normative allocations of energy and fuel have not been progressively reduced across the board despite the national policy of resource conservation, and in some instances showed a steady increase in fuel or energy consumed. In the case of synthetic rubber, the overall reduction in fuel consumption can probably be traced back to the closure of the plant at Erevan.

However, under present conditions, there may be some inherent flaws in the uncontrolled pursuit of resource conservation as a goal in itself, which is demonstrated by the fact that as much as 60 per cent of air pollution control installations are old, worn out, or obsolete, not to mention those which operate below design performance levels for other reasons.[80] As yet there is no economic incentive to expend financial and material resources to curtail related ecological damage.

A decision not to undertake waste reduction, resource conservation, reprocessing, and recycling means that cleansing, neutralisation, and disposal installations must be provided. In the past, the usual forms of chemical waste disposal were unmonitored burial of solid and sludge wastes,[81] release of waste water into rivers and streams, injection of liquids and sludges into subterranean faults[82] and mines,[83] or unrestricted emissions of exhaust gases into the air.

7.18 Share of Fuel and Energy Resources Expended on Production of Different Types of Products

	1985	1986	1987	1988
Electricity (kWh/ton)				
Oil Refining				
Allocated	33	33	34	34
Consumed	33	34	34	35
Calcium Carbide				
Allocated	3114	3134	3093	3177
Consumed	3161	3081	3190	3280
Fuel (million kilocalories/ton)				
Refining, excluding gas condensate				
Allocated	188	186	184	188
Consumed	187	184	185	187
Synthetic Rubber				
Allocated	29000	28900	28407	28250
Consumed	28354	28561	28288	28209
Chemical Fibres and Threads				
Allocated	14702	14777	14666	14604
Consumed	14944	14413	14303	13706
Synthetic Resin and Plastic				
Allocated	5360	5305	5129	5143
Consumed	5168	5120	5082	4935
Caustic Electrolytic Soda				
Allocated	3516	3569	3543	3595
Consumed	3594	3537	3596	3564

Source: Narodnoe khozyaistvo SSSR v 1988, pp. 312–13.

The extent to which such unsatisfactory techniques are still widely practised is uncertain.

The terms 'cleansing', 'neutralisation', and 'disposal' imply that a toxic substance is subjected to mechanical, biological-chemical, or thermal processes to the extent that on release it no longer presents a threat to human health or the environment. However, in principle, both Soviet and Western scientists point out that such installations do not completely protect nature, as they can simply be a means of transferring dangerous substances from one natural sphere to another where the threat is less obvious.[84] According to Lishchin, 80 per cent by volume of liquid organic effluents are subjected to thermal methods of waste reduction and/or neutralisation and about 17 per cent to biological-chemical methods.[85] These approaches are also found in the West, where the appropriateness of a given method is sometimes questioned in specific environmental contexts.[86]

Borodin estimated that about the order of 24 billion rubles will be needed by the year 2005 to introduce a full programme of resource conservation and to construct waste management installations for the chemical industry as a whole.[87]

Notes

1   B N Lishchin, et al, Ekonomika obezvrezhivaniya promyshlennykh stokov khimicheskikh predpriyatii, *Khimicheskaya promyshlennost'*, no. 11, 1987, pp. 701–3.

2   Ibid.

3   This is established, but of an evolutionary nature in the United States. There are passing references to various Soviet systems in which wastes are classed numerically, apparently to signal the potential hazardous characteristic of the materials. No information has been found that explains these systems, which leads to further questions: Is any such system mandatory, and if so which one; and, is such a system comprehensively applied, and in what circumstances? For example, see G Ya Chegrinets, et al, Sanitarno-gigienicheskaya kharakteristika zhidkikh azotnykh udobrenii – otkhodov proizvodstva v besstochnoi sisteme vodosnabzheniya khimicheskogo kombinata, *Gigiena i sanitariya*, no. 6, 1988, pp. 75–7, where certain recycled wastes are classified as presenting a '4th class danger' to the health of rats.

4   This is reasonably established in a number of Western countries in regulation if not in practice.

5   Again, established, but a continuing concern in the West.

6   V K Borodin, Okhrane prirody – povsednevnoe vnimanie, *Khimicheskaya promyshlennost'*, no. 2, 1989, pp. 83–7.

7   V I Ovchinnikov, Vklad khimikov v vypolnenie Prodovol'stvennoi programmy strany, *Khimicheskaya promyshlennost'*, no. 5, 1988, pp. 259–64.

8   I P Narkevich, Ozonovyi sloi: znachenie i okhrana ot razrusheniya, *Khimicheskaya promyshlennost'*, no. 1, 1989, pp. 3–7. See also, A Frokin, Oglyanis' v trevoge, *Pravda*, 4 August 1988, p. 2, who discusses the lack of a chemical waste management programme for chlorine by-products and wastes.

9   See for instance N D Afanas'ev, et al, Purification of Waste Gases During the Agglomeration of Phosphate Raw Materials, *Soviet Chemical Industry*, no. 1, 1986, pp. 56–8 (translation from *Khimicheskaya promyshlennost'*). The authors assert that during the development of experimental production technologies to be used with Karatau apatite, 'in view of the lack of experience of the chemical industry in purifying large amounts of gases containing toxic components with different physico-chemical properties', they also had to design and develop special pollution control technologies. See also, G A Denzanov, et al, Snizhenie poter' ammiaka i ftora v proizvodstve ftorida-biftorida ammoniya i beloi sazhi, *Khimicheskaya promyshlennost'*, no. 3, 1987, pp. 166–7, (translated in *Soviet Chemical Industry*). The authors discuss the importance of retooling the production process so that the percentages of ammonia and fluorine used are increased and thereby industry can reduce the relative volume of pollutants that must be controlled.

The chemical industry is required to effect water, energy, and raw materials conservation. Three terms are often mentioned in respect of the conservation function: resource conservation means that lesser amounts of energy and raw materials per unit of output are used in the manufacturing of a given product; reprocessing means that wastes from one production process become the raw material for another; and recycling is a type of reprocessing, which occurs when materials that would otherwise be discarded are reused within the same industry. The most common forms of reprocessing involve large volume solid wastes, such as ash, cinder, and gypsum that are used to make construction materials, while the most common form of recycling in the chemical industry is of water. A further term is used in respect of recycled water – that of repeat-use, which means literally what the words suggest. The difference between the two terms is indistinct, although the sophistication of the technology may be a definitive point.

10   E I Taubman, Prav li ministr? *Priroda i chelovek*, no. 5, 1989, pp. 12–14. See also, G N Vorozhtsov, Anilinokrasochnaya promyshlennost' – itogi i perspektivy, *Khimicheskaya promyshlennost'*, no. 11, 1987, pp. 656–60 (translated in *Soviet Chemical Industry*). The author asserts that the industry has a considerable programme of new construction in the 12th and 13th plan periods, for which low waste productions 'will be created'. He also notes that the industry will seek foreign investment and cooperation in expansion of dyes, pigments, optical whiteners, auxiliary textile substances, and other important products.

11   For detailed information about the chemical industry by branch activity, see Matthew Sagers, *The Soviet Chemical Industry*, Washington, DC: D C Heath, 1990.

12   L Kelim, Kontseptsiya razvitiya khimicheskoi promyshlennosti v XIII pyatletke i do 2000 g, *Khimicheskaya promyshlennost'*, no. 12, 1988, pp. 759–60; Yu A Bespalov, Vazhneishe zadachi khimicheskoi promyshlennosti, *Khimicheskaya promyshlennost'*, no. 3, 1987, pp. 131–5; V K Borodin, Zadache otraslevogo profsoyuza i ego vklad v uskorenie sotsial'no-ekonomicheskogo razvitiya khimicheskikh otraslei promyshlennosti, *Khimicheskaya promyshlennost'*, no. 4, 1987, pp. 195–202. 'In the chemical, petrochemical, and oil refining industries during the 12th plan period, there are to be increases in the production of chemicals and petrochemical products by 30–2 per cent, mineral fertilisers by 127 per cent, plastics and resins to 6.8–7.1 million tons, chemical fibres and filaments to 1.85 million tons, and tyre production by 1.7 times.' Yu A Bespalov, *Khimicheskaya promyshlennost'*, no. 3, 1987, pp. 131–5; V I Ovchinnikov, *Khimicheskaya promyshlennost'*, no. 5, 1988, op cit.

13   A M Aleshin, Osnovnaya khimicheskaya promyshlennost' za sem'desyat let Sovetskoi vlasti, *Khimicheskaya promyshlennost'*, no. 11, 1987, pp. 644–9; L Kelim, *Khimicheskaya promyshlennost'*, no. 12, 1988, ibid.

14   G Denisov, Vybor, *Meditsinskaya gazeta*, 14 July 1989, pp. 1–2.

15   Statement by O M Nefedov, *Vestnik Akademiya Nauk SSSR*, no. 2, 1989, pp. 105–107.

16   *Narodnoe khozyaistvo SSSR za 70 let*, p. 126.

17   V B Dem'yanov, E N Zheltov, Optimal'nyi uroven' tsentralizatsii – vazhnyi faktor uglublenniya spetsializatsii remontnoi sluzhby Minkhimproma SSSR pri vypolnenii kapital'nogo remonta osnovnykh fondov, *Khimicheskaya promyshlennost'*, no. 4, 1988, pp. 246–50 (translated in *Soviet Chemical Industry*).

18   V E Kir'yanchuk in *Tscentral'noe chernozem'e*, Izd: Voronezhskogo universiteta, 1986, p. 4. Interestingly, the author believes that no territorial redistribution of the chemical industry is envisaged in the Central Black Earth Region, where there are 'tense balances in respect of the raw material base, fuel and water resources.' The reasons for relocating plants notwithstanding, the budgetary effect will be on the resources allocated for new construction.

19   V P Kutyrev, Obshchesoyuznye smotriny sibiri, *EKO*, no. 2, 1986, pp. 103–135; A G Aganbegan, Chtoby prirastat' sibir'iu, *Priroda i chelovek*, no. 10, 1984, pp. 18–23.

20   I K Komarov, *Novaya investsionnaya politika i stroitel' stvo*, Mysl', 1988, pp. 31, 34–5.

21   A A Novikov, V N Vinogradov, S D Evenchik, Osnovnye napravleniya nauchno-tekhnicheskogo progressa v osnovnoi khimicheskoi promyshlennosti v period 1986–1990 gg i do 2000 g, *Khimicheskaya promyshlennost'*, no. 3, 1986, pp. 131–3. The article ends with a notation that 'the Ministry of Chemical Machine Building, and the Ministry of Instruments should be reconstructed and retooled so that production of modern chemical equipment will be secured.'

22   Statement by O Abdirakhmanov, *Novyi Mir*, no. 5, 1989, pp. 202–3. See also the interview by E Prikhod'ko, Pustaya kolybel', *Meditsinskaya gazeta*, no. 99, 18 August 1989, p. 2, in which V E Radzinskii, a medical doctor, discussed truly horrendous environmentally-induced maternal and child health problems in Turkmenia. He said, 'Without improvements in chemicalisation, the problems of child mortality cannot be resolved.' Most statistics about the state and condition of public health in the Soviet Union continue to be suppressed. Those which have been published, including the infant mortality rates cited here, would be better understood should these data become available. The infant mortality rates mentioned in the text probably refer to Karakalpak ASSR, but equally they could reflect difficulties in a number of regions and towns scattered through the Soviet Union where environmental conditions are especially severe and where the condition of public health has deteriorated. It is certain that the provision of health care services, supplies, and personnel does not keep pace with demand.

23   V K Borodin, *Khimicheskaya promyshlennost'*, no. 2, 1989, op cit. N V Kuznetsov, Okhrane okruzhayushchei sredy – zabotu i vnimanie kazhdogo kollektiva i truzhenika, *Khimicheskaya promyshlennost'*, no. 5, 1988, pp. 313–316. F T Morgun, Ekologiya v sisteme planirovaniya, *Planovoe khozyaistvo*, no. 12, 1988, pp. 53–63. The importance of these centres and their scientific subdivisions (that will be devoted to specific pollution problems generated by manufacturing) cannot be overstated, and it is noteworthy that individual republics will probably establish scientific centres as well.

24   M Shakhanov, Gor' Kaya Sol' Arala, *Sovetskie profsoyuzy*, no. 8, 1989, pp. 18–19 wrote that DDT was routinely used in Kzyl' Ordinsk Oblast, and reported the presence of several proscribed chemicals such as CSP hexachlorine.

25   A Sokolov, Prodaem kolshak dla vulkana, *Priroda i chelovek*, no. 3, 1989, pp. 12–13; Mezha, *Priroda i chelovek*, no. 3, 1989, pp. 14–17.

26   Povyshat' organizovannost' i distsiplinu na proizvodstve, sotsialno-ekonomicheskoe razvitie SSSR v pervom kvartale 1989 g, *Ekonomicheskaya gazeta*, no. 18, 1989, p. 15, noted that Goskompriroda took decisions concerning the unsuitable construction of the Pavlodarsk plant for vitamin production, and the need to reprofile chemical plants at Berezovsk (Odessa *oblast*) and Kaustnik (Volgograd area). A statement by V A Koptyug, *Vestnik Akademiya Nauk SSSR*, no. 5, 1989, pp. 60–4, however, suggested rather bitterly that 'Goskompriroda is barely visible' at present.

27   V K Borodin, *Khimicheskaya promyshlennost'*, no. 2, 1989, *supra*.

28   A Arbatov, S Bogolyubov, L Sobolev, *Ecology*, Moscow: Novosti, 1989, p. 58: 'In the chemical industry the level of water recycling is 74 per cent on average, reaching 97 per cent at a few plants...'.

29   L Kelim, *Khimicheskaya promyshlennost'*, no. 12, 1988, op cit. The article noted that the priorities for the reconstruction and retooling programme have not been fully elaborated. Borodin, ibid, stated that workers in the medical and microbiological industries are exposed in the course of their workday to more than 1500 chemical products for which no studies have been conducted; this meant they suffered from 'dangerous working conditions' that were made worse by the external emissions of such substances.

30   A L Breitberg and A Kosyakov, Predotvratit' zagryaznenie vodoemov, *Mashinostroitel'*, no. 6, 1986, pp. 25–26.

31   V K Borodin, *Khimicheskaya promyshlennost'*, no. 2, 1989, op cit.

32   This figure is mentioned in an article by E Velikov, M Styrikovich, and V Maslennikov, Platit tot, kto zagryaznyaet, *Ekonomicheskaya gazeta*, no. 33, 1989, p. 18.

33   F T Morgun, *Planovoe khozyaistvo*, no. 12, 1988, op cit. However, it is significant that the normatives for investment, that are to include cost-benefit and damage-cost analyses of technological options, are incomplete. K Gofman, The Payments for Consumption of Natural Resources and Environmental Pollution – New Approaches in the Soviet Economy, paper presented in Sweden, c 1988.

34   M P Ratanov, et al, Mediko-geograficheskie problemy zagryazneniya vozdushnogo basseina gorodskikh aglomeratsii, *Vestnik MGU, Seriya geografiya*, no. 2, 1989, pp. 65–72; M G Slin'ko, Resheniya kollegii - v zhizn'!, *Khimicheskaya promyshlennost'*, no. 7, 1988, pp. 444–7, provided additional information about the programme, 'Progress 1995', under which the chemical industry will respond to ecological requirements in the city of Moscow, noting that a plant for the production of technical photoplastics was closed in the first quarter of 1988. By 1990 other chemical plants will be reprofiled, depending on the availability of capital funds. See also, V Shchepotkin, Schet pred'yavlen prirodoi, *Izvestiya*, 15 September 1987, p. 3: Pollution of the Chirchik River is one of the main ways that pollution is spread in and from Tashkent; reportedly about 55 per cent of all untreated waste water in Uzbekistan is discharged into it.

35   N V Kuznetsov, *Khimicheskaya promyshlennost'*, no. 5, 1988, op cit. The article gave an example of air and water pollution at Ufa, where the environmental regulatory inspectors' concern about health 'takes precedence' over departmental interests. The researchers point out that Ufa is reportedly one of the most polluted cities in the Soviet Union, largely due to the presence of the chemical industries.

36   Information obtained during discussions with a delegation from the Western Caucasus Economic Institute, located in Rostov-on-Don, May 1989. See also, M G Slin'ko, *Khimicheskaya promyshlennost'*, no. 7, 1988, op cit, which noted that a series of new polytechnic universities are to be built to provide graduate specialists for the chemical industry, now experiencing a shortfall of 6,000 annually. The article did not mention whether the programme would train cadres for nature protection work, although the additional studentships could afford an opportunity to fill personnel gaps.

37   B Laskorin, et al, Eshche odna 'stroike' veka? *Izvestiya*, 3 April 1989, p. 2.

38   V I Ovchinnikov, *Khimicheskaya promyshlennost'*, no. 5, 1988, op cit.

39   *Meditsinskaya gazeta*, 14 July 1989, op cit.

40   Eto ne podarok, *Kommunist*, no. 5, 1989, pp. 75–81. (*Current Digest of the Soviet Press* published summaries of several articles behind this debate.)

41   B Laskorin, et al, *Izvestiya*, 3 April 1989, op cit.

42   Ibid.

43   A project of even larger scale (at 30–120 billion rubles) is being envisaged in respect of Yamal natural gas, and this is being even more bitterly denounced than the Tyumen project. See V Tsarev, Yamal b'et trevogu, *Ekonomicheskaya gazeta*, no. 32, 1989, p. 19. Laskorin, ibid, indicated that development of Yamal will cost 250–300 billion rubles over the next several planning periods.

44   V Gubarev, Ekologiya bez kosmetiki, *Pravda*, 7 September 1987.

45   Z Balayan, Erevan v bede. Do kakikh por? *Literaturnaya gazeta*, 7 October 1987, p. 1.

46   N V Kuznetsov, *Khimicheskaya promyshlennost'*, no. 5, 1988, op cit.

47   Z M Lazarev, F F Daitov, Kompleksnoe reshenie voprosov okhrany okruzhayushchei sredy na neftekhimicheskom predpriyatii, *Gigiena i sanitariya*, no. 1, 1987, pp. 61–2.

48　A M Aleshin, *Khimicheskaya promyshlennost'*, no. 11, 1987, op cit.
49　L Kelim, Krupneishii kontrakt podpisan, *Khimicheskaya promyshlennost'*, no. 2, 1989, p. 159.
50　O G Oganov, M V Makarenko, Kompleksnoe razvitie organizatsii remontov khimicheskikh proizvodstv na osnove zarubezhnogo opyta, *Khimicheskaya promyshlennost'*, no. 6, 1988, pp. 363–70, op cit, stated that without realistic costing, *khozraschet* in the chemical industry would remain an economy myth.
51　Yu Bespalov, Vazhneishie zadachi khimicheskoi promyshlennosti, *Khimicheskaya promyshlennost'*, no. 3, 1987, pp. 131–5. A discussion of the existence of unused capacity in more specific terms is found in D P Miller, L V Murzov, Ispol'zovanie koeffitsienta proportsional'nosti proizvodtsvennykh moshchnostei dla rascheta fondootdachi, *Khimicheskaya promyshlennost'*, no. 12, 1988, pp. 749–50.
52　G Mishin, Zamorozhennyi rubl', *Ekonomicheskaya gazeta*, no. 17, 1989, p. 6.
53　V I Ovchinnikov, *Khimicheskaya promyshlennost'*, no. 5, 1988, op cit.
54　Ibid.
55　A A Novikov, V N Vinogradov, S D Evenchik, *Khimicheskaya promyshlennost'*, no. 3, 1986, op cit.
56　Prirost promyshlennoi produktsii za schet rosta proizvoditel'nosti truda po pyatiletkam, v protsentakh, *Vestnik statistiki*, no. 5, 1987, p. 61.
57　Lecture by Peter Aven, All-Union Institute for Systems Studies, Moscow, in Glasgow, 16 January 1990.
58　G Mishin, *Ekonomicheskaya gazeta*, no. 17, 1989, op cit.
59　O G Oganov, M V Makarenko, *Khimicheskaya promyshlennost'*, no. 6, 1988, op cit.
60　V K Borodin, The Chemists Trade Union on the 70th Anniversary of the Great October Revolution, *Soviet Chemical Industry*, no. 11, 1987, pp. 1–4.
61　O G Oganov, *Khimicheskaya promyshlennost'*, no. 6, 1988, *supra*.
62　Ibid.
63　This has been proposed in the metallurgical industry, and it can be assumed that, once approved by central authorities, the practice will also be applied in the chemical industry.
64　*Meditsinskaya gazeta*, no. 89, 14 July 1989, op cit.
65　V Shchepotkin, Schet pred'yavlen prirodoi, *Izvestiya*, 15 September 1987, p. 2.
66　N V Kuznetsov, *Khimicheskaya promyshlennost'*, no. 5, 1988, op cit.
67　V K Borodin, *Khimicheskaya promyshlennost'*, no. 2, 1989, op cit.
68　O G Oganov et al, *Khimicheskaya promyshlennost'*, no. 6, 1988, op cit. A long discussion of these points is in A Nove, The Investment Process in the USSR, *Berichte des Bundesinstitut für Ostwissenschaftliche und internationale Studien*, no. 53, 1989. Nove cites a series of articles in *EKO*, no. 4, 1988, pp. 83–107, in which O G Oganov indicated that when all sources of funding are considered 40 billion rubles are spent on repairs to the active parts of capital assets. Oganov also cited the presence of 70,000 repair organisations and units which employ several million workers.
69　*Narodnoe khozyaistvo SSSR v 1988 g*, p. 546–548.
70　Ekonomika strany – itogi goda, *Izvestiya*, 28 January 1990, pp. 1–4.
71　Laskorin, et al, *Izvestiya*, 3 April 1989, p. 2; *Kommunist*, no. 5, 1989, pp. 75–81, op cit.
72　O G Oganov, *Khimicheskaya promyshlennost'*, no. 6, 1988, op cit.
73　L Kelim, Vychislitel'naya tekhnika – katalizatop nauchno-tekhnicheskogo progressa, *Khimicheskaya promyshlennost'*, no. 1, 1989, pp. 74–5.
74　I P Narkevich, Klassifikatsiya promyshlennykh otkhodov, *Khimicheskaya promyshlennost'*, no. 4, 1988, pp. 243–50 (translation in *Soviet Chemical Industry*; and I P Narkevich, Ecological Safety and the Activity of National and International Organisations in Maintaining It, *Soviet Chemical Industry*, no. 5, 1988, pp. 77–83.
75　Such a method is proposed by A Kolosov, Okhrana okruzhayushchei sredy v

usloviyakh intensifikatsii ekonomiki, *Voprosy ekonomiki*, no. 12, 1985, pp. 90–8 (translated in *Problems of Economics*).

76   V M Kirillov, O G Vorob'ev, Ekologicheskii analyiz khimicheskoi tekhnologii, *Khimicheskaya promyshlennost'*, no. 7, 1989, pp. 548–51.

77   A A Astakhov, Osnovnye napravleniya sovershenstvovaniya finansov predpriyatii khimicheskoi promyshlennosti v usloviyakh polnogo khozrascheta, *Khimicheskaya promyshlennost'*, no. 9, 1987, pp. 515–20.

78   O G Oganov, *Khimicheskaya promyshlennost'*, no. 6, 1988, op cit; V K Borodin, *Khimicheskaya promyshlennost'*, no. 2, 1989, op cit; G M Mkrtchyan, L A Bondarenko, V M Sokolov, Ot zapretov – k malootkhodnym tekhnologiyam, *EKO*, no. 2, 1989, pp. 124–32.

79   *Kommunist*, no. 5, 1989, op cit.

80   *Vestnik statistiki*, no. 6, 1988, op cit.

81   This reference discusses an issue of agricultural chemicals that have been delivered to the consumer or distributor, but were subsequently banned or recalled. Chemical plant managers may argue that disposal of such products, even though they are of a massive volume, is not within their purview. However, the example demonstrates the linkage between the industry and safe waste disposal and the effects of the most common disposal practice – burial. *Environmental Management Abstracts*, no. 2, 1988, p. 18, cites an example in Moldavia, where burial of banned agricultural chemicals is causing pollution:

> In the Moldavian SSR chemicals are polluting surface and ground waters as well as atmospheric air and soil. The chemicals and products of their decomposition are accumulated in agricultural products, objects of flora and fauna. Reserves of DDT, which is not used anymore nowadays, amount to about 1,000 tonnes only in the soil layer. A large content of DDT has been found in the soils under orchards of the old type. The Dneister River is contaminated with copper compounds, organic chlorine preparations, ammonia and nitrate nitrogen along its whole length. The Prut River is contaminated with the same substances but a tendency for an increase in average annual copper concentration is noted in it. Small rivers of the republic are characterised by increased pollution. The farms accumulated over 800 tonnes of poisonous chemicals, which has become inapplicable or their use had been prohibited and which had to be buried or processed. Measures are considered for improving the state of the environment in rural regions of the Moldavian SSR. The most important one is to set up a material and technical base for chemicalisation of agriculture (it is necessary to construct 24 standard warehouses for storing poisonous chemicals and mineral fertilisers, 384 stationary filling stations, 278 grounds for seed disinfection, etc.).

82   M Urmanski, Rentabel'no li sinee nebo? *Gazovaya promyshlennost'*, no. 3, 1987, pp. 36–9, noted a statement by A Bordiugov, head of the department for nature protection at the Technical Administration of the Ministry of Gas Industry, in which he expressed uncertainty about the ecological safety of injecting liquid wastes into subterranean areas. The researchers suggest that the gas industry's concern, in this instance of water containing methanol and other pollutants, is analogous to the chemical industry's practices. For example, consider the horror with which the public greeted the Agricultural Ministry's suggestion that polluted waste water from the new Odessa superphosphate plant should also be injected underground. See *Priroda i chelovek*, no. 5, 1989, op cit.

83   An example is provided here of the formation of wastes in the manufacturing of potassium fertilisers. The case is representative of those instances where the raw materials are of reasonably high quality, but industries working with the Karatau

apatite deposits will find the problem multiplied many-fold. *Environmental Management Abstracts*, no. 5, 1988, p. 37. 'Solid and liquid wastes are formed in potassium fertiliser production which mass amounts to 25 and 15 per cent, respectively, of the mined ore. The paper considers a possibility to reduce the volume of wastes stored on the ground surface by means of placing up to 60–70 per cent of the salt wastes and sludges into underground workings...'.

84   G M Mkrtchyan, et al, *EKO*, no. 2, 1989, op cit. Given the official reports above that as much as 60 per cent of air pollution control installations are worn out or obsolete, it is possible the same situation obtains in respect of water treatment.

85   B N Lishchin, et al, *Khimicheskaya promyshlennost'*, no. 11, 1987, op cit.

86   J Hirshhorn, et al, *Strategies for Chemical Waste Management*, Office of Technology Assessment, US Congress, Washington, DC, 1983. In general, the concerns are:
   • that most chemical wastes are toxic by virtue of a variety of contaminants contained in a single waste stream. At present, waste may not be adequately managed due to the lack of laboratory facilities to identify the dangerous characteristics of the waste in the first instance.
   • the current Soviet practice of permitting effluents on the basis of a maximum volume of single contaminants in effluents may not respond to the needs of the chemical industry given the variable nature of the waste stream.
   • the incineration of wastes is an effective method to neutralise only some liquid wastes, although it is usually efficient to reduce the volume of wastes. Incineration is effective at specific temperatures (corresponding to individual components of the waste stream), and then usually only in combination with equipment to trap and neutralise remaining contaminants in the gaseous emissions or residual solids or sludge wastes. The availability of high efficiency incinerators is not known, and current practice is significantly to rely on existing units, for example, at electric power stations rather than environmentally regulated, free-standing incinerators dedicated to waste disposal.

87   V K Borodin, *Khimicheskaya promyshlennost'*, no. 2, 1989, op cit.

Appendices

**Appendix 1   State Capital Budget for Nature Protection and the
Rational Use of Natural Resources in 1989**
(millions of rubles)

			of which						
	Total Capital Budget		Water Resources		Atmospheric Air		Land		Subsoil & Mineral Resources
	Used	% PF¹	Used	% PF	Used	% PF	Used	% PF	Used	% PF
USSR, all²	3255	86	2166	85	404	76	441	104	140	86
of which										
FEC³	597	93	328	92	103	83	97	123	53	85
• Ministry of Energy	123	94	95	95	19	82	1	196	–	–
• Ministry of Atomic Power	87	109	84	108	2	97	.3	172	–	–
• Ministry of Oil & Gas	159	101	57	93	33	86	69	118	–	–
• Concern 'Gasprom'	166	86	39	79	49	81	24	142	46	81
• Ministry of Coal	48	80	39	75	–	–	2	99	7	117
• Ministry of Oil & Gas Construction	14	85	14	86	–	–	.5	75	–	–

Metallurgical Complex	403	86	220	89	115	78	6	102	59	94
• Ministry of Metallurgy	360	83	181	83	111	77	6	105	59	94
• Concern 'Noril'sk Nikel''	43	133	39	135	4	116	0	2	–	–
Chemical-Forestry Complex	522	75	317	78	132	68	19	91	24	78
• Ministry of Petro-chemicals	181	68	112	72	56	58	4	73	8	108
• Association 'Agrokhim'	178	86	93	91	37	71	14	102	14	72
• Ministry of Medical Industry	43	75	36	72	7	93	.3	79	–	–
• Ministry of Forestry Industry	112	74	70	74	32	85	1	65	–	–
• MGO 'Tekhnokhim'	8	88	6	116	–	–	–	–	2	54

Notes: [1] PF means 'Per cent of Plan Fulfilled'.
  [2] The reader is cautioned that the branches within the three complexes represented in the table are delineated somewhat differently than elsewhere in the text. For example, the two ministries for ferrous and non-ferrous metallurgical production are given here as a single USSR ministry. The table from which these figures are taken represent about half of the amount *expended* in the national economy for nature protection and the rational use of nature. The table states that 86 per cent of the budget was expended, which implies that the budget allocation was 3.7 billion rubles for 1989. In addition, about 1.1 billion rubles were expended (of 1.25 billion available) by the republics to protect air, land, and water resources (exclusive of any on subsoil and mineral resources). The data apparently do not total all that which was expended in the national economy or by the three sectors included in the table.
  [3] FEC means 'Fuel and Energy Complex'.

Source: *Vestnik statistiki*, no. 6, 1990, p. 42.

Appendix 2 Commissioning of Nature Protection Installations Due to the State Capital Budget in 1989[1]

Installations for:

	Waste Water Treatment, ts cu m/day[2]		Circulating Water Supplies, ts cu m/day		Trapping & Neutralising Exhaust Gases ts cu m/hr	
	Commissioned	% PF[3]	Commissioned	% PF	Commissioned	% PF
USSR, all[4]	4352	50	15897	52	31222	56
FEC4	398	47	10736	46	7865	33
• Ministry of Energy	108	52	1519	22	6529	43
• Ministry of Atomic Power	28	26	9189	56	1209	15
• Ministry of Oil & Gas	120	49	8	19	63	100
• Concern 'Gasprom'	38	104	15	–	64	100
• Ministry of Coal	102	40	5	59	–	–
Metallurgical Complex	856	92	795	42	9089	72
Chemical-Forestry Complex	408	56	2670	70	2584	62
• Ministry of Petrochemicals	125	54	238	37	1336	69
• Association 'Agrokhim'	186	72	1805	74	423	95
• Ministry of Medical Industry	22	21	415	91	817	73
• Ministry of Forestry Industry	75	55	212	81	8	1

Notes: [1] The source for this table also included data for newly commissioned capacity due to expenditure by the republics. Such capacity commissioned in 1989 totalled 1747 thousand cubic metres for sewage treatment, 686 thousand cubic metres in circulating water, and 2253 thousand cubic meters per hour for exhaust gas trapping and neutralisation. Thus, of total waste water treatment capacity introduced in 1989, about 40 per cent was due to investment incurred by the republics.

[2] ts cu m/day means thousand cubic meters per day.

[3] % PF means 'Per cent of Plan Fulfilled'.

[4] FEC means 'Fuel and Energy Complex'.

Source: *Vestnik statistiki*, no. 6, 1990, p. 42.

Index

Academy of Sciences, 4
Advisory Committee, 4
Aganbegyan, A G, 67, 83
Agricultural Chemicals, Ministry of, 35
Agricultural Fertilizers, Ministry of, 179
Agriculture, 33–4, 96
  ecological consequences of, 52–9
  future requirements of, 59–62
  planning for, 35–40
  water use by *see* irrigation
Agro-Industrial Committee (Gosagro-
    prom), 35, 38
air pollution
  from chemical industry, 176
  from electric power industry, 111–13,
      114–20, 120–2
  from metallurgical industry, 142, 155,
      157–61
  monitoring and control of, 105–6,
      107–11, 115, 144, 155–7, 161–
      2
  from pulp and paper industry, 79–80,
      84–5, 87
Almalyk, 158
Amu Darya river and basin, 55, 56, 58
Andzero-Sudzansk, 20
Aral Sea, 4, 43, 52, 55–7

Arkhangelsk, 82, 84
Armenia
  metallurgical industry in, 134
  water systems in, 14, 15, 42, 43, 44
    costs of, 46
    irrigation, 48, 51, 54, 60
    sewage, 17, 24
Arnasaisk, Lake, 57
Ashikol, Lake, 57
Assy River Basin, 56
Astakhov, A A, 193
Astrakhan, 118, 193
Atomic Safety, Committee on, 5
automation
  in chemical industry, 190–1
  of irrigation, 50
  in metallurgical industry, 139–40
  of pollution control, 86–7
Azerbaidzhan
  chemicals in, 175
  water systems in, 14, 42, 43, 44
    costs of, 46
    irrigation, 48, 51, 54, 60
    sewage, 17, 24
Azov, Sea of, 52

Baikal, Lake, 7, 11–12, 30n25, 43, 67

Bakyrchiksk, 133
Balkash, lake, 52
Balkhash, 158
Balti, 116
Baltic Sea, 79
bankruptcies, 36
basic industrial production funds (BIPF)
    see capital
Belorussia, 5
    water systems in, 14, 15, 42, 43, 44
        irrigation, 48, 51, 60
        sewage, 17, 24
boiling installations, 83
Bol'shoi Kamen', 20
Borodin, V K, 172, 175, 198
Boshchekul'sk, 133
Bratsk, 20, 83, 84, 85, 158, 160
bufitos (agricultural chemical), 33
Buguchansk reservoir, 83
Bumazhnaya promyshlennost (journal),
    70, 83

capital and investment programmes
    in agriculture, 35–40
        irrigation, 59–62
    in chemical industry, 177–8, 180–90,
        193–4
        environmental, 172, 178–80, 195
    in electric power industry, 98–105
        environmental options, 92, 105–
        20
    in metallurgical industry, 129–42
        environmental, 142–4, 152–5, 161–
        2
    in pulp and paper industry, 69–77
        for pollution control, 86–8
    unreliability of data on, 8–9
carbon oxides, 110, 119, 160
Caspian Sea, 43
Central Committee, 4, 35, 38
Central Statistical Administration
    (Goskomstat), 105–6
Chazov, E, 13
Chelyabinsk, 158
Chemical Industry, Ministry of, 179
chemical and petrochemical industries,
    16
    capital assets of, 180–90

economic and social background of,
    173–7
    investment in, 177–8, 193–4
        environmental, 172, 178–80
        waste management in, 192–3, 194–8
Chemical and Petroleum Machine
    Building, Ministry of, 174
chemicals
    in agriculture, 33, 36, 50–1, 53, 179
    in pulp and paper industry, 79–81, 83
    see also chemical and petrochemical
Chernobyl', 5, 41–2, 93
Chimkent, 158
Chu River Basin, 56
climate and water use, 20–1
coal
    mining of, 92, 99, 101
    in power generation, 93, 94, 96, 113,
        115
commercial linkages *see* foreign link-
    ages
Committees *see individual committees*
Communist Party, 5
Construction, Ministry of, 22
Cooper, Caron, 96
cooperatives in agriculture, 38
cost-benefit analyses, 7
    see also khozraschet
Council of People's Deputies, 2, 3, 4,
    156
credit system, 36–7
crisis, environmental, 1–2

Dagestan, 42, 47–8
DDT, 175, 203n81
Dengizkul' Lake, 57
desertification, 33
    of Aral Sea area, 4, 43, 52, 55–7
disposal of waste *see* storage
Donets Basin, 93, 118
drainage of land *see* irrigation
dust emissions, 116–17, 121, 157–9,
    161–2

Eco-centres, 5
Ecology laboratory, 5
economic reforms, 6–8
    see also khozraschet

Egrashev, A, 58
Ekibastuz, 93, 113, 118, 119
EKO (journal), 188
elections and 'green' issues, 2
electric power industry, 12, 24, 88, 138, 145, 169n115
  characteristics of, 91, 92–105
  environmental options for, 92, 105–20
  future investments in, 120–2
electrification programme, 38
energy conservation, 95–7
Energy Programme, 93, 94, 105
Environmental Commission, 187
environmental groups, 2
environmental investment *see under* capital and investment
Erevan, 196
Estonia
  electric power generation in, 116
  water systems in, 14, 15, 42, 43, 44
    irrigation, 48, 51, 60
    sewage, 17, 24

farms, state and collective, 36–7, 39, 40, 47
Ferrous Metallurgy, Ministry of, 155
Finance, Ministry of, 193
fines and penalties
  for excessive water use, 49
  for pollution, 68, 85
Finland, 68, 81, 120
Fishery Industries, Ministry of, 4
Five Year Plans
  and chemical industry, 179, 184, 186
  and electric power industry, 94
  and irrigation, 59
  and metallurgical industry, 137, 150, 158
  and pulp and paper industry, 68, 71, 78, 79, 86
  and water resources, 12, 25, 27–8
Food Programme, 35
foreign linkages
  in chemical industry, 178, 179–80
  in pulp and paper industry, 68, 77, 86
forestry management, 68
Forestry Products Industry, 71–7

  see also pulp and paper
fuel industry, 98, 99, 100, 102, 103, 106
  see also coal; gas; oil

gas, natural, 92, 96, 105, 114, 178
gas emissions *see* air pollution
General Guidelines for the Chemicalisation of the National Economy, 173
Georgia
  agriculture in, 41
  metallurgical industry in, 134
  water systems in, 14, 15, 42, 43, 44
    costs of, 46
    irrigation, 48, 51, 53, 54, 60
    sewage, 17, 24
Gorbachev, Mikhail S, 35, 38, 129, 185
Gosagroprom, 35, 38
Goskomgidromet, 4, 105, 106, 112, 115, 158
Goskompriroda, 2–5, 105, 106, 175
Goskomstat, 105–6
Gosplan, 4, 38, 70
Great Britain, 120
Gur'evsk, 175
Gusev, A A, 22

Health, USSR Ministry of, 4, 105
health expenditure, 112–13
households
  electricity use by, 96
  water use by, 14–15, 16
Housing and Municipal Management, Ministry of, 21
housing policies, 15, 128
hydroelectric power, 91, 92, 94, 95, 97
Hydrometeorology, USSR State Committee on (Goskomgidromet), 4, 105, 106, 112, 115, 158

imports
  of electric power equipment, 120
  of pulp and paper products, 69
  of technology, 68
  see also foreign linkages
industry
  cost of water to, 45–6
  electricity use by, 96

location of, 37, 128–9, 174
use of water by, 14, 15–16
waste water from, 18–19
see also individual industries
inflation, 78
Inspectorate for Monitoring the Operations of Gas Treatment and Dust Extraction Devices, 106
investment *see* capital and investment
Irkutsk, 5, 175
irrigation and drainage, 34, 51–2
costs of water from, 45–8
evaluation of need for, 41–5
productivity from, 39–40
required improvements in, 58–62
and salination problems, 52–3, 55–8
technology in, 49–50
wastage in, 48–9, 53–5
Irrigation Service, 40, 47
Issik-Kul', Lake, 52
Izrael, Yuri, 23, 112, 161, 178

Japan, 68
joint ventures *see* foreign linkages

Kairaktinsk, 133
Kalinin, 19
Kamyshlybash Lake, 57
Kansk-Achinsk, 93, 113, 118, 119
Karakumsk canal, 56
Karatau, 179
Karmanovsk, 111
Kashirsk, 111
Kattashop Lake, 57
Katun project, 95
Kazakhstan
chemical industry in, 174, 179
electric power generation in, 93, 113
metallurgical industry in, 128, 148, 158, 159
water systems in, 14, 42, 43
costs of, 46
irrigation, 48, 51, 54, 56, 60
sewage, 17, 24
Kemerov, 133
Khabarovsk, 5
Khachaturov, T S, 13, 25, 26, 121–2, 145, 147

Kharitonov, N A, 138
Kharkov, 20
khozraschet, 6
in agriculture, 37–8
in chemical industry, 174, 181, 193
in electric power industry, 115
in metallurgical industry, 128
in pulp and paper industry, 68
Kirgizia
water systems in, 14, 15, 42, 43
costs of, 46
irrigation, 48, 51, 53, 54, 56, 60
sewage, 17, 24
Kirillov, V A, 192
Kiselev, B G, 132
Kizelovskii, 117
Kohtla-Jarve, 116
Koktenkol'sk, 133
Kola North, 156, 160
Kolosov, A, 145
Kommunarsk, 160
Kotlass, 82
Krasnoyarsk, 160
Krastel, 187
Kuzbas, 93
Kuznetsk, 118, 133

laboratories, environmental, 5, 175
Ladoga, Lake, 29n25, 67, 84, 87
Lapin, V I, 136
Latvia
metallurgical industries in, 134
water systems in, 14, 42, 43, 44
irrigation, 48, 51
sewage, 17, 24, 26
leaseholds, inheritable, 38
Lemeshev, M Ya, 49
Leningrad, 5, 175
Lipet'sk oblast, 129
Lithuania
water systems in, 14, 15, 42, 43, 44
irrigation, 48, 51, 60
sewage, 17, 24
Lishchin, B N, 192, 197
location of industries, 37, 128–9, 174
Loiter, M, 60

machine-building industry, 68, 77, 78–9

Magadan, 20
Magnitogorsk, 134, 138
metallurgical industry, 16, 127
  development of, 128–9
  investment in, 129–42
    environmental, 142–4, 152–5, 161–2
  pollution by, 128, 129, 144–51, 155–62
military expenditure, xii
Minashina, N G, 60–1
Mineral Fertilisers, Ministry of, 184, 187
Ministries *see individual Ministries*
Minlesprom, 85
Minvodkhoz, 4, 35, 36–7, 40–1, 57–8
Mishin, G, 137
Mitsubishi company, 179–80
Moldavia
  chemicals in, 203n81
  water systems in, 14, 15, 42, 43, 44
    costs of, 46, 47
    irrigation, 48, 51, 54, 60
    sewage, 17, 24
Morgun, F T, 2, 3, 5, 143, 175
Moscow, 5, 13, 19, 176
Moscow basin (coalfield), 93, 117, 118
Murgaba river, 56
Murmansk, 158

Narkevich, I P, 192
Nature Protection, State Committee for, (Goskompriroda), 2–5, 105, 106, 175
Nekrasov, A S, 113
nitrogen oxides, 110, 112, 119
Nizhni Tagil, 133, 156
Non-ferrous Metallurgy, Ministry of, 143, 151, 161
Noril'sk, 5, 158, 159, 175
normatives *see* standards
Nove, Alec, 181
Novgorod, 20–1
Novosibirsk, 5, 175
nuclear power, 91, 92–3, 94, 95

Odessa, 173, 187
Oganov, O G, 188
oil

in electricity generation, 94, 96
extraction and refining of, 16, 92, 93, 99, 101, 114
see also chemical and petrochemical
Okulovsky Pulp Plant, 87
Omsk, 20
Ovchinnikov, V I, 172
Ozernyi collector canal, 58

Pechenganikel', 158
penalties *see* fines
Perm, 5, 83, 111, 175
permafrost, 53
Petrochemical Industry, Ministry of, 179
petrochemicals *see* chemical and petrochemical industry
Petroleum Machine Building, Ministry of, 115
Petropavlovsk-Kamchatka, 5, 20, 175
Pitkyaranta Pulp Plant, 87
planning authorities *see individual Ministries and Committees*
Planning Committee, (Gosplan), 4, 38, 70
Plans *see* Five Year Plans
pollution controls, 6–7
  see also air pollution *and also under* water
private sector in agriculture, 38
product substitution, 7–8
pulp and paper industry, 67–8
  economic problems of, 69–79
  pollution problems in, 79–85
  production by, 68–9
  required investment in, 86–8
  water use by, 16, 79

rents for land, 36, 37
resource conservation and recycling, 7
  in chemical industry, 192, 194–8
  in electric power industry, 92, 118
  in metallurgical industry, 141–2, 145–6, 160–1
  in pulp and paper industry, 79–81, 83, 87
  of water *see under* water
river diversions, 42, 43
Rostov oblast, 26

Russian Soviet Federal Socialist Republic (RSFSR)
  environmental laboratories in, 5
  water systems in, 14, 15, 19–20, 21, 42, 43, 44
    costs of, 46
    irrigation, 48, 51, 54, 60
    sewage, 17, 24, 25–6
Rustavsk, 134
Rzhev waterworks and canal, 19

safety of workers in chemicals, 175
salination, 52–3, 55–8
Samarkand, 160
Sanitary and Epidemiological Service, 4–5, 21
Sarkanais, 134
Sarykamyshsk, Lake, 57, 58
scientific research in pulp and paper industry, 77–8, 81, 82
Severonikel', 158
sewage systems, 11, 16–27, 61–2, 65n53
Shabad, T, 113
shale fuel, 116, 118
Sheinin, L B, 47
Siberia
  and chemical industry, 174, 175
  metallurgical industry in, 128
  power generation in, 93, 95
  see also individual areas, lakes etc
Sokol, 83
standards (normatives)
  for air and water pollution, 84–5, 108–11
  in waste water management, 21–3
Standards, State Committee on, 115
storage and disposal of waste
  in chemical industry, 196–8
  in metallurgical industry, 144–5
  in pulp and paper industry, 84, 88
Styrikovich, M A, 113, 120, 156
Sudoch'e, Lake, 57
sulphur
  as pollutant, 79, 80, 109, 110, 112, 138, 160
  removal of, 83–4, 114–15, 117–18, 119, 120–2, 162
    for recycling, 87, 92, 118, 161

Supreme Soviet, 187
Svema, 187
Sverdlovsk, 136, 158, 159
Syr Darya river and basin, 55, 56, 59

Tadzhikstan
  water systems in, 14, 15, 42, 43, 44
    costs of, 46
    irrigation, 48, 51, 53, 54, 56, 60
    sewage, 17, 24, 26–7
Talasa River Basin, 55, 56
Tallinn, 85
Tashkent, 176
taxation policy, 36–7
technology, Soviet, inadequacy of, 67–8, 69–70, 79, 83
Tedzhena River Basin, 56
thermal energy, 169n115
Tipisev, A, 79, 81
Tomsk, 20
Turin (USSR), 82, 83
Turkmenia
  water systems in, 14, 15, 42, 43, 44
    costs of, 46, 47
    irrigation, 48, 51, 53, 54, 56, 60
    sewage, 17, 24
turn-key arrangements, 77, 86
Tyumen, 178, 180, 189

Ufa, 177
Uglegorsk, 111
Ukraine, 5
  agriculture in, 41–2
  chemical industry in, 187
  metallurgical industry in, 128, 134
  water systems in, 14, 15, 42, 43, 44
    costs of, 46, 47
    irrigation, 48, 51, 54, 60
    sewage, 17, 24
  wood processing industry in, 84–5
Ulan Ude, 20
Ural river, 79
Urals region, 27, 93, 141
urban areas
  air pollution in, 111–13, 155–6
  sewage systems in, 16–21, 23–7
  water supplies in, 12–15
Ust'-Ilimsk, 83

Ust'-Kamenogorsk, 158
Uzbekistan
    water systems in, 14, 42, 43, 44
        costs of, 46
        irrigation, 48, 51, 53, 54, 56, 60
        sewage, 17, 24

valuation of land, 36, 37
Vladivostock, 5, 175
Vnit'sk, 187
Vnukov, A K, 120
Volga river, 79
Vorontsev, N N, 3

water
    consumption of, 13–15, 43–4
    cost and pricing of, 45–7, 49, 83
    pollution of
        in chemical industry, 176
        in pulp and paper industry, 79–82,
            84

recycling of, 15–16, 44
    in chemical industry, 175, 176
    in metallurgical industry, 146, 149,
        152–4
    in pulp and paper industry, 82–3,
        86, 88
resources of, 11–12, 41–3
waste, treatment of, 16–27, 61–2, 65
    n53, 87–8, 107, 146–51, 154–5
Water Management, Ministry of,
    (Minvodkhoz), 4, 35, 36–7, 40–1,
    57–8
Western Caucasus Economic Region, 177
wood processing industry *see* Forestry
    Products Industry

Yamal, 178

Zalogin, N G, 121
Zaparozhe, 111, 158, 159
Zeravshana river, 55, 56